Anglais pour débutants 2

ENGLISH? OF COURSE!

Student Activity Book

Rédaction : Lily Dabby
Révision pédagogique : Sylvie Beauchemin
Suzanne Chénier
Marielle Hurtubise
Claude Laurin
Conception graphique : Jo-Anne Guindon
Éditique : Sylvie Fauvelle
Révision linguistique : Rachelle Van Dyk
Ghislaine Jean
Martine Joly
Impression : Centre franco-ontarien de ressources pédagogiques

Le ministère de l'Éducation de l'Ontario a fourni une aide financière pour la réalisation de ce projet. Cet apport financier ne doit pas pour autant être perçu comme une approbation ministérielle pour l'utilisation du matériel produit. Cette publication n'engage que l'opinion de son auteure, laquelle ne représente pas nécessairement celle du Ministère.

435, rue Donald, Ottawa ON K1K 4X5
Commandes : Tél. : (613) 747-1553
Téléc. : (613) 747-0866
Site Web : www.librairieducentre.com
C. élec. : commandes@librairieducentre.com

ISBN 2-89581-217-9
Dépôt légal — troisième trimestre 2008
Bibliothèque et Archives Canada

Imprimé au Canada Printed in Canada

Contents

UNIT IV: You and Your Planet

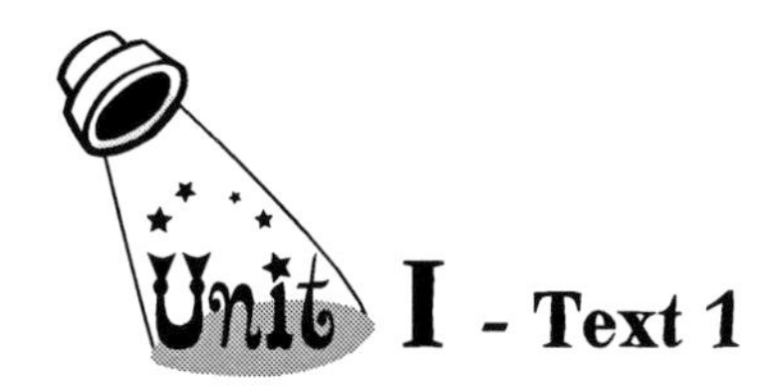

Unit I - Text 1

Welcome to École secondaire Des Ponts!

Activity 1, Part 1
Your teacher will read one number from each set below. Circle the number that you hear.

Numbers:

0 = zero 1 = one 2 = two 3 = three 4 = four 5 = five	6 = six 7 = seven 8 = eight 9 = nine 10 = ten	11 = eleven 12 = twelve 13 = thirteen 14 = fourteen 15 = fifteen	16 = sixteen 17 = seventeen 18 = eighteen 19 = nineteen 20 = twenty

1. 7 – 3 – 9
2. 6 – 3 – 8
3. 1 – 0 – 10
4. 2 – 5 – 8
5. 1 – 16 – 9
6. 14 – 4 – 19
7. 7 – 15 – 7
8. 5 – 15 – 8
9. 0 – 17 – 7
10. 9 – 5 – 8
11. 4 – 11 – 7
12. 20 – 8 – 18
13. 5 – 9 – 12
14. 6 – 7 – 0
15. 5 – 13 – 8

Activity 1, Part 2
Make the following words plural. Write each word in the correct column.

Words	People	Things
bell board boy chair chalkboard class classroom clock desk dictionary girl journal man narrator notebook student teacher	1. example: boys 2. ______ 3. ______ 4. ______ 5. ______ 6. ______ 7. ______ 8. ______ 9. ______ 10. ______ 11. ______	1. example: bells 2. ______ 3. ______ 4. ______ 5. ______ 6. ______ 7. ______ 8. ______ 9. ______ 10. ______ 11. ______

Activity 1, Part 3
a. Look around your classroom. Write the correct number in each blank.
b. Circle the correct singular or plural words in your answers.

Example: How many clocks are there in your classroom?
There (is) (are) one (clock) (clocks) in my classroom.

1. How many chairs are there in your classroom?

   There (is) (are) ____________ (chair) (chairs) in my classroom.

2. How many desks are there in your classroom?

   There (is) (are) ____________ (desk) (desks) in my classroom.

3. How many chalkboards are there in your classroom?

   There (is) (are) ____________ (chalkboard) (chalkboards) in my classroom.

4. How many teachers are there in your classroom?

   There (is) (are) ____________ (teacher) (teachers) in my classroom.

5. How many new students are there in your classroom?

   There (is) (are) ____________ new (student) (students) in my classroom.

6. How many boys are there in your classroom?

   There (is) (are) ____________ (boy) (boys) in my classroom.

Activity 1, Part 4
Answer the following questions about your school.

1. What is the name of your school?

   ____

2. What is the name of your APD (Anglais pour débutants) teacher?

   ____

3. How many girls are there in your APD class (today)?

   ____

4. How many boys are there in your APD class (today)?

   ____

5. How many students are there in your APD class (today)?

   ____

Activity 2, Part 1

Write the definition of the words and expressions that are new to you.

Vocabulary List

I. Nouns	II. Verbs
1. answer: ________	1. to answer: ________
2. bell: ________	2. to arrange: ________
3. board: ________	3. to ask: ________
4. boy: ________	4. to bring: ________
5. chair: ________	5. to change: ________
6. chalkboard: ________	6. to circle: ________
7. clock: ________	7. to count: ________
8. circle: ________	8. to end: ________
9. class: ________	9. to enter: ________
10. classroom: ________	10. to know: ________
11. day: ________	11. to like: ________
12. definition: ________	12. to listen: ________
13. desk: ________	13. to look: ________
14. dictionary: ________	14. to meet: ________
15. girl: ________	15. to point: ________
16. school: ________	16. to pronounce: ________
17. journal: ________	17. to put: ________
18. a. man: ________	18. to read: ________
b. woman: ________	19. to ring: ________
19. name: ________	20. to sit down: ________
20. narrator: ________	21. to smile: ________
21. notebook: ________	22. to stand up: ________
22. number: ________	23. to study: ________
23. question: ________	24. to talk: ________
24. school: ________	25. to turn around: ________
25. sentence: ________	26. to use: ________
26. sound: ________	27. to wait: ________
27. student: ________	28. to walk: ________
28. teacher: ________	29. to want: ________
29. word: ________	30. to write: ________
1. person (singular): ________ 2. people (plural): ________	

Would you please...? Please How many...are there? There is... (singular) There are... (plural)	Good morning. How are you? I am fine, thank you. Fine, thanks. What is your name? My name is... How do you do? Nice to meet you. Pleased to meet you.	Welcome to... Thank you very much. Thanks. Bye! See you later. Goodbye. Have a good day.

Activity 2, Part 2
Text 1: Welcome to École secondaire Des Ponts!

Narrator: *The students enter. There are seven students in the classroom. They talk and smile. The bell rings. The students sit down and wait for the APD teacher. A man enters the classroom.*

Teacher: Good morning, class.

Students: Good morning.

Teacher: How are you?

Students: Fine, thank you. How are you?

Teacher: I am fine, thanks.

Narrator: *The teacher smiles. He looks at the desks and chairs in the classroom.*

Teacher: Class, would you please arrange the desks and chairs in a circle?

Narrator: *The students stand up, arrange the desks and chairs in a circle, and sit down.*

Teacher: Thank you.

Narrator: *The teacher walks to the chalkboard. He writes his name on the board. He turns around and points to his name.*

Teacher: My name is Mr. Perreault. I am your APD teacher.

Narrator: *Mr. Perreault sits down. How many students are there? He counts the students. There are seven students. There are three boys and four girls in his class. He looks at Tina.*

Mr. Perreault: What is your name?

Tina: My name is Tina.

Mr. Perreault: Nice to meet you, Tina.

Tina: Nice to meet you too, Mr. Perreault.

Mr. Perreault: Welcome to APD class, Tina.

Tina: Thank you very much, Mr. Perreault.

Narrator: *Mr. Perreault looks at Omar.*

Mr. Perreault: What is your name?

Omar: My name is Omar.

Mr. Perreault: How do you do, Omar?

Omar: Very well. How do you do, Mr. Perreault?

Mr. Perreault: Welcome to APD class, Omar.

Omar: Thank you, Mr. Perreault.

Narrator: *Mr. Perreault looks at Hamid.*

Mr. Perreault: What is your name?

Hamid: My name is Hamid.

Mr. Perreault: Pleased to meet you, Hamid.

Hamid: Pleased to meet you too, Mr. Perreault.

Mr. Perreault: Welcome to APD class.

Hamid: Thanks, Mr. Perreault.

Narrator: *Mr. Perreault meets every student in his class. He meets Tina, Omar, Chantal, Hamid, Toni, Keiko and Ricardo. He likes his students. They are very polite. Mr. Perreault and his students talk. He asks many questions. The students answer his questions. The students ask questions too, and he answers every question. Mr. Perreault looks at the clock. He stands up, walks to the chalkboard, and writes two words on the board: "dictionary" and "notebook".*

Mr. Perreault: Students, please bring a notebook and dictionary to class every day. Your notebook and your dictionary are very important. The notebook is your "APD Journal". I want you to write in your APD Journal every day! I want you to use the French-English dictionary every day too.

Narrator: *The bell rings. The students stand up.*

Chantal: Bye, Mr. Perreault.

Hamid: See you later.

Mr. Perreault: Goodbye. Have a good day! And please remember to bring your dictionary and notebook to class each day.

Activity 2, Part 3
Comprehension Questions
Answer the following questions on Text 1.

1. What is the name of the school?

____

2. What is the name of the APD teacher?

____

3. How many girls are there in the class?

____

4. How many boys are there in the class?

____

5. How many students are there in the class?

____

Activity 2, Part 4
Number the following sentences in the correct order. Refer to Text 1.

_____ Nice to meet you too, Mr. Perreault.
_____ How are you?
_____ Thank you very much, Mr. Perreault.
_____ My name is Tina.
_____ Welcome to APD class.
_____ Fine, thank you. How are you?
__1__ Good morning, class.
_____ I am fine, thanks.
_____ Nice to meet you, Tina.
_____ What is your name?

Activity 3, Part 1
Say the following verbs in the third person singular. Do they end with an "s", "z", or "iz" sound? Write each verb in the correct column.

	"s" sound	"z" sound	"iz" sound
answers arranges **asks** brings enters likes looks meets points **rings** sits smiles stands talks turns **uses**	1. example: **asks** 2. ________ 3. ________ 4. ________ 5. ________ 6. ________ 7. ________ 8. ________ 9. ________ 10. ________	1. example: **rings** 2. ________ 3. ________ 4. ________ 5. ________ 6. ________ 7. ________ 8. ________ 9. ________ 10. ________	1. example: **uses** 2. ________ 3. ________ 4. ________ 5. ________ 6. ________ 7. ________ 8. ________ 9. ________ 10. ________

Activity 3, Part 2

a. Rewrite the following sentences in the plural. Make sure that the subjects and verbs agree.

Example: The teacher talks to the student. (3 changes)
The teacher**s** tal**k** to the student**s**.

1. The student walks to the classroom. (3 changes)

____

2. The student talks to the teacher. (3)

____

3. The girl writes the answer on the chalkboard. (4)

____

4. The teacher speaks to the student. (3)

____

5. The student waits for the teacher. (3)

____

6. The student arranges the desk and chair. (4)

____

b. Rewrite the following sentences in the singular. Make sure that the subjects and verbs agree.

Example: The boys talk to the teachers. (3 changes)
The **boy talks** to the **teacher**.

1. The girls talk to the boys. (3 changes)

____

2. The students sit at the desks. (3)

____

3. The girls want to look at the answers on the chalkboards. (4)

____

4. The students read in the classrooms. (3)

____

Activity 3, Part 3
Write the correct verb in each blank. Make sure that the verb agrees with the subject.

Example: The teacher **enters** the classroom.
The students **enter** the classroom.

answer
arrange
ask
enter
meet
ring
sit
smile
wait
walk
write

Example: The teacher **smiles** at his students.

1. The bell ______________________.
2. The students ______________________ for the APD teacher.
3. The teacher ______________________ the classroom.
4. He ______________________ to the chalkboard.
5. He ______________________ his name on the chalkboard.
6. The students ______________________ the desks and chairs in a circle.
7. The students ______________________ in a circle.
8. Mr. Perreault ______________________ all the students in his class.
9. Mr. Perreault ______________________ questions.
10. The students ______________________ the questions.

Activity 3, Part 4
Circle the correct verb in each of the following sentences. Make sure that the verb agrees with the subject.

Example: Tina (bring) (**brings**) her dictionary to class.

1. Omar (look) (looks) at the clock.
2. The students (wait) (waits) for the APD teacher.
3. The students (arrange) (arranges) the desks and chairs in a circle.
4. Mr. Perreault (point) (points) to his name on the chalkboard.
5. The students (turn) (turns) around and (look) (looks) at the chalkboard.
6. Mr. Perreault (count) (counts) the students in his class.
7. The students (want) (wants) to talk to Mr. Perreault.
8. Mr. Perreault (use) (uses) the chalkboard in the classroom.
9. The students (like) (likes) Mr. Perreault.

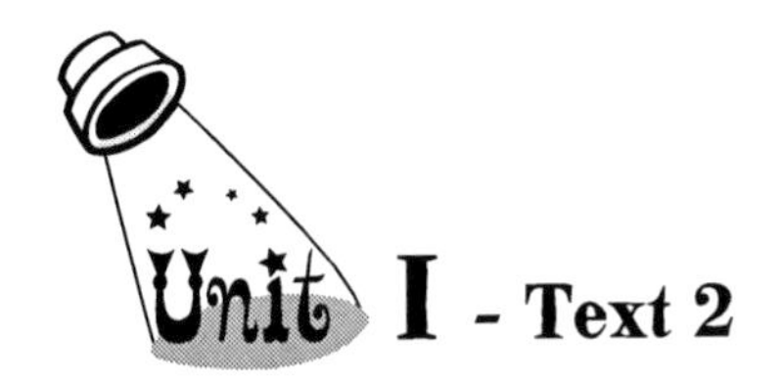

Unit I - Text 2

Two Journal Entries

Activity 1, Part 1
Write the correct possessive adjective ("his", "her", or "their") in each blank.

1. Tina brings ______________ dictionary to class.
2. The students like ______________ teacher, Mr. Perreault.
3. Omar likes ______________ friends.
4. Chantal likes ______________ art teacher very much.
5. Hamid and Omar bring notebooks to ______________ APD class.
6. Mr. Perreault writes ______________ name on the chalkboard.
7. Tina and Chantal sit at ______________ desks when the bell rings.
8. Mrs. Roy teaches APD in ______________ classroom.
9. Mr. Perreault teaches APD in ______________ classroom.
10. Mrs. St-Louis, the principal, is in ______________ office.
11. Omar likes ______________ gym teacher very much.
12. Hamid likes ______________ history teacher very much.
13. Tina and Omar eat ______________ lunch in the cafeteria.
14. Mr. Perreault enters ______________ classroom when the bell rings.
15. Mr. Perreault and Mrs. Roy welcome ______________ students to class.

Activity 1, Part 2
Rewrite the following sentences in the plural.
Change the verbs, nouns and possessive adjectives too.
Example: The teacher talks to his student. (4 changes)
The teacher**s** tal**k** to **their** student**s**.

1. The student walks to his classroom. (4 changes)

____

2. The student talks to his teacher. (4)

____

3. The girl writes her answer on the chalkboard. (5)

____

4. The teacher speaks to her student. (4)

____

5. The student waits for her APD teacher. (4)

____

6. The student arranges his desk and chair in his classroom. (7)

____

Activity 1, Part 3
Write the definition of the words and expressions that are new to you.

Vocabulary List

I. Questions	**IV. Staff**
1. Where?: ______	1. counsellor: ______
2. Who?: ______	2. janitor: ______
3. Whose?: ______	3. librarian: ______
	4. nurse: ______
II. School Building	5. principal: ______
1. auditorium: ______	6. a. assistant principal: ______
2. a. bathroom: ______	b. vice-principal: ______
b. toilet: ______	7. secretary: ______
c. washroom: ______	8. staff: ______
3. cafeteria: ______	
4. a. gymnasium: ______	**V. Subjects**
b. gym: ______	1. art: ______
5. a. laboratories: ______	2. chemistry: ______
b. labs: ______	3. computer science: ______
6. library: ______	4. drama: ______
7. office: ______	5. history: ______
8. building: ______	6. a. physical education: ______
9. floor: ______	b. phys. ed.: ______
	c. gym : ______
III. Titles	7. science: ______
1. a. Mr.: ______	8. (other) subjects: ______
b. Mrs.: ______	______
c. Ms.: ______	______
d. Miss: ______	
2. title: ______	

VI. Homonyms:

1. a. four: ____________________
   b. for: ____________________
2. a. to: ____________________
   b. too: ____________________
   c. two: ____________________

VII. Verbs

1. to begin: ____________________
2. to choose: ____________________
3. to clean: ____________________
4. to come: ____________________
5. to complete: ____________________
6. to eat: ____________________
7. to find: ____________________
8. to give: ____________________
9. to go: ____________________
10. to help: ____________________
11. to introduce: ____________________
12. to play: ____________________
13. to receive: ____________________
14. to show: ____________________
15. to speak: ____________________
16. to teach: ____________________
17. to welcome: ____________________
18. to work: ____________________

VIII. Nouns

1. day: ____________________
   a. morning: ____________________
   b. afternoon: ____________________
   c. evening: ____________________
2. credit: ____________________
3. friend: ____________________
4. journal entry: ____________________
5. general assembly: ____________________
6. list: ____________________
7. lunch: ____________________
8. mistake: ____________________
9. schedule: ____________________

IX. Adjectives

1. a. each: ____________________
   b. every: ____________________
2. a. new: ____________________
   b. old: ____________________
3. many: ____________________
4. (the) following: ____________________
5. sick: ____________________

X. Adverbs

1. after: ____________________
2. before: ____________________
3. finally: ____________________
4. early: ____________________
5. then: ____________________
6. also: ____________________
7. too: ____________________

XI. WHO? (subject pronoun)		**WHOSE?** (possessive adjective)
I	➜	my
you	➜	your
he	➜	his
she	➜	her
we	➜	our
they	➜	their

XII. Ordinal Numbers

1 ➜ 1st = first	6 ➜ 6th = sixth
2 ➜ 2nd = second	7 ➜ 7th = seventh
3 ➜ 3rd = third	8 ➜ 8th = eighth
4 ➜ 4th = fourth	9 ➜ 9th = ninth
5 ➜ 5th = fifth	10 ➜ 10th = tenth

Activity 1, Part 4

a. Introduce the new teachers to your parents.

Example: Introduce teacher 1: This is my **APD** teacher. **His** name is Mr. Perreault.

1. Mr. Perreault APD	2. Miss Perron History	3. Mrs. Lévesque Art	4. Mr. Boulanger Chemistry
5. Ms. Charbonneau Computer Science	6. Mr. Larivière Dramatic Arts	7. Miss Bélanger Science	8. Mr. Perron Phys. Ed.

1. Introduce teacher 2: This is my ____________________ teacher. _______ name is Miss Perron.
2. Introduce teacher 3: This is my ____________________ teacher. _______ name is Mrs. Lévesque.
3. Introduce teacher 4: This is my ____________________ teacher. _______ name is Mr. Boulanger.
4. Introduce teacher 5: This is my ____________________ teacher. _______ name is Ms. Charbonneau.
5. Introduce teacher 6: This is my ____________________ teacher. _______ name is Mr. Larivière.
6. Introduce teacher 7: This is my ____________________ teacher. _______ name is Miss Bélanger.
7. Introduce teacher 8: This is my ____________________ teacher. _______ name is Mr. Perron.

b. Answer the following questions, making sure to use correct pronouns and possessive adjectives.

Example: Who is teacher 1? **He** is my APD teacher. **His** name is Mr. Perreault.

1. Who is teacher 2? _______ is my history teacher. _______ name is Miss Perron.
2. Who is teacher 3? _______ is my art teacher. _______ name is Mrs. Lévesque.
3. Who is teacher 4? _______ is my chemistry teacher. _______ name is Mr. Boulanger.
4. Who is teacher 5? _______ is my computer science teacher. _______ name is Ms. Charbonneau.
5. Who is teacher 6? _______ is my drama teacher. _______ name is Mr. Larivière.
6. Who is teacher 7? _______ is my science teacher. _______ name is Miss Bélanger.
7. Who is teacher 8? _______ is my phys. ed. teacher. _______ name is Mr. Perron.

Activity 1, Part 5

List your teachers in the first column. Use Mr., Mrs., Ms. and Miss to introduce your teachers.

Names of Your Teachers	Subjects They Teach
1. ____________________	This is ________________. ______ is my ______________teacher.
2. ____________________	This is my ____________teacher. ______ name is ______________.
3. ____________________	This is ________________. ______ is my ______________teacher.
4. ____________________	This is my ____________teacher. ______ name is ______________.
5. ____________________	This is ________________. ______ is my ______________teacher.

Activity 1, Part 6
Text 2A: Chantal's Journal Entry

The name of my school is École secondaire Des Ponts. Many people work at our school. We have a principal. Her name is Mrs. St-Louis. There is also a vice-principal. His name is Mr. Marin. There are two secretaries at our school. Their names are Mrs. McDonald and Mrs. Dubois. We have one school nurse. Her name is Miss Morel. There are two janitors. Mr. Lacroix works in the morning, and Mrs. Nadon works in the afternoon and evening. There is also a school counsellor. His name is Mr. Bleau. There are many people who work at our school.

Activity 1, Part 7
Answer the following questions in complete sentences. Refer to *Chantal's Journal Entry*.

1. How many principals are there at École secondaire Des Ponts?

____

2. Who is the principal?

____

3. What is the name of the vice-principal?

____

4. How many secretaries are there at École secondaire Des Ponts?

____

5. What are their names?

____

6. Is there a nurse at École secondaire Des Ponts?

____

7. What is his or her name?

____

8. How many janitors work at École secondaire Des Ponts?

____

9. What are their names?

____

10. When do they work? (morning? afternoon? evening?)

____

Activity 1, Part 8

Write the correct verb in each blank. Use each verb only once. Make sure that the verb agrees with the subject.

begin
come
eat
end
give
go
introduce
meet
receive
ring
show
sit
speak
wait
walk
welcome

On the first day of school, students (1) ________________ to school early in the morning. They (2) ________________ with their old friends. They also (3) ________________ the new students. They (4) ________________ the new students the offices, library, gym, cafeteria, auditorium, lab and classrooms in the school building. When the bell (5) ________________, students (6) ________________ to the auditorium. In the auditorium, they (7) ________________ in their chairs and (8) ________________ for the general assembly to begin. The general assembly (9) ________________ when the principal (10) ________________ the students. The principal and vice-principal then (11) ________________ the staff, namely, the teachers, librarian, nurse, secretaries, janitors and school counsellors. The school counsellors (12) ________________ the students their school schedules. After the students (13) ________________ their schedules, the general assembly (14) ________________. Students (15) ________________ to the cafeteria to (16) ________________ lunch. After lunch, students go to their first afternoon class.

Activity 2, Part 1

Use the apostrophe "s" to indicate the possessive in the following sentences.

Example: The journal entry of Omar is new.
Omar's journal entry is new.

1. The journal of Omar is on his desk.

____

2. The dictionary of Hamid is on his desk.

____

3. The notebook of Tina is on her desk.

____

4. The name of the teacher is on the chalkboard.

____

5. The APD teacher of Tina is Mr. Perreault.

____

6. The students of Mr. Perreault are in the classroom.

____

Activity 2, Part 2

Answer the following questions. Refer to the list below.

Example: Who is the fifth teacher in the list?
The **fifth** teacher is **Miss Charbonneau**.

1. Miss Perreault APD	2. Miss Perron History	3. Mrs. Lévesque Art	4. Mr. Boulanger Chemistry
5. Miss Charbonneau Computer Science	6. Mr. Larivière Dramatic Arts	7. Miss Bélanger Science	8. Mr. Perron Phys. Ed.

1. Who is the third teacher in the list? The __________ teacher is ____________________.
2. Who is the seventh teacher in the list? The __________ teacher is ____________________.
3. Who is the second teacher in the list? The __________ teacher is ____________________.
4. Who is the sixth teacher in the list? The __________ teacher is ____________________.
5. Who is the eighth teacher in the list? The __________ teacher is ____________________.

Activity 2, Part 3

a. Find the correct occupation in the list below to answer each question. Write your answers in complete sentences.

Example: Who works with students in the classroom?
The **teacher** works with students in the classroom.

vice-principal	janitor	principal	staff
counsellor	librarian	secretary	**teacher**

1. Who talks to students about courses and credits?

____

2. Who lends books to students?

---

3. Who are the people who work at a school?

---

4. Who is the "boss" of the school?

---

5. Who answers the telephone in the school office?

---

6. Who helps the principal?

---

7. Who keeps the school clean?

---

b. Find the correct place in the list below to answer each question. Write your answers in complete sentences.

Example: Where do students go to ask questions about the school?
Students go to the **school office** to ask questions about the school.

auditorium	gym	library	principal's office
cafeteria	lab	nurse's office	**school office**

1. Where do students go when they are sick?

---

2. Where do students go to eat lunch?

---

3. Where do students go to do chemistry experiments?

---

4. Where do students go to study or do research?

---

5. Where do students go to play volleyball or basketball?

---

6. Where do students go to speak to the principal?

____

7. Where do students go for a general assembly?

____

Activity 2, Part 4
Text 2B: Omar's Journal Entry

On the first day of school, students like to come to school early in the morning. They like to speak with their old friends. They also want to meet the new students. They show the new students the offices, library, gym, cafeteria, auditorium, labs and classrooms in the school building. When the bell rings, the students walk to the auditorium. In the auditorium, they sit and wait for the general assembly to begin. The general assembly begins when the principal welcomes the students. The principal and vice-principal introduce the staff. First, they introduce the teachers. Next, they introduce the librarian, nurse, secretaries and janitors. Finally, they introduce the school counsellors. The school counsellors give the students their school schedules. The general assembly ends after the students receive their schedules. The students go to the cafeteria to eat lunch. After lunch, the students go to their first afternoon class.

Activity 2, Part 5
Number the following sentences in the correct order. Look for the words "first", "next", "after" and "finally" to help you put the sentences in order. Refer to *Omar's Journal Entry*.

______ The general assembly ends after the students receive their school schedule.

______ The general assembly begins when the principal welcomes the students.

______ The students speak with their old friends and meet the new students.

______ After they eat lunch in the cafeteria, the students go to their afternoon classes.

______ Finally, they introduce the school counsellors.

___1___ Students come to school early in the morning.

______ When the bell rings, the students walk to the auditorium and wait for the general assembly to begin.

______ Next, they introduce the librarian, nurse, secretaries and janitors.

______ The students eat lunch in the cafeteria.

______ They show the new students the school offices, library, gym, cafeteria, etc.

______ First, the principal and vice-principal introduce the teachers.

Activity 2, Part 6
Rewrite the sentences correctly. (There are 10 mistakes.)

The general assembly begin when the principal welcomes the student, and the general assembly end after the students receives his school schedules. After he eat lunch in the cafeteria, students go to her afternoon classes. The students meets Mr. Perreault, and Mr. Perreault meet her students.

____

____

____

____

____

____

____

____

Activity 2, Part 7
Associate each word on the right with its opposite on the left.

Example: ___F___ Mr.

1. ________ teacher
2. ________ new
3. ________ morning
4. ________ boy
5. ________ to ask
6. ________ to begin
7. ________ to give
8. ________ to come
9. ________ to sit
10. ________ to answer

A. afternoon
B. to answer
C. to end
D. girl
E. to go
F. Mrs.
G. old
H. to question
I. to receive
J. to stand
K. student

Activity 2, Part 8
Answer the following questions. Refer to Activity 1, Part 5. (Write the names of your teachers.)

1. Who is the fifth teacher on your list? The **fifth** teacher is ________________.
2. Who is the third teacher on your list? The ________ teacher is ________________.
3. Who is the second teacher on your list? The ________ teacher is ________________.
4. Who is the first teacher on your list? The ________ teacher is ________________.
5. Who is the fourth teacher on your list? The ________ teacher is ________________.

I - Text 3

The First Afternoon Class

Activity 1, Part 1
Circle the adjectives and underline the adverbs in each of the following sentences.

1. The students study the vocabulary lists carefully.
2. Paper clips hold papers together temporarily.
3. The schedules are permanent.
4. The students walk slowly to the cafeteria.
5. Each student receives a schedule.
6. I come to school early.
7. The teacher gives a book to each student.
8. He is a new student.
9. She is the new librarian.
10. Mr. Lalonde has many students in his class.
11. We go to class after lunch.
12. We speak with friends before the bell rings.

Activity 1, Part 2
Write the definition of the words and expressions that are new to you.

Vocabulary List

I. School Supplies	10. a. pencil: ____________
1. binder: ____________	b. colouring pencil: ____________
2. book: ____________	11. pencil case: ____________
3. calculator: ____________	12. ruler: ____________
4. eraser: ____________	13. school bag: ____________
5. glue: ____________	14. scissors (pair of): ____________
6. notebook: ____________	15. sharpener: ____________
7. paper: ____________	16. stapler: ____________
8. paper clip: ____________	17. supplies: ____________
9. pen: ____________	18. a. transparent tape: ____________
	b. scotch tape: ____________

II. Nouns

1. period: ____________________
2. break: ____________________
3. classmate: ____________________
4. course: ____________________
5. home: ____________________
6. locker: ____________________
7. lunchtime: ____________________
8. metal: ____________________
9. paragraph: ____________________
10. picture: ____________________
11. ring: ____________________
12. a. spare (period): ____________________
    b. free (period): ____________________

III. Adjectives and Adverbs

1. a. big: ____________________
   b. small: ____________________
2. a. dull: ____________________
   b. sharp: ____________________
3. together: ____________________

adjective + ly ➜ adverb

1. a. careful: ____________________
   b. carefully: ____________________
2. a. correct: ____________________
   b. correctly: ____________________
3. a. permanent: ____________________
   b. permanently: ____________________
4. a. slow: ____________________
   b. slowly: ____________________

For adjectives that end with a consonant "y", change the "y" to "i" and add "ly":

....

5. a. temporary: ____________________
   b. temporarily: ____________________

IV. Verbs

1. to buy: ____________________
2. to cut: ____________________
3. to discuss: ____________________
4. to draw: ____________________
5. to erase: ____________________
6. to examine: ____________________
7. to read: ____________________
8. to see: ____________________
9. to tell: ____________________
10. to try: ____________________
11. to underline: ____________________
12. a. can (verb): ____________________
    b. cannot: ____________________
    c. can't: ____________________
13. a. may: ____________________
    b. may not: ____________________

....

subject pronoun

it ➜ [a thing/an animal]

they ➜ [persons, animals, or things]

V. Other Words

1. below: ____________________
2. following: ____________________

Activity 1, Part 3

What do students use? Select the word from the list on the left that best answers each of the following questions.

binder book calculator eraser glue locker notebook pair of scissors paper paper clip pen pencil pencil case ruler school bag sharpener stapler	**Example:** Students read it. What is it? It is a book. 1. It looks like a big book. It has three metal rings. Students put papers in it. What is it? __________ 2. Students write with it. They can erase their answers. What is it? __________ 3. Students put it on (the back of) pictures to permanently attach them to papers or posters. What is it? __________ 4. When students write with it, they cannot erase their answers. What is it? __________ 5. Students cut paper with it. What is it? __________ 6. Students use it to answer math questions. What is it? __________ 7. Students come to school with it and they go home with it. They put their school supplies, books, binders, etc. in it. What is it? __________ 8. When students come to school in the morning, they put their jackets and some books and notebooks in it. What is it? __________ 9. Students write their journal entries in it. What is it? __________ 10. Students put their small school supplies (pencils, erasers, etc.) in it. What is it? __________ 11. Students use it to hold two or three sheets of paper together temporarily. It is made of metal. What is it? __________

	12. Students use it to attach two or three sheets of paper permanently. It is made of metal. What is it? ________________________________
	13. Students use it when they need to change their answers. What is it? ________________________________
	14. Students write on it. It is found in notebooks and binders. What is it? ________________________________
	15. Students draw lines with it. What is it? ________________________________
	16. Students use it to make their dull pencils sharp. What is it? ________________________________

Activity 1, Part 4

Use the correct subject pronoun (I, you, he, she, it, we, you, or they) and the correct possessive adjective (my, your, his, her, our, their) in the following sentences.

1. Jonathan buys ______________ lunch at the school cafeteria every day.
2. This is your locker. ______________ is new.
3. ______________ go to our afternoon classes after lunch.
4. When the bell rings, I sit in ______________ chair.
5. My friend, Marianne, likes ______________ new math teacher.
6. We eat ______________ lunch in the school cafeteria.
7. My friend, Marianne, likes school. ______________ likes her new friends.
8. The students in my class bring ______________ dictionaries.
9. ______________ can bring your lunch to school or buy your lunch at the cafeteria.
10. You bring ______________ lunch to school every day.
11. Your pencil is old. ______________ is dull.
12. Students come to school early in the morning. ______________ like to speak with their friends before classes begin.
13. When the bell rings, ______________ sit at my desk and wait for the class to begin.
14. ______________ buys his lunch at the school cafeteria every day.
15. The students use ______________ dictionaries in class.

Activity 2, Part 1

Use "May I..." when you want to ask for permission. Write the questions a student asks if he or she wants to...

Example: ... use your dictionary: May I use your dictionary?

1. ... go to the bathroom:

____

2. ... ask a question:

____

3. ... speak to you after class:

____

Activity 2, Part 2

Text 3: The First Afternoon Class

After students eat their lunches, they go to their first afternoon class. In the classroom, they meet their teacher and classmates. The students ask the teacher questions about the school and the course. The teacher answers their questions.

The teacher asks the students to examine their schedules carefully. The teacher tells the students to see their school counsellor after class if there are mistakes in their schedules.

Before the end of class, the teacher gives each student his or her locker number and the books for the course. Finally, the teacher gives the students a list of school supplies to buy. This is Mr. Perreault's list:

binder	notebook	ruler
colouring pencils	paper	(a pair of) scissors
dictionary	paper clips	sharpener
eraser	pen	stapler
glue	pencil case	scotch tape

Activity 2, Part 3

Correct the following sentences.

Example: Students eat their lunches after their afternoon classes.
Students eat their lunches **before** their afternoon classes.

1. The teacher tells the students to see the principal if there are mistakes in their schedules.

 ____

2. The counsellor gives students their locker numbers.

 ____

3. The students buy their books after school today.

 ____

4. The office gives books to the students.

 ____

5. Students eat their lunches in the auditorium after the general assembly.

 ____

Activity 2, Part 4

Number the following sentences in the correct order. Refer to *The First Afternoon Class*. Look for the words "first", "after" and "finally" to help you put the sentences in the correct order.

_______ The teacher asks the students to examine their schedules slowly and carefully.

_______ The teacher writes his or her name on the chalkboard.

_______ The teacher also gives the books for the course to the students.

_______ The teacher tells the students to see the school counsellor after class if there are mistakes in their schedules.

___1___ First, the students eat their lunches.

_______ The students ask the teacher questions about the school and the course.

_______ Finally, the teacher gives the students a list of school supplies to buy.

_______ The teacher meets the students in his or her class.

_______ The teacher gives each student his or her locker number.

_______ After lunch, the students go to their first afternoon class.

_______ The teacher answers their questions.

Activity 2, Part 5

What do students do? Fill in the blanks using verbs from the list on the left. Make sure that the subjects and verbs agree.

answer **ask** bring buy may may not cut discuss draw erase examine give put read tell try show speak work	**Example:** The teacher **asks** questions. 1. The students ______________ to speak English in class. 2. The students ______________ the questions. 3. In art class, many students paint or ______________ pictures. 4. In art class, students use scissors to ______________ pictures for their collages. 5. In math class, the teacher tells the students to use a pencil. When the students use a pencil they can ______________ answers that are not correct. 6. Many students like to ______________ comic books. 7. Students ______________ their books and notebooks on their desks when the bell rings. 8. Students ______________ their school bags to school in the morning. 9. Students ______________ their tests to their teacher before the end of class. 10. The art students ______________ their posters and pictures to their friends. 11. In APD class, students ______________ English. 12. In the chemistry class, students ______________ in groups of two or three. 13. Students ______________ eat their lunches in the classroom. 14. Students ______________ eat in the cafeteria. 15. Students ______________ many things under the microscope. 16. Students ______________ their schedules with their school counsellor. 17. The teacher ______________ the students to go to their lockers. 18. The students ______________ their school supplies after school.

Unit I - Text 4
Show Me Your Schedule, Please

Activity 1, Part 1
Use the correct verbs (do, does, have, has) in the following sentences.

1. He ________________ his homework at 7:00 in the morning.
2. You ________________ your homework after school, don't you?
3. I ________________ one pencil.
4. She ________________ her projects on the weekend.
5. They ________________ their projects together.
6. We ________________ many books and notebooks in our lockers.
7. I ________________ your book in my locker.
8. Do you ________________ many interesting projects in your computer science class?
9. She ________________ her computer projects at school.
10. We ________________ our projects in the library.
11. She ________________ pictures of celebrities in her locker.
12. They ________________ their homework when they have spares.
13. He ________________ a new dictionary.
14. They ________________ APD class after lunch.
15. I ________________ many old and new friends at my school.

Activity 1, Part 2
Solve the following equations and write them in full. (You may use a calculator.)

Example: 13 + 4 = ? ➜ Thirteen plus four equals seventeen.

21 = twenty-one	26 = twenty-six	40 = forty	101 = one hundred and one
22 = twenty-two	27 = twenty-seven	50 = fifty	110 = one hundred and ten
23 = twenty-three	28 = twenty-eight	60 = sixty	200 = two hundred
24 = twenty-four	29 = twenty-nine	70 = seventy	300 = three hundred
25 = twenty-five	30 = thirty	80 = eighty	900 = nine hundred
		90 = ninety	1,000 = one thousand
		100 = one hundred	

math words and symbols: plus: + minus: – equals: =
times: × divided by: ÷

1. $71 - 15 = ?$

2. $8 \times 12 = ?$

3. $2916 + 34 = ?$

4. $369 \div 3 = ?$

5. $341 - 25 = ?$

6. $218 + 52 = ?$

7. $80 \times 12 = ?$

8. $1119 - 34 = ?$

9. $1269 \div 3 = ?$

10. $44 - 16 = ?$

Activity 1, Part 3

Crossword Puzzle: Solve the following crossword puzzle by solving the equations.

DOWN

1. eighteen minus three =
2. three times four =
3. eighty minus sixty =
4. fifty plus twenty =
5. nineteen plus eleven plus ten =
6. two times five =
7. thirty-nine divided by three =
8. ninety minus thirty =
9. seventy plus twenty =
10. forty divided by ten =

ACROSS

11. forty times two =
12. sixteen minus five =
13. twelve plus two =
14. fifteen plus four =
15. three times six =
16. twenty-five times four =
17. fourteen plus three =
18. four times four =
19. one hundred divided by two =
20. seventeen plus thirteen =

Activity 1, Part 4
Write the definition of the words and expressions that are new to you.

Vocabulary List

I. Math Symbols and Words

1. divided by: ____________
2. equals: ____________
3. minus: ____________
4. plus: ____________
5. times: ____________

II. Time

What time is it, please?

1. time: ____________
2. hour: ____________
3. minute: ____________
4. second: ____________
5. (3:00) 3 o'clock: ____________
6. half past: ____________
7. a quarter past: ____________
8. a quarter to: ____________
9. week: ____________
10. weekday: ____________
    a. Monday: ____________
    b. Tuesday: ____________
    c. Wednesday: ____________
    d. Thursday: ____________
    e. Friday: ____________
11. weekend: ____________
    a. Saturday: ____________
    b. Sunday: ____________
12. year: ____________

III. Nouns

1. crossword puzzle: ____________
    a. down: ____________
    b. across: ____________
2. homework: ____________
3. letter: ____________
4. project: ____________

IV. Adjectives

1. dear: ____________
2. different: ____________
3. a. first: ____________
    b. last: ____________
4. good: ____________
5. all: ____________
6. a. short: ____________
    b. long: ____________

V. Adverbs

1. a. once: ____________
    b. twice: ____________
2. all the time: ____________
3. a. always: ____________
    b. never: ____________
4. again: ____________

VI. Expressions

1. Take care: ____________
2. a. from 4:00 to 6:00: ____________
    b. from 4:00 until 6:00: ____________

VII. Verbs	11. to do: ______________________
1. to add: ______________________	I do / we do
2. to finish: ______________________	you do / you do
3. to hear: ______________________	he/she/it does / they do
4. to hope: ______________________	a. do not ➔ don't
5. to miss: ______________________	b. does not ➔ doesn't
6. to move: ______________________	12. to have: ______________________
7. to promise: ______________________	I have / we have
8. to return: ______________________	you have / you have
9. to start: ______________________	he/she/it has / they have
10. to take away: ______________________	....
	VIII. Other Expressions
	1. for example: ______________________
	2. in point form: ______________________

Activity 1, Part 5
Answer the following questions in point form.

Homographs: words that have the same spelling but different meanings

for example: to spring: ________________ to fall: ________________

the spring: ________________ the fall: ________________

We change the time on our clocks twice a year. We set our clocks ahead one hour on the second Sunday in March at 2 o'clock in the morning. We set our clocks back one hour on the first Sunday in November at 2 o'clock in the morning. That is why we say, "Spring forward and fall back."

Do you understand the homographs in the expression?

week
weekdays Monday (Mon.) Tuesday (Tues.) Wednesday (Wed.) Thursday (Thurs.) Friday (Fri.)
weekend Saturday (Sat.) Sunday (Sun.)

Answer the following questions in point form.

1. How many days are there in a week?

____

2. How many weekdays are there in a week?

____

3. a. How many days are there in a weekend?

____

b. What are their names?

____

4. How many weekdays begin with the letter "T"?

____

(If Sunday is the first day of the week...)

5. What is the second day of the week?

____

6. What is the seventh day of the week?

____

7. What is the fifth day of the week?

____

8. What is the third day of the week?

____

9. What is the sixth day of the week?

____

10. What is the fourth day of the week?

____

Activity 2, Part 1

a. Listen to your teacher and answer the question: "What time is it, please?"
b. Draw the short hour hand and long minute hand on the clocks below.

1.	2.	3.
4.	5.	6.
7.	8.	9.
10.	11.	12.

Activity 2, Part 2

What time is it, please?	time:	o'clock
What is the time, please?	hour:	half past (30 minutes)
	minute:	quarter past/to (15 minutes)

a. Write the correct time, using digital time (in hours and minutes).

Example: What time is it, please? It is 7:01. **It is seven-o-one.**
What is the time, please? It is 4:30. **It is four-thirty.**
What is the time, please? It is 4:35. **It is four thirty-five.**

1. What time is it, please? It is 9:06. ______________________.
2. What time is it, please? It is 3:30. ______________________.
3. What time is it, please? It is 4:08. ______________________.
4. What time is it, please? It is 1:05. ______________________.
5. What time is it, please? It is 5:55. ______________________.

b. Write the correct time, using "o'clock" or "half past".

Example: What time is it, please? It is 1:00. **It is one o'clock.**
What is the time, please? It is 1:30. **It is half past one.**

1. What time is it, please? It is 11:00. ______________________.
2. What time is it, please? It is 3:30. ______________________.
3. What time is it, please? It is 4:30. ______________________.
4. What time is it, please? It is 7:00. ______________________.
5. What time is it, please? It is 5:30. ______________________.

c. Write the correct time, using "a quarter past" or "a quarter to".

Example: What time is it, please? It is 7:15. **It is a quarter past seven.**
What is the time, please? It is 7:45. **It is a quarter to eight.**

1. What time is it, please? It is 9:15. ______________________.
2. What time is it, please? It is 3:45. ______________________.
3. What time is it, please? It is 4:45. ______________________.
4. What time is it, please? It is 1:15. ______________________.
5. What time is it, please? It is 2:45. ______________________.

d. Write the correct time, using "minutes past" or "minutes to".

Example: What time is it please? It is 6:13. **It is thirteen minutes past six.**
What is the time please? It is 6:48. **It is twelve minutes to seven.**

1. What time is it, please? It is 9:06. ______________________.
2. What time is it, please? It is 3:30. ______________________.
3. What time is it, please? It is 4:08. ______________________.
4. What time is it, please? It is 1:05. ______________________.
5. What time is it, please? It is 5:55. ______________________.

e. Write the correct time, using "minutes past" and "minutes to".

(31-59) minutes past the hour		(1-29) minutes to the hour
5:31 = It is thirty-one minutes past five.	or	It is twenty-nine minutes to six.
5:40 = It is forty minutes past five.	or	It is twenty minutes to six.
5:45 = It is forty-five minutes past five.	or	It is fifteen minutes to six.
5:55 = It is fifty-five minutes past five.	or	It is five minutes to six.

1. What time is it please? It is 9:36. ______________________.
   or ______________________.
2. What time is it, please? It is 3:40. ______________________.
   or ______________________.
3. What time is it, please? It is 4:08. ______________________.
   or ______________________.
4. What time is it, please? It is 1:05. ______________________.
   or ______________________.
5. What time is it, please? It is 7:45. ______________________.
   or ______________________.

Activity 2, Part 3
Text 4: Hamid's Letter

Tina, Chantal, Hamid, Omar and Josef are good friends. When Josef and his family moved to Argentina, Tina, Chantal, Hamid and Omar promised to write letters to Josef. This is Hamid's letter to Josef.

September 14, 200__

Dear Josef,

How are you? I hope you are fine. How is your new school? Do you like your courses? Do you like your teachers? Have you made new friends?

We are fine. I see Tina, Chantal and Omar at school every day. We miss you very much. We talk about you all the time. We like your letters. We have APD class with a new teacher. His name is Mr. Perreault.

Our schedule is different this year. School begins at nine o'clock. The first period is from nine o'clock to ten o'clock, and then we have our first break. Our first break is from ten o'clock until a quarter past ten. Our second period begins at a quarter past ten and ends at a quarter past eleven, and then we have our second break from a quarter past eleven until twenty-five minutes past eleven. Our third period begins at twenty-five minutes past eleven and finishes at twenty-five minutes past twelve, and then we have our lunch period. It starts at twelve twenty-five and finishes at one o'clock. It is only thirty-five minutes long. Our fourth period is our first afternoon period. It is from one until two, and then we have our third break from two until ten minutes past two. Our last and fifth period is from ten minutes past two until ten minutes past three.

Oh no! I hear the bell. Take care!

Your friend,
Hamid

Activity 2, Part 4
Examine Hamid's schedule.

PERIOD	Monday	Tuesday	Wednesday	Thursday	Friday
1.	Français	Chemistry	Français	Chemistry	Français
2.	History	History	Chemistry	History	Chemistry
3.	Art	Math	Math	Art	Math
4.	APD	Computer Science	APD	Computer Science	APD
5.	Computer Science	Phys. Ed.	(spare)	Phys. Ed.	Phys. Ed.

Decide whether each of the following statements is true or false. Correct the false statements.

Example: Hamid has chemistry class in the afternoon.

False: Hamid has chemistry class in the **morning**.

1. Hamid's APD class is before lunchtime.

2. Hamid has Art three times a week.

3. Hamid has Chemistry twice a week.

4. Hamid has Computer Science once a week.

5. Hamid has Phys. Ed. on Mondays, Tuesdays and Thursdays.

6. Hamid has a spare twice a week.

7. Hamid has Français in the morning.

8. Hamid's art class is on Mondays and Wednesdays.

9. Hamid's history class is in the afternoon.

10. Hamid's math class is in the afternoon.

Activity 2, Part 5
Read Hamid's letter again and complete his schedule.

PERIOD	TIME
Period 1	(9:00 – 10:00)

Activity 2, Part 6

a. **Complete your school schedule. Include school subjects, names of teachers (use Mr., Mrs., Ms. or Miss), room numbers, spares or free periods, breaks and lunchtime.**

Period – Time	Monday	Tuesday	Wednesday	Thursday	Friday

b. **Write five sentences about your schedule. Remember to use the subject pronoun "I" and the possessive adjective "my".**

1. ______________________________
2. ______________________________
3. ______________________________
4. ______________________________
5. ______________________________

Activity 2, Part 7

Use "always", "never", or "sometimes" to complete the following sentences describing Hamid's schedule.

1. Hamid's APD class is ____________________ in the afternoon.
2. Hamid's français class is ____________________ in the morning.
3. Hamid's math class is ____________________ in the morning.
4. Hamid's computer science class is ____________________ in the morning.
5. Hamid's gym class is ____________________ in the morning.
6. Hamid's biology class is ____________________ in the morning.
7. Hamid's history class is ____________________ in the morning.
8. Hamid's computer science class is ____________________ in the afternoon.
9. There are ____________________ two breaks in the morning.
10. There is ____________________ one break in the afternoon.
11. My math class is ____________________ in the afternoon.
12. My gym class is ____________________ in the afternoon.
13. My history class is ____________________ in the morning.
14. My français class is ____________________ in the morning.
15. My biology class is ____________________ in the morning.

Activity 2, Part 8

Look at your schedule and Hamid's schedule to answer the following questions.

Example: Does Hamid have... class in the morning? Yes, he does./No, he doesn't.
Do you have français class in the morning? Yes, I do./No, I don't.

1. Does Hamid have a math class in the morning? ______________________________.
2. Do you have an APD class in the morning? ______________________________.
3. Does Hamid have a phys. ed. class in the morning? ______________________________.
4. Does Hamid have an APD class three times a week? ______________________________.
5. Do you have a computer science class every day? ______________________________.
6. Do you have a français class five times a week? ______________________________.
7. Does Hamid have a spare twice a week? ______________________________.
8. Do you have a spare twice a week? ______________________________.
9. Does Hamid have a math class in the afternoon? ______________________________.
10. Do you have a computer science class every day? ______________________________.
11. Do you have an APD class in the morning? ______________________________.
12. Does Hamid have an art class once a week? ______________________________.
13. Do you have a phys. ed. class in the afternoon? ______________________________.
14. Does Hamid have a français class five times a week? ______________________________.
15. Does Hamid have an APD class in the afternoon? ______________________________.

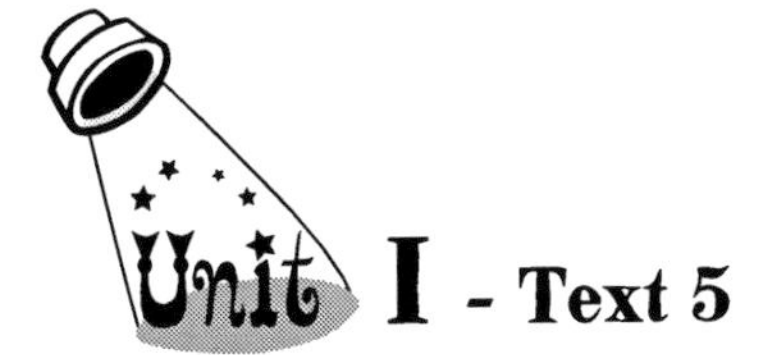

Unit I - Text 5

Names Are Fascinating!

Activity 1, Part 1

a. Read the letters out loud.

b. Listen to your teacher carefully and circle the correct letter in each group.

1.	A	E	Y	I	8.	G	J	K	H	15.	X	S	Z	C
2.	B	D	T	Z	9.	O	L	P	N	16.	S	X	U	W
3.	A	K	J	Y	10.	G	I	J	Y	17.	Z	Q	E	I
4.	Q	U	V	Y	11.	U	Q	W	Y	18.	Q	X	H	A
5.	Z	C	S	V	12.	H	A	K	J	19.	H	G	J	K
6.	E	I	U	A	13.	B	F	G	H	20.	I	E	A	U
7.	B	F	H	A	14.	A	I	U	E	21.	S	X	U	Q

Activity 1, Part 2

Listen carefully and write the letters that your teacher reads out. Rewrite the letters in the correct order. What's the word?

Example: E E A T R H C → TEACHER

1. ___ ___ ___ ___ ___ ___ ___ ___ ___ ___

The word is ______________________________

2. ___ ___ ___ ___ ___ ___ ___ ___ ___ ___

The word is ______________________________

3. ___ ___ ___ ___ ___ ___ ___ ___ ___ ___

The word is ______________________________

4. ___ ___ ___ ___ ___ ___ ___ ___ ___

The word is ______________________________

5. ___ ___ ___ ___ ___ ___ ___ ___ ___

The word is ______________________________

6. ___ ___ ___ ___ ___ ___ ___ ___ ___ ___

The word is ______________________________

Activity 1, Part 3
Write the definition of the words that are new to you.

Vocabulary List

I. Names

1. full name: ____
2. a. first name: ____
   b. given name: ____
3. a. family name: ____
   b. last name: ____
   c. surname: ____
4. a. middle name: ____
   b. middle initial: ____
5. maiden name: ____
6. name of spouse: ____
7. nickname: ____

II. Nouns

1. baby: ____
2. celebrity: ____
3. country: ____
4. chart: ____
5. joy: ____
6. language: ____
7. meaning: ____
8. news: ____
9. schoolmate: ____
10. son: ____
11. thing: ____

III. Letters of the Alphabet

1. alphabet: ____
2. a. letter: ____
   b. capital letter: ____
3. consonant: ____
4. vowel: ____

IV. Verbs

1. to adopt: ____
2. to belong: ____
3. to come (from): ____
4. to follow: ____
5. to get: ____
6. to hyphenate: ____
7. to interview: ____
8. to keep: ____
9. to marry: ____
10. to match: ____
11. to mean: ____
12. to refer: ____
13. to say: ____
14. a. to sound like: ____
    b. to look like: ____
15. to stop: ____
16. to think: ____

V. Adjectives

1. a. different: ____
   b. same: ____
   c. similar: ____
2. fascinating: ____
3. interesting: ____
4. multicultural: ____

VI. Other Words

1. but: ____
2. other: ____

VII. Questions	2. When?: ______
1. What?: ______	a. later: ______
2. When?: ______	b. finally: ______
3. Where?: ______	3. How often?: ______
4. Who?: ______	a. always (100% of the time)
5. Whose?: ______	b. usually (75%-99% of the time)
6. Why?: ______	c. sometimes (50% of the time)
7. How?: ______	4. How many?: ______
8. How often?: ______	a. some: ______
9. How many?: ______	b. only (one): ______
VIII. Questions and Answers	c. many: ______
1. Why?: ______	d. more (than): ______
a. because: ______	

Activity 1, Part 4

a. Write eight questions using words from the vocabulary list.

b. Ask a classmate the questions and write your classmate's answers.

1. What do you ______?

______.

2. When do you ______?

______.

3. Where do you ______?

______.

4. Who is your ______ teacher?

______.

5. When do you ______?

______.

6. How many ______ do you have?

______.

Activity 1, Part 5

Fill in each blank with the word from the list that is the opposite of the underlined word.

after afternoon big different dull first listen many short sit small **vowels** write	**Example:** She likes consonants but he likes **vowels**. 1. He likes big chairs but she likes ____________ chairs. 2. He likes to stand up but she likes to ____________ down. 3. He likes to speak but she likes to ____________. 4. His pictures are the same but her pictures are ____________. 5. She likes to read long books but he likes to read ____________ books. 6. Her pencil is ____________, not sharp. She needs a good sharpener. 7. He likes to read but she likes to ____________. 8. He speaks some languages but she speaks ____________ languages. 9. She has a small school bag but he has a ____________ school bag. 10. His APD class is before lunch but my APD class is ____________ lunch. 11. He likes the last exercise but she likes the ____________ exercise. 12. My français class is in the morning but his français class is in the ____________.

Activity 2, Part 1

Text 5: Names Are Fascinating!

Names are fascinating! In some countries, like Indonesia, people have only one name. In other countries, like Portugal and Brazil, some people have six or more names. In many countries, people usually have three names. They have a "given" or "first" name, a "middle" name, and a "family" name.

Many given or middle names have male and female versions. For example, the name "Louise" is the female version of "Louis". Many first and middle names have short forms too. For example, Cathy is the short form of Catherine.

There are also variations of names in different languages. For example, the Spanish name "Maria" and the French name "Marie" are variations of the English name "Mary".

Did you know that girls and women have maiden names, but boys and men don't? What is a maiden name? In many countries, when a woman marries, she stops using her maiden name and adopts her husband's family name. But in some countries like Somalia, a married woman does not adopt her husband's family name. She keeps her maiden name.

Did you know that the family name does not always follow the first and middle names? In countries like China and Vietnam, people say or write their family names first, and then they say or write their first and middle names. The most popular family name in the world is Li. More than 87 million people have it!

Did you know that name traditions are changing? Some children have hyphenated family names. Why? Because some parents give their children the father's family name and the mother's maiden name (e.g., Jeanne Lamasse-Gendron).

Names are interesting because they have different sources and meanings. For example, names like "Marie" or "Jérôme" come from different religions or mythologies. Many family names like "Fisher" or "Cooke" started with the occupation of the families. Many family names mean "son of" or "belonging to". For example, "Samuelson" means "son" of Samuel and "MacDonald" means "belonging to" the family of Donald. "O'", "bin," "Fitz," "zadeh," "ski" and "ov" also mean "son of" or "belonging to". Sometimes, names refer to family characteristics like "Long" or "Short". Many names like "da Vinci" or "Esfahani" refer to the place in which the family originally lived. Finally, some people have names like "Rose" or "Joy" that are also the names of things.

Babies receive very interesting names, but sometimes they get nicknames like "Tiger" or "Einstein". People give nicknames to friends, members of their family, or celebrities. Do you have a nickname? Do your brothers or sisters have nicknames? Can you think of three celebrities who have nicknames?

Usually there is a reason behind a nickname. What is the reason behind the nicknames of some of your classmates, or those of certain celebrities?

Activity 2, Part 2

a. Match the following male names with their female versions.

1. _____ Jules	A. Jacqueline
2. _____ Samuel	B. Patricia
3. _____ Patrick	C. Samantha
4. _____ Robert	D. Julia
5. _____ Jack	E. Roberta

b. Can you think of three others?

_________________________ : _________________________

_________________________ : _________________________

_________________________ : _________________________

Activity 2, Part 3

a. Match the short forms on the right with the original names on the left.

1. My name is William. Many people call me ______________.	A. Lin
2. My name is Robert. Many people call me ______________.	B. Bill
3. My name is Margaret. Many people call me ______________.	C. Jim
4. My name is Richard. Many people call me ______________.	D. Chuck
5. My name is Charles. Many people call me ______________.	E. Maggie, Peggy
6. My name is James. Many people call me ______________.	F. Dick
7. My name is Carolyn. Many people call me ______________.	G. Bob

b. Can you think of three other names?

Original Name **Short Form**

______________________ : ______________________

______________________ : ______________________

______________________ : ______________________

Activity 2, Part 4

Can you match the variations of the following names? Write the letter of the English name next to the matching name on the left.

1. _____ Yusuf	A. John
2. _____ Guillaume	B. Steven
3. _____ Juanita	C. Joseph
4. _____ Giovanni, Juan	D. Richard
5. _____ Miguel	E. William
6. _____ Estefan	F. Mary
7. _____ Ricardo	G. Angela
8. _____ Miriam	H. Michael
9. _____ Giorgio	I. George
10. _____ Angélique	J. Jane

Activity 2, Part 5

Interview your classmates. What are the sources or meanings of their names? Complete the chart below with the names of your classmates and schoolmates, and the names of historical figures and people in the news.

Religion or Mythology	Occupation	Characteristics
______________________	______________________	______________________
______________________	______________________	______________________
______________________	______________________	______________________
"Son of" or "Belonging to"	**Geography**	**Nouns**
______________________	______________________	______________________
______________________	______________________	______________________
______________________	______________________	______________________

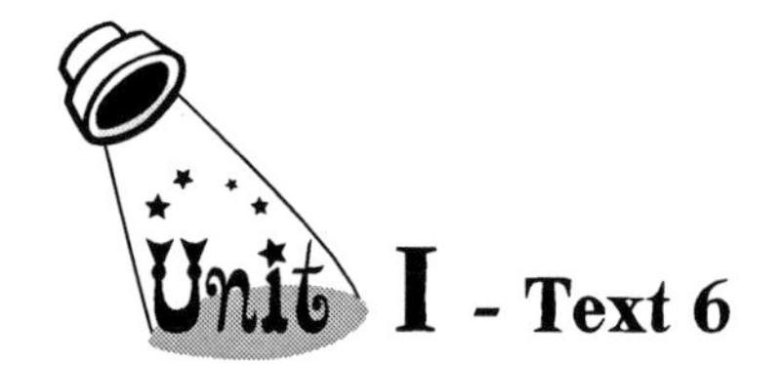

Unit I - Text 6

More Information, Please

Activity 1, Part 1
Write the definition of the words and expressions that are new to you.

Vocabulary List

I. Forms

1. application form: ______________
2. health form: ______________
3. information form: ______________
4. job application form: ______________
5. registration form: ______________

II. Dates

1. age: ______________
2. birthday: ______________
3. calendar: ______________
4. date: ______________
5. day (1st to 31st): ______________
6. month: ______________
   a. January (Jan.)
   b. February (Feb.)
   c. March (Mar.)
   d. April (Apr.)
   e. May (May)
   f. June (June)
   g. July (July)
   h. August (Aug.)
   i. September (Sept.)
   j. October (Oct.)
   k. November (Nov.)
   l. December (Dec.)
7. a. year: ______________
   b. leap year: ______________
8. a. school year (September to June)
   b. grade: ______________

III. Verbs

1. to be born: ______________
2. to call: ______________
3. to print: ______________
4. to remember: ______________
5. to sing: ______________

IV. Nouns

1. abbreviation: ______________
2. birth: ______________
3. check: ______________
4. cycle: ______________
5. party: ______________
6. song: ______________
7. a. sun: ______________
   b. moon: ______________
8. world: ______________

V. Other Words

1. all the rest: ______________
2. except: ______________
3. a. after: ______________
   b. before: ______________
   c. between: ______________

VI. Adjective/Adverb

clear/ly: ______________

VII. Adjectives

1. complicated: ______________
2. important: ______________

Ordinal Numbers		
11 ➔ 11th = eleventh 12 ➔ 12th = twelfth 13 ➔ 13th = thirteenth 14 ➔ 14th = fourteenth 15 ➔ 15th = fifteenth	16 ➔ 16th = sixteenth 17 ➔ 17th = seventeenth 18 ➔ 18th = eighteenth 19 ➔ 19th = nineteenth 20 ➔ 20th = twentieth	21 ➔ 21st = twenty-first 22 ➔ 22nd = twenty-second 23 ➔ 23rd = twenty-third 24th, 25th, 26th, 27th, 28th, 29th, 30th 31st = thirty-first

Activity 1, Part 2
Answer the following questions in complete sentences.

Example: What is the tenth month of the year? **October is the tenth month of the year.**

1. What is the fourth month of the year?

   ______________________________.

2. What is the eleventh month of the year?

   ______________________________.

3. What is the first month of the year?

   ______________________________.

4. What is the eighth month of the year?

   ______________________________.

5. What is the seventh month of the year?

   ______________________________.

6. What is the third month of the year?

   ______________________________.

7. What is the second month of the year?

   ______________________________.

Activity 1, Part 3
Complete the sentences below.

1. There are 7 days in every ______________.
2. There are 12 months in every ______________.
3. There are 365 ______________ in a year.
4. There are 52 ______________ in every year.
5. Every ______________ has 30 or 31 days, except February.

6. The day after Saturday is ______________________________.
7. The day before Monday is ______________________________.
8. The day between Wednesday and Friday is ______________________________.
9. Saturday and Sunday are called the ______________________________.
10. Monday, Tuesday, Wednesday, Thursday and Friday are called ______________________________.
11. The two days of the week that begin with the letter "T" are ______________________________ and ______________________________.
12. There are two days of the week that begin with the letter "S": ______________________________ and ______________________________.
13. You do not pronounce the first letter "D" in this weekday: ______________________________.

Activity 1, Part 4
Text 6: More Information, Please

There are many different forms we complete. For example, we complete school registration forms, health forms, job application forms and many others. Forms ask for information. When we complete a form, we print our answers clearly because all forms are important. First, forms ask for our full name. They also ask for our date of birth.

Date of Birth

A person's date of birth is sometimes complicated! Why? Because there are many different calendars in the world. For example, there is the Christian calendar, Hebrew calendar, Hindu calendar, Muslim calendar and many others.

To complete a form in Canada, we write our "Gregorian" date of birth. What is the Gregorian calendar? It is the Christian calendar. The Gregorian calendar year is more than 2,000 years old. Do you know why? Because it begins with the year of the birth of Jesus Christ. He was born more than 2,000 years ago. The letters "B.C.", which stand for before Christ, refer to years before his birth.

Days and months of the Gregorian calendar are based on Greek or Roman myths or mythological characters. For example, March refers to Mars, the god of war.

Many holidays date back to Roman times as well. The celebration of Valentine's Day began in the time of the Roman Empire and Easter is associated with the arrival of spring.

Note that many holidays in Canada are celebrated on a Monday so that people can have a long weekend. In Ontario, there is also a civic holiday in August.

The Gregorian calendar changes with the cycle of the sun. (The months do not change every 28 days with the cycle of the moon.) It divides the 365 days of the year into 12 months. There are sometimes 28, 29, 30, or 31 days in a month. It is complicated. Children sing this short song to remember how many days there are in each month:

Thirty days hath September,

April, June and November.

All the rest have thirty-one,

except February alone,

Which hath four and twenty-four

'til leap year gives it one day more.

The Gregorian calendar has a leap year once every four years. The leap year has 366 days. The month of February has 29 days in the leap year. If your birthday is on February 29th, how old are you? Do you count your age in years or birthday parties?

Here are the 12 months of the Gregorian year and their abbreviations, in English.

January (Jan.)	April (Apr.)	July (July)	October (Oct.)
February (Feb.)	May (May)	August (Aug.)	November (Nov.)
March (Mar.)	June (June)	September (Sept.)	December (Dec.)

It is a different year in different calendars. Each calendar numbers the years differently for a reason. Why do different calendars number the years differently? That is a good question!

Many calendar dates and holidays in Canada are associated with religious beliefs, for example Christmas and Easter.

Valentine's Day is associated with poems, heart shapes, chocolates and flowers.

There are many different ways of celebrating birthdays. In Canada, gifts, a cake, party hats, streamers and balloons, blowing out candles with an extra candle for good luck, making a wish, singing a birthday song, etc. are all part of the traditional way of celebrating birthdays.

How does your family celebrate birthdays?

How are different holidays celebrated around the world?

Activity 1, Part 5
Look at your calendar and write the correct dates below. Use abbreviations for the dates.
Example: January 17, 2002 → Jan. 17, 2002

1. The first Tuesday in March: ______________________
2. The fourth Monday in September: ______________________
3. The second Friday in October: ______________________
4. The third Wednesday in May: ______________________
5. The first Thursday in February: ______________________

Activity 1, Part 6
Number the following days in the correct order. Check a calendar if necessary.

_______ Halloween

___1___ New Year's Day

_______ Canada Day

_______ Groundhog Day

_______ Christmas Day

_______ Labour Day

_______ Valentine's Day

_______ Remembrance Day

_______ Christmas Eve

_______ Thanksgiving Day

_______ St. Jean Baptiste Day

Activity 1, Part 7
Answer the following questions in complete sentences.

Example: How many days **does** January have? ➔ January **has** 31 days.
How many days **do** April and June have? ➔ April and June **have** 30 days.

1. How many days does February have in a leap year?

____.

2. How many days do March and July have?

____.

3. How many days does August have?

____.

4. How many days do April and June have?

____.

5. How many days do October and December have?

____.

6. How many days does February usually have?

____.

Activity 1, Part 8
Write the date in numbers: YYYY (year) / MM (month) / DD (day).

Example: July 16, 1989 → 1989/07/16

1. February 15, 1981 ______ / ______ / ______
2. September 25, 1987 ______ / ______ / ______
3. April 19, 1999 ______ / ______ / ______
4. December 11, 2000 ______ / ______ / ______
5. March 1, 2002 ______ / ______ / ______

Activity 1, Part 9
Write the following dates in full.
Example: 1992/03/14 → March 14, 1992

1. 2005/06/01: ______________________________
2. 2003/09/14: ______________________________
3. 2009/05/19: ______________________________
4. 1912/11/15: ______________________________
5. 2001/07/03: ______________________________
6. 2012/12/12: ______________________________
7. 1901/08/01: ______________________________

Activity 2, Part 1
Check library resources or visit a website to find out why calendars number the years differently.
Example:

The Gregorian calendar (2000):
The Gregorian calendar starts with the year of the birth of Jesus Christ.

1. The Hindu calendar (2057):

______________________________.

2. The Jewish calendar (5761):

______________________________.

3. The Muslim calendar (1421):

______________________________.

4. Other calendar:

______________________________.

Activity 2, Part 2

Examine this year's calendar and write the date (or start date) for the following. Check a website if necessary.

Example: Halloween is on (day of the week), October 31, 20 ___ ___.

1. Labour Day: (Canada/USA) ______________________________.
2. Rosh Hashanah: (Jewish) ______________________________.
3. Yom Kippur: (Jewish) ______________________________.
4. Thanksgiving Day: (Canada) ______________________________.
5. Divali: (Hindu) ______________________________.
6. Ramadan: (Muslim) ______________________________.
7. Id-ul-Fitr: (Muslim) ______________________________.
8. Halloween: (Canada/USA) ______________________________.
9. Remembrance Day: (Canada/USA/Europe) ______________________________.
10. Kwanzaa: (African) ______________________________.
11. Christmas Day: (Christian) ______________________________.
12. New Year's Eve: (Christian) ______________________________.
13. New Year's Day: (Christian) ______________________________.
14. Yuan Tan: (Chinese) ______________________________.
15. Groundhog Day: (Canada/USA) ______________________________.
16. Valentine's Day: (Canada/USA) ______________________________.
17. St. Patrick's Day: (Canada/USA/Ireland) ______________________________.
18. April Fool's Day: (Canada/USA/France) ______________________________.
19. Mother's Day: (Canada/USA) ______________________________.
20. Father's Day: (Canada/USA) ______________________________.
21. Victoria Day: (Canada) ______________________________.
22. St. Jean Baptiste Day: (Canada) ______________________________.
23. Canada Day: (Canada) ______________________________.
24. Independence Day: (USA) ______________________________.
25. Bastille Day: (France) ______________________________.

Activity 2, Part 3
a. Evaluation Criteria: Research

Name: ______________________________ Date: ____________________

Selected Calendar Date: ____

Criteria	Level 1	Level 2	Level 3	Level 4
Research is – complete – clear – organized Paragraph is free of errors in – spelling – punctuation – capitalization – the conjugation of regular verbs – the plural and possessive forms of nouns – subject-verb agreement – the negative and interrogative forms of sentences				
Student uses complete sentences and correct vocabulary to communicate information.				
Comments/Suggestions				

b. Evaluation Criteria: Poster

Name: ______________________________ Date: ______________

Selected Calendar Date: ______________________________

Criteria	Level 1	Level 2	Level 3	Level 4
Title is clear and original.				
Title is correctly written.				
Poster is neat, clear and well laid out.				
Poster is original and creative.				
Poster makes effective use of colour, fonts, graphics, etc.				
Poster is detailed and complete.				
Poster presentation is clear, complete and interesting.				
Correct vocabulary and sentence structure are used thoughout presentation.				
Correct pronunciation and grammar are used throughout presentation.				

Comments/Suggestions:

Unit I - Text 7

Where Do You Live?

Activity 1, Part 1
What is Your Nationality?

Some nationalities end with -ISH.

Country		*Nationality*
Denmark	➜	Danish
Finland	➜	Finnish
Great Britain	➜	British
Ireland	➜	Irish
Poland	➜	Polish
Scotland	➜	Scottish
Spain	➜	Spanish
Sweden	➜	Swedish
Turkey	➜	Turkish

Some nationalities end with -IAN.

Country		*Nationality*
Algeria	➜	Algerian
Argentina	➜	Argentinian
Australia	➜	Australian
Brazil	➜	Brazilian
Canada	➜	Canadian
Colombia	➜	Colombian
Egypt	➜	Egyptian
Ethiopia	➜	Ethiopian
India	➜	Indian
Iran	➜	Iranian
Italy	➜	Italian
Jordan	➜	Jordanian
Syria	➜	Syrian
Belgium	➜	Belgian

Exceptions

Country		*Nationality*
France	➜	French
Germany	➜	German
Greece	➜	Greek
The Netherlands	➜	Dutch
Norway	➜	Norwegian
Peru	➜	Peruvian
The Philippines	➜	Filipino
Switzerland	➜	Swiss

Some nationalities end with -ESE.

Country		*Nationality*
Burma	➜	Burmese
China	➜	Chinese
Japan	➜	Japanese
Lebanon	➜	Lebanese
Portugal	➜	Portugese
Taiwan	➜	Taiwanese
Vietnam	➜	Vietnamese

Some nationalities end with -AN.

Country		*Nationality*
Afghanistan	➜	Afghan
Cuba	➜	Cuban
Jamaica	➜	Jamaican
Mexico	➜	Mexican
Morocco	➜	Moroccan
The United States of America	➜	American

Some nationalities end with -I.

Country		*Nationality*
Iraq	➜	Iraqi
Israel	➜	Israeli
Kuwait	➜	Kuwaiti
Pakistan	➜	Pakistani
Somalia	➜	Somali

Some nationalities end with -EAN.

Country		*Nationality*
Chile	➜	Chilean
Korea	➜	Korean

Activity 1, Part 2

a. Write complete sentences to describe the nationality of each person.

Example: Omar/Ethiopia: ➜ This is my friend, Omar. He is from Ethiopia. He is Ethiopian.
Lisa/Poland: ➜ This is my friend Lisa. She is from Poland. She is Polish.
Jean and Cathy. ➜ These are my friends Jean and Cathy. They are from Canada. They are Canadian.

1. Juan/Chile:

____.

2. Henri and Julie/France:

____.

3. Marie/Peru:

____.

4. Myriam and Avi/Israel:

____.

b. Write complete sentences to describe the nationality of each person.

Example: Omar/Ethiopia: ➜ Omar is from Ethiopia. He is Ethiopian.
Lisa, Stasha /Poland: ➜ Lisa and Stasha are from Poland. They are Polish.

1. I/Spain:

____.

2. Marie/Ireland:

____.

3. Pierre and Marc/France:

____.

4. Ahmed and I/Somalia:

____.

5. You/Canada:

____.

6. Mr. Chisho and I/Japan:

____.

7. Ms. Swinna/Denmark:

    ____.

8. Frederick and Lisa/Switzerland:

    ____.

9. Miss Ling/China:

    ____.

10. Mr. Cobbs/Great Britain:

    ____.

11. Michel and I/Belgium:

    ____.

12. Louisa and I/Spain:

    ____.

13. I/Finland:

    ____.

14. John and Janet/United States:

    ____.

15. Hassan/Turkey:

    ____.

Activity 1, Part 3
Text 7: Where Do You Live?

Forms usually ask questions about your country of birth, country of residence and country of citizenship. Your country of birth is the country in which you were born. Your country of residence is the country in which you live. And your country of citizenship is the country in which you have obtained (or could obtain) a passport.

People who are citizens of a country usually have a passport or can get a passport in that country. For example, if you are a citizen of the United States, you have or can get an American passport. If you are a citizen of Brazil, you have a Brazilian passport.

Often, our country of citizenship, our country of birth and our country of residence are the same, but not always.

Our country of citizenship is sometimes complicated because different countries have different laws.

Usually, if you are born in a country, you are a citizen of the country. For example, if you are born in Canada, you are a Canadian citizen.

Many people choose their country of citizenship when they immigrate. Many Canadians and Americans immigrated to North America from other countries around the world.

Passports

Some people have more than one passport because they are citizens of more than one country. For example, if you are a Canadian citizen, you can also be a citizen of another country. How many students are there in your class with only one citizenship? What is their citizenship?

How many students are there in your class with more than one citizenship? What are their citizenships?

There are also many people who have different nationalities but the same passport. Do you know what this passport is called? It is called the European Union Passport. Many Europeans have a "European" passport, but only if they are citizens of the countries that are members of the European Union. This is the history of the European Union.

1. First, Belgium, Germany, France, Italy, Luxembourg and the Netherlands created a small "union" called the "European Union" in 1951.
2. In 1973, Denmark, Ireland and the United Kingdom joined the European Union.
3. In 1981, Greece joined the European Union.
4. Then, in 1986, Spain and Portugal joined the European Union.
5. In 1995, Austria, Finland and Sweden joined the European Union.
6. On May 1, 2004, many former communist countries such as Poland and Slovakia joined the European Union.

More countries in eastern and southern Europe want to join the union too.

The citizens of these different European countries have their national citizenships and their European citizenships. That means if you are French, you have a French European Union passport, and if you are Spanish, you have a Spanish European Union passport.

Why did these countries create the European Union? That is a good question!

Did you know that...

- While Australia is the world's smallest continent, it's also the world's largest island?
- The first letter of every continent's name is the same as the last: AmericA, AntarcticA, EuropE, AsiA, AustraliA, AfricA?
- The Great Wall of China is the largest construction project ever undertaken by humans, and its stones could build an 8-foot wall around the world along the equator?
- There is a city called Rome on every continent in the world?
- Approximately 50% of the earth is covered by the Pacific Ocean?
- There are about 5,000 languages in the world?
- All the planets in our solar system could be placed inside the planet Jupiter?

Activity 1, Part 4

Imagine you are making new "continental unions". Look at a map and place ten countries in the unions below. Write the names of the countries and their capital cities in English.

AFRICAN Union		(North and South) AMERICAN Union	
Country	Capital City	Country	Capital City
1. ________		1. ________	
2. ________		2. ________	
3. ________		3. ________	
4. ________		4. ________	
5. ________		5. ________	
6. ________		6. ________	
7. ________		7. ________	
8. ________		8. ________	
9. ________		9. ________	
10. ________		10. ________	

ASIAN Union			
Country	Capital City	Country	Capital City
1. ________		6. ________	
2. ________		7. ________	
3. ________		8. ________	
4. ________		9. ________	
5. ________		10. ________	

Activity 1, Part 5
Singular or plural? Fill in each blank with the singular or plural of a word in the left-hand column. Use each word only once.

Africa America Asia Australia capital city city continent country Earth Europe land North province South state town village water	We live on a planet called (1) ____________________. Earth is divided into (2) ____________________ and (3) ____________________. The land is divided into five big areas called (4) ____________________. The names of the five big areas are (5) ____________________, (6) ____________________, (7) ____________________, (8) ____________________ and (9) ____________________. The American continent is divided into (10) ____________________ and (11) ____________________ America. Each continent is divided into (12) ____________________. Some countries like Canada are divided into (13) ____________________. Some countries like the United States are divided into (14) ____________________. Each country has only one (15) ____________________. However, in each country there are some large (16) ____________________ and many small (17) ____________________ and (18) ____________________.

Activity 2, Part 1
Write the definition of the words and expressions that are new to you.

Vocabulary List

I. Words About Our World	
1. planet: ____________________	7. a. country: ____________________
2. earth: ____________________	b. (of) residence: ____________________
3. world: ____________________	c. (of) citizenship: ____________________
4. a. land: ____________________	d. nationality: ____________________
b. water: ____________________	8. province: ____________________
5. a. map: ____________________	9. state: ____________________
b. globe: ____________________	10. capital city: ____________________
6. continent: ____________________	11. city: ____________________
	12. town: ____________________
	13. village: ____________________

II. Address

1. apartment: ______
2. house: ______
3. north: ______
4. south: ______
5. east: ______
6. west: ______
7. avenue: ______
8. boulevard: ______
9. crescent: ______
10. road: ______
11. street: ______
12. postal code: ______

III. Telephone

1. area code: ______
2. telephone number: ______
3. extension: ______
4. a. business (bus.) telephone number: ______

   b. work number: ______

IV. Verbs

1. to become: ______
2. to immigrate: ______
3. to join: ______
4. to list: ______
5. to live: ______
6. to make certain: ______
7. to spell: ______

V. Nouns

1. case: ______
2. law: ______
3. member: ______
4. passport: ______

VI. How Often

1. always: ______
2. often: ______
3. sometimes: ______
4. never: ______

Activity 2, Part 2

Addresses are usually very long. That is why we use abbreviations.

Find the correct abbreviations for the following words and Canadian provinces.

1. __B__ apartment	A. c/o
2. _____ Avenue	B. apt.
3. _____ Boulevard	C. Ave.
4. _____ Crescent	D. Blvd.
5. _____ Road	E. Cres.
6. _____ Street	F. Dr.
7. _____ North	G. E.
8. _____ South	H. N.
9. _____ East	I. Rte.
10. _____ West	J. Rd.
11. _____ care of	K S.
12. _____ Route	L. St.
13. _____ Drive	M. W.
14. _____ British Columbia	N. Alta., AB
15. _____ Alberta	O. B.C., BC
16. _____ Saskatchewan	P. Man., MB
17. _____ Manitoba	Q. N.B., NB
18. _____ Nunavut	R. N.L., NL
19. _____ Ontario	S. N.S., NS
20. _____ Quebec	T. Ont., ON
21. _____ New Brunswick	U. Nunavut, NU
22. _____ Nova Scotia	V. P.E.I., PE
23. _____ Prince Edward Island	W. Que., QC
24. _____ Newfoundland and Labrador	X. Sask., SK
25. _____ Yukon	Y. Yukon, YT
26. _____ Northwest Territories	Z. N.W.T., NT

Activity 2, Part 3
Write your school address in the return address area, and then write your own address as if you were sending this envelope to yourself.

Return Address

____
____
____
____

Canada

Name ______________________

Number + Street ______________________

City + Province ______________________

Postal Code ______________________

Activity 2, Part 4
Complete the following form with your own information. Print neatly and pay attention to capitalization.

Student ID Card

Last Name: ______________________ First Name: ______________________

Date of Birth: ______________________ Age: ______________________

Country of Birth: ______________________ Nationality: ______________________

Home Address: ____
(Number and Street)

____
(City) (Province)

____
(Postal Code) (Telephone Number)

Name of Parent or Guardian: ____

School Address: ____
(Number and Street)

____
(City) (Province)

____
(Postal Code) (Telephone Number)

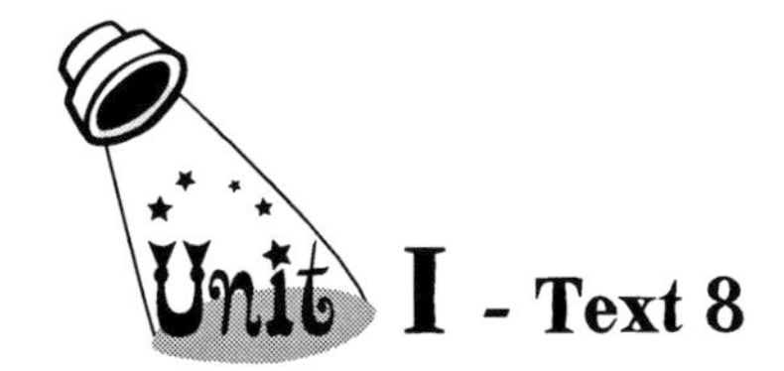

Family and Next of Kin

Unit I - Text 8

Activity 1, Part 1
Write the definition of the words and expressions that are new to you.

Vocabulary List

I. Family

1. relation/relationship: ____________
2. family tree: ____________
3. a. family: ____________
   b. nuclear family: ____________
   c. extended family: ____________
   d. adoptive family: ____________
   e. step family: ____________
4. parent: ____________
   a. mother: ____________
   b. father: ____________
   c. (mother's/father's) side: ____________
5. child/children (plural): ____________
   a. daughter: ____________
   b. son: ____________
6. grandparent: ____________
   a. grandfather: ____________
   b. grandmother: ____________
7. grandchild: ____________
   a. granddaughter: ____________
   b. grandson: ____________
8. a. partner: ____________
   b. spouse: ____________
   c. husband: ____________
   d. wife: ____________
9. sibling: ____________
   a. brother: ____________
   b. sister: ____________
10. (other) relative: ____________
    a. aunt: ____________
    b. uncle: ____________
    c. cousin: ____________
11. child of your brother/sister: ____________
    a. nephew: ____________
    b. niece: ____________
12. in-law: ____________
    (father-, mother-, sister-, brother-,
    daughter-, son-, parents-in-law)
13. godparent: ____________
14. guardian: ____________

II. Marital Status

1. divorced: ____________
2. married: ____________
3. other: ____________
4. single: ____________
5. widowed: ____________

III. Nouns

1. card: ____________
2. clinic: ____________
3. health: ____________
4. insurance: ____________
5. landed immigrant: ____________
6. lawyer: ____________
7. physician/doctor: ____________
8. refugee: ____________
9. resident: ____________
10. test: ____________
11. widow: ____________
12. widower: ____________

IV. Verbs	3. medical: ______________
1. to contact: ______________	4. real: ______________
2. to imagine: ______________	**VI. Expressions**
V. Adjectives	1. in case of emergency: ______________
1. close: ______________	2. OHIP/Ontario Health Insurance Plan: ______________
2. dead: ______________	3. next of kin: ______________

Activity 1, Part 2
Choose the correct marital status and write the letter on the short line. Use each letter only once.

1. _____ My spouse is dead.	A. divorced
2. _____ I am not married.	B. married
3. _____ I have papers from my lawyer. They say I am not married anymore.	C. other
4. _____ I am not married, but I live with my partner.	D. single
5. _____ I live with my spouse.	E. widowed

Activity 1, Part 3
Crossword Puzzle. Solve the crossword by writing the name of a family member.

DOWN

1. I am a woman. I am married to a man. He is my ______________.
2. We are three siblings. He is my brother. She is my ______________.
3. The son of my brother or sister is my ______________.
4. I have two parents: my mother and my ______________.
5. The child of my aunt or uncle is my ______________.
6. We are three siblings. She is my sister. He is my ______________.
7. The brother of my father or mother is my ______________.

ACROSS

8. I have four grandparents: two grandfathers and two ______________.
9. I have two children: a girl, my daughter, and a boy, my ______________.
10. The mother and father of my mother are my grandmother and my ______________.
11. The sister of my mother or the sister of my father is my ______________.
12. I am a man. I am married to a woman. She is my ______________.
13. I have two parents: my father and my ______________.
14. The daughter of my brother or my sister is my ______________.
15. I have two children. My boy is my son; my girl is my ______________.

Activity 1, Part 4
Text 8: Family and Next of Kin

Forms often ask for information about family and next of kin. If you are married, you may write information about your spouse too. Usually, you write the maiden name of your wife or the full name of your husband. You sometimes write the occupation and the business telephone number of your spouse.

Some forms ask for the name, business telephone number and address of your family physician. They also ask for your OHIP number. Do you know what "OHIP" is? It is the Ontario Health Insurance Plan. In Ontario, every resident, landed immigrant, or refugee waiting to become a Canadian citizen has an OHIP card. Before you can see the doctor or do medical tests, clinics and laboratories, make sure you have your OHIP card.

Forms sometimes ask for the name, relationship and telephone number of your "next of kin". That means a close family member. You usually write the name of a family member who lives in your city. Sometimes you write the names of your parents, your brother or sister, or your spouse. Sometimes you write the name of one of your children, a niece, a nephew, or another member of your family. If you don't have a family member who lives in your city, you write the name of a close friend. This information is needed in case there is a medical emergency.

Whose name do you write? Who are the members of your family? In many countries, people live in "nuclear" families. The members of the nuclear family are usually the parents and the children. In other countries, people live in "extended" families. The members of the extended family are all the members of the family: parents, grandparents, children and grandchildren, nephews, nieces, aunts, uncles, cousins and in-laws.

Activity 1, Part 5

List the names of your family members. Indicate their relationship to you.

First Name: ____________________ Relationship: ____________________

____________________ ____________________

____________________ ____________________

____________________ ____________________

____________________ ____________________

____________________ ____________________

____________________ ____________________

Activity 1, Part 6

Imagine this is your family tree. Look at it carefully and answer the questions that follow.

(+ = married)

Richard Dubuc + Joanne Viau (Dubuc)
Georges Thibault + Danielle Forget (Thibault)
Julie Dubuc
Donald Dubuc + Anne Thibault (Dubuc)
Roger Thibault
Jean Dubuc
YOU
Lucie Dubuc + Antoine Joly
Daniel Joly
Geneviève Joly

Example: Who is Danielle Forget (Thibault)? **She is my grandmother on my mother's side.**

1. Who is Anne Thibault (Dubuc)? ____________________.
2. Who is Donald Dubuc? ____________________.
3. Who is Jean Dubuc? ____________________.
4. Who is Lucie Dubuc? ____________________.
5. Who is Daniel Joly? ____________________.
6. Who is Geneviève Joly? ____________________.
7. Who is Julie Dubuc? ____________________.
8. Who is Roger Thibault? ____________________.
9. Who is Richard Dubuc? ____________________.
10. Who is Joanne Viau (Dubuc)? ____________________.
11. Who is Georges Thibault? ____________________.
12. Who is Antoine Joly? ____________________.

Please Complete This Form

I - Text 9

Activity 1, Part 1
Circle the letters of the words that should be capitalized in the following sentences.

1. My school is located on main street next to the shell gas station.
2. Tomorrow i will send a birthday card to my uncle tom, who will be 40 years old next tuesday.
3. An american, neil armstrong, was the first man to land on the moon. this historic event took place in july 1969.
4. I went to see the movie "The raiders of the lost ark" with my friend mary.
5. Tom and helen visited the parliament buildings in ottawa, ontario.

Activity 1, Part 2
Complete your own information form.

Surname/Family Name:	First/Given Name:	Middle Name:

Grade: ___________	Age: ________	Date of Birth (yyyy/mm/dd): ___/___/___	Sex: M ☐ F ☐

Address:	Apt. No.	City/Town	Province	Postal Code

Next of Kin's name:	Relationship:	Telephone Number (Home):	Telephone Number (Work):

Family Physician:	Country of Residence:
Telephone Number:	
OHIP Number:	Country of Citizenship:

Activity 1, Part 3
Listen carefully to your teacher and complete the form below. Print clearly.

Surname/Family Name:	First/Given Name:	Middle Name:	
Age: ________ / Date of Birth (yyyy/mm/dd): ___/___/___	Marital Status: Married ☐ Single ☐ Divorced ☐ Other ☐	Sex: M ☐ F ☐	
Address: Apt. No.	City/Town	Province	Postal Code
Spouse's Name: Spouse's Occupation:	Telephone Number (Home): Telephone Number (Work):		
Family Physician: Address: Telephone Number:	Country of Residence: Country of Citizenship:		
Next of Kin's name:	Telephone Number:	Relationship:	

Activity 1, Part 4
Circle the letters of the words that should be capitalized in the following paragraph.

Hello. my name is christophe jules arial. my wife, karine bourdon, and i are new to this city. we both work close to école secondaire des ponts. i am a computer technician and she is a lab technician. we live in a big apartment building on merton ave. our apartment is on the fourth floor. i was born in montreal, quebec on the 3rd of august. if you would like to visit our places of work, please ask your teacher to call karine or me at 111-555-1291.

Activity 1, Part 5

Read Toni's journal entry and complete her registration form. Print the information clearly. List the missing information. Compare your list to a classmate's list and give a few reasons that would justify the missing information.

Text 9: Please Complete this Form

Hi. My name is Toni Gardoni. But Toni is not my given name. My real name is Antonia Lena Gardoni. I was born on March 6 in Florence, Italy. I am an Italian citizen, but I am also very proud to be a Canadian citizen. I am 16 years old and I am in Grade 10. I live on 326 Franklin Street. My postal code is K1L 1A2. I live with my mother, Helena Verdi, and my sister and two brothers. Our home phone number is 111-555-3963.

My mother is a school counsellor. She works at a school. She works from 8:30 to 5:30 on weekdays. I call her at work sometimes. Her number is 111-555-9731.

My father is a nurse. He works for our family physician, Dr. Michaud, at the General Clinic.

Surname/Family Name:		First/Given Name:		Middle Name:
Age: ______	Date of Birth (yyyy/mm/dd): ____/____/____			Sex: M ☐ F ☐
Address:	Apt. No.	City/Town	Province	Postal Code
Mother's maiden name: Mother's occupation:		Telephone Number (home): Telephone Number (work):		
Father's name in full: Father's occupation:		Telephone Number (home): Telephone Number (work):		
Grade:		OHIP Number:		
Family physician: Address: Telephone Number:		Country of Residence: Country of Citizenship:		
Next of Kin's name:	Telephone Number:		Relationship:	
Signature:		Date:		

Activity 1, Part 6

a. Put the words in order to form questions.

Example: your What name is first?
What is your first name?

b. Use the questions to interview a classmate.

Questions	Answers
Example: your What name is first?	What is your first name?
family What name your is?	
name have middle you Do a?	
you old How are?	
country your What of birth is?	
is What city of birth your?	
birth date is What of your?	
citizenship is country What your of?	
is What postal code your?	
are What in grade you?	
maiden What mother's your name is?	
mother's What occupation your is?	
full What father's your name is?	
father's What occupation your is?	
many have How do sisters you?	
is name What her?	
their names What are?	
many have How do brothers you?	
is name What his?	
their names What are?	
is français Who teacher your?	
your the street What name is of?	
code What your postal is?	
your area What is code?	

Activity 1, Part 7
Write a paragraph (50-70 words) about your classmate and insert it in your portfolio along with your other journal entries.

Draft:

Final Copy:

Activity 1, Part 8
Hand in your journal entries at the end of this unit so your teacher can mark them.

Journal Entries

Name: ______________________ Date: ______________

Evaluation Criteria	Yes	No	Comments
1. All journal entries have been handed in.			
2. Journal entries are detailed and complete.			
3. Ideas are: – clear – original – well developed			
4. Journal entries demonstrate understanding of topic and vocabulary.			
5. Journal entries contain few (or no) spelling or grammar errors.			

Comments/Suggestions:

II - Text 10

Which Committee Are You Going to Join?

Activity 1, Part 1
Listen carefully and write the letter A or E in each blank as your teacher says each word.

1.	M_____T	M_____T
2.	F_____D	F_____D
3.	D_____N	D_____N
4.	M_____N	M_____N
5.	S_____T	S_____T

Activity 1, Part 2
Listen carefully and write the letter I or O in each blank as your teacher says each word.

1.	D_____G	D_____G
2.	R_____B	R_____B
3.	T_____M	T_____M
4.	KN_____T	KN_____T
5.	P_____T	P_____T

Activity 1, Part 3
Listen carefully and write the letter A, E, or I in each blank as your teacher says each word.

1.	S_____T	S_____T	S_____T
2.	P_____T	P_____T	P_____T
3.	P_____N	P_____N	P_____N
4.	B_____G	B_____G	B_____G
5.	H_____M	H_____M	H_____M
6.	L_____D	L_____D	L_____D
7.	B_____D	B_____D	B_____D
8.	B_____N	B_____N	B_____N
9.	B_____T	B_____T	B_____T
10.	D_____N	D_____N	D_____N

Activity 1, Part 4
Listen carefully and write the letter A, E, I, or O in each blank as your teacher says each word.

1. B_____G B_____G B_____G B_____G
2. P_____T P_____T P_____T P_____T
3. T_____N T_____N T_____N T_____N
4. D_____N D_____N D_____N D_____N
5. M_____SS M_____SS M_____SS M_____SS

Activity 1, Part 5
Listen carefully and write the letter O or U in each blank as your teacher says each word.

1. B_____G B_____G
2. C_____B C_____B
3. C_____D C_____D
4. C_____T C_____T
5. D_____CK D_____CK
6. D_____G D_____G
7. G_____T G_____T
8. ST_____CK ST_____CK
9. M_____M M_____M
10. N_____T N_____T

Activity 1, Part 6
Listen carefully and write the letter A, E, I, O, or U in each blank as your teacher says each word.

1. ST_____CK ST_____CK ST_____CK ST_____CK
2. B_____N B_____N B_____N B_____N
3. L_____CK L_____CK L_____CK L_____CK
4. B_____T B_____T B_____T B_____T
5. P_____CK P_____CK P_____CK P_____CK
6. H_____M H_____M H_____M H_____M
7. H_____T H_____T H_____T H_____T
8. J_____G J_____G J_____G J_____G
9. DR_____ NK DR _____NK DR_____ NK

Activity 1, Part 7
Listen carefully and write the letter A, E, I, O, or U in each blank as your teacher reads each sentence.

1. THE C____TS G____T THE H____T D____GS ____ND THE B____G B____NS FROM THE BL____CK B____G.
2. B____N S____T ____N THE D____CK ____N THE H____T S____N WITH H____S S____N.

Activity 1, Part 8
To shorten a name, people often use the first letter of each name or word. This is called an acronym. For example, the students at École secondaire Des Ponts refer to their school as ESDP (E for École, S for secondaire, D for Des and P for Ponts).
Can you write the correct acronyms for the following?

1. National Basketball Association: ____ ____ ____
2. Auto Immune Deficiency Syndrome: ____ ____ ____ ____
3. Canadian Broadcasting Corporation: ____ ____ ____
4. General Motors: ____ ____
5. National Hockey League: ____ ____ ____
6. Federal Bureau of Investigation: ____ ____ ____
7. American Broadcasting Corporation: ____ ____ ____
8. New Democratic Party: ____ ____ ____
9. National Football League: ____ ____ ____
10. British Broadcasting Corporation: ____ ____ ____
11. United Nations: ____ ____
12. General Electric: ____ ____
13. Parti Québecois: ____ ____
14. World Wide Web: ____ ____ ____
15. North American Free Trade Agreement: ____ ____ ____ ____ ____
16. Progressive Conservative: ____ ____
17. British Airways: ____ ____

List three other acronyms:

18. ________________________________: ____ ____ ____ ____
19. ________________________________: ____ ____ ____ ____
20. ________________________________: ____ ____ ____ ____

Activity 1, Part 9

Use the correct possessive adjective (my, your, his, her, its, our, or their) in each of the following sentences.

1. The school is in a new building. ________________ name is École secondaire Des Ponts.
2. I am Tina. When I meet David, I will lend him ________________ dictionary until he has time to buy one.
3. Hamid and Omar are going to join the soccer team. ________________ soccer team will practice three times a week.
4. You and I have the same art class. ________________ art class is in the afternoon.
5. I have a new school bag. ________________ new school bag is small.
6. Here is my new school bag. ________________ colour is green.
7. Chantal does ________________ homework in the evening.
8. You have computer and art classes. ________________ classes are in the morning.
9. Omar's pencil does not write well. ________________ point is dull.
10. You and I use the same computer. ________________ computer is new.
11. David has ________________ transcripts and letters of recommendation.
12. Mrs. Girard, the secretary, sits at ________________ desk.
13. Parents often come with ________________ sons and daughters on the first day of school.
14. The Welcoming Committee hopes to do ________________ job well.
15. Chantal has an old chair. ________________ colour is red.

Activity 1, Part 10

Rewrite the following sentences in the plural.

Example: The student plants a tree. (3-1: three changes; take one word away)
The students plant ( ) trees.

1. The child plants a rose bush. (3-1)

   ____.

2. The cafeteria lunch always looks good. (2)

   ____.

3. Her family has a new schedule. (4-1)

   ____.

4. The student does her homework on the weekend. (4)

   ____.

5. The teacher asks the student to find the country and the city on the map. (7)

   ____.

Activity 2, Part 1

Rewrite the following sentences in the future tense. Use "will" + the simple form of the verb.

Example: David meets Tina.
David **will meet** Tina.

1. David comes to school on Tuesday or Wednesday.

____.

2. David sees the offices and classrooms.

____.

3. David asks many questions.

____.

4. David thinks about the various school activities.

____.

5. David joins his favourite committee next week.

____.

6. David asks about after-school activities too.

____.

7. David meets many teachers and students on his first day at ESDP.

____.

8. David gets a locker for the year.

____.

9. David eats lunch with the members of the Welcoming Committee.

____.

10. David feels comfortable with his new friends.

____.

Activity 2, Part 2

Rewrite the following sentences in the future tense. Use "to be going" + the infinitive of the verb.

Example: Tina meets David when he arrives.
Tina **is going to meet** David when he arrives.

1. Tina shows the school to David.

____.

2. She answers all of his questions.

____.

3. She explains the jobs of the different committees.

____.

4. She tells David about the after-school activities too.

____.

5. Tina encourages David to join the activities that he likes.

____.

6. Tina explains the school calendar to David.

____.

7. She introduces David to many teachers and students.

____.

8. Before lunchtime, she finds David.

____.

9. They walk to the cafeteria and eat lunch with the rest of the Welcoming Committee.

____.

10. Tina shows David how to return home.

____.

Activity 2, Part 3
Write the definition of the words and expressions that are new to you.

Vocabulary List

I. Nouns	9. menu: ____________
1. acronym: ____________	10. music: ____________
2. activity: ____________	11. opinion: ____________
3. bush: ____________	12. P.S.: ____________
4. committee: ____________	13. plant: ____________
5. computer graphics: ____________	14. poster: ____________
6. flower: ____________	15. regards: ____________
7. ice cream: ____________	16. sports: ____________
8. job: ____________	17. team: ____________
	18. tree: ____________

II. Adjectives

1. artistic: ______________
2. beautiful: ______________
3. busy: ______________
4. comfortable: ______________
5. dear: ______________
6. exciting: ______________
7. favourite: ______________
8. green: ______________
9. red: ______________
10. special: ______________
11. sure: ______________
12. with/without: ______________

III. Adverbs

1. next: ______________
2. soon: ______________
3. today: ______________
4. tonight: ______________
5. tomorrow: ______________

IV. Verbs

1. to arrive: ______________
2. to decorate: ______________
3. to drink: ______________
4. to encourage: ______________
5. to enjoy: ______________
6. to explain: ______________
7. to feel: ______________
8. to guess: ______________
9. to make: ______________
10. to plan: ______________
11. to plant: ______________
12. to recycle: ______________
13. to research: ______________
14. to spend time: ______________
15. to take turns: ______________
16. to telephone: ______________
17. to water: ______________

V. Expressions

1. Take care.
2. That's right.

....

subject pronoun		**possessive adjective**
it	➜	its

adjective		**comparative**		**superlative**
good	➜	better	➜	best

FUTURE Time
in (2 days/2 weeks/2 months/2 years) next (week/Monday/month/spring/year) tomorrow/today tonight this (week/Wednesday/month/spring/year)

"will" + infinitive (without "to")			**"to be going" + infinitive (with "to")**		
I		eat	I am		eat
you		drink	you are		drink
he/she/it	**will**	play	he/she/it is	**going to**	play
we		run	we are		run
they		walk	they are		walk

Activity 2, Part 4
Make a list of the things that are good, better, and best.

In your opinion...	Which is good?	Which is better?	Which is the best?
ice cream........flavour	vanilla	chocolate	strawberry
1. music........to listen to			
2. sport........for exercise			
3. month......for walking			
4. drink............for lunch			

Write a sentence comparing each item with the others in the same category.

Example: I think that vanilla is a good ice cream flavour, chocolate is a better ice cream flavour, and strawberry is the best ice cream flavour!

1. I think that ______________________________
______________________________.
2. I think that ______________________________
______________________________.
3. I think that ______________________________
______________________________.
4. I think that ______________________________
______________________________.

Activity 2, Part 5
Text 10: Which Committee Are You Going to Join?

______________________, 20____.

Dear Josef,

I hope you are fine doing well.

I want to tell you about our first week at ESDP. This year, our first week at school is very busy, but it is also very exciting. We are busy with our classes and our homework, but we are also busy with a new and exciting school program called "The World of ESDP". This program hopes to make ESDP the best school in the city. I will explain the program to you.

First, there are many small committees in this program. Each committee has a different job. Each student at ESDP will research the job of each committee and choose the committee he or she wants to join. When we join a committee, we begin our different jobs. For example, there is the Cafeteria Committee. Its job is to make the cafeteria a very special place to eat. The members will choose lunchtime music and plan cafeteria menus each week. They will also plan multicultural lunches twice a year.

There is also the Green Committee. Its job is to encourage recycling, water the plants in the school and plant flowers, bushes and trees in the spring.

The Decorating Committee has a very interesting job too. Many of the students who are artistic and enjoy computer graphics want to join the Decorating Committee. Its job is to decorate the school and make it beautiful. For example, members will decorate the school with posters of all the special projects and activities.

There is also the Welcoming Committee. I think I am going to join the Welcoming Committee today. Can you guess what this committee does? Can you guess what my job will be? That's right! My job will be to welcome new students to ESDP and to our city!

There are going to be only five members in the Welcoming Committee and the members will take turns spending time with every new student who comes to ESDP. We are going to have a new student at ESDP next week. His name is David Thien. He and his family are immigrants and will arrive on the weekend. David will come to ESDP on Tuesday or Wednesday. Our job will be to show David the classrooms, offices and other places at our school, and answer his questions. We will also encourage David to join committees and after-school activities. And all the members of the Welcoming Committee will eat lunch with David every day for the first week he is at our school. After one week, we are sure that David will feel that he has friends at ESDP and that he will feel comfortable at his new school.

I will tell you about David's first week at ESDP in my next letter. Take care and write soon.

Your friend,
Tina

P.S.: Please give my regards to your parents, sisters and brothers.

Activity 2, Part 6

a. List four after-school sports activities at your school.

1. ______________________ 3. ______________________

2. ______________________ 4. ______________________

b. Name the school sports teams you are going to join this year. Explain why you chose them.

____

____

c. List three committees at your school and explain their jobs.

1. The ______________________________ Committee.

   Its job is to ____

   ____.

2. The ______________________________ Committee.

   Its job is to ____

   ____.

3. The ______________________________ Committee.

   Its job is to ____

   ____.

d. Which committee are you going to join this year? Why?

____

____

____

Activity 2, Part 7

Associate each word on the right with its antonym on the left.

Example: __D__ husband	A. last
1. _____ new	B. temporary
2. _____ big	C. never
3. _____ before	D. wife
4. _____ short	E. fall
5. _____ always	F. same
6. _____ different	G. sharp
7. _____ spring	H. old
8. _____ permanent	I. long
9. _____ dull	J. after
10. _____ first	K. small

Activity 2, Part 8
Write a friendly letter using the following format and conventions.

_______________, 20____
(Date)

Dear ______________________,
(Salutation)

____

____

____

____

____

____

____

____

____

____

____

____

______________________,
(Complimentary close)

____
(Signature)

P.S.: ____

Activity 2, Part 9
Answer the following questions in complete sentences using the future tense.

1. At what time are you going to go home today?

____.

2. Which friend are you going to telephone tonight?

____.

3. When will you finish your next APD journal entry?

____.

4. What are you going to buy tomorrow?

____.

5. Where will your brother (or sister) go on the weekend?

____.

6. What will you eat or drink after school today?

____.

7. At what time are you going to finish your homework tonight?

____.

Activity 2, Part 10

Put the words in order to form questions. Use correct punctuation.

Example: are today What going do we to?

What are we going to do today?

1. come to When he class will gym?

____?

2. their When they write test will?

____?

3. test they write When their are to going?

____?

4. school their buy Where they supplies will?

____?

5. her What do with notebook will she old?

____?

6. school What drink after will today you?

____?

7. you play time going At are soccer what to today?

____?

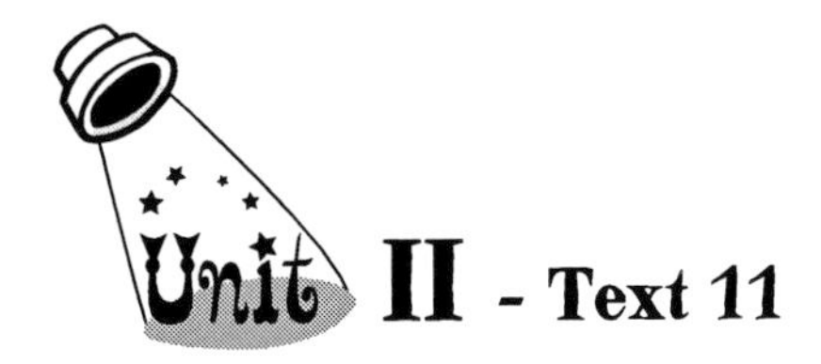

II - Text 11

What Did Josef Do on the First Day of School?

Activity 1, Part 1
Write the definition of the words and expressions that are new to you.

Vocabulary List

I. Nouns

1. recommendation: ____________
2. breakfast: ____________
3. game: ____________
4. transcripts: ____________
5. door: ____________
6. lot of: ____________

II. Adjectives

1. a few: ____________
2. a. difficult: ____________
   b. easy: ____________
3. excited: ____________
4. fun: ____________
5. great: ____________
6. a. happy: ____________
   b. sad: ____________
7. kind: ____________
8. necessary: ____________
9. nervous: ____________
10. nice: ____________
11. a. regular: ____________
    b. irregular: ____________
12. ready: ____________

III. Verbs

1. describe: ____________
2. knock: ____________
3. prepare: ____________
4. thank: ____________
5. wave: ____________
6. wish: ____________

IV. Future Time/Past Time

in (2 days) ➜ (2 days) ago
next (week) ➜ last (week)
tomorrow ➜ yesterday
today ➜ yesterday
tonight ➜ last night
this (week) ➜ last (week)

V. Irregular Simple Past Tense

to be
I am ➜ I was
you are ➜ you were
he/she/it is ➜ he/she/it was
we are ➜ we were
they are ➜ they were

to have
I have ➜ I had
you have ➜ you had
he/she/it has ➜ he/she/it had
we have ➜ we had
they have ➜ they had

to do
I do ➜ I did
you do ➜ you did
he/she/it does ➜ he/she/it did
we do ➜ we did
they do ➜ they did

Activity 1, Part 2
Text 11: What Did Josef Do on the First Day of School?

(today's date)

Dear Tina, Hamid, Omar and Chantal,

Thank you very much for your letters. I like to read each one many times. I miss you and ESDP. I also miss our classes and our projects with Mrs. Roy.

The new committees you have this year sound very interesting and exciting. I think the committees will make ESDP one of the best schools in Canada! I know that Tina joined the Welcoming Committee, but what about the rest of you? Which committees are you going to join?

I am glad that you like your new APD teacher, but you did not describe Mr. Perreault! Please describe him in your next letter. He sounds like a very interesting teacher. I also want to know more about the two-month project he wants you to do. It sounds like a lot of fun, but it also sounds like a lot of work!

You started school two weeks ago, but I started only yesterday. Let me tell you about my first day in my new school.

First, my father called last week and arranged for an interview with the principal at 8:00 in the morning. My mother prepared a special breakfast for the family because she knows I am always nervous when I have an interview. At 7:15 we finished breakfast, and my parents and I walked to school together.

When we arrived at the school, we entered the school office and talked to the secretary. We asked many questions. I like her very much. She is very nice. Her name is Mrs. Girard. She smiled and welcomed me to the school. Next, we followed Mrs. Girard to the principal's office. She knocked on his door and we entered his office. He interviewed me and asked many questions about ESDP and Canadian schools in general. I think I answered all his questions well. The interview lasted twenty minutes. When my parents and I returned to the school office, we completed the school registration form.

Next, Mrs. Girard called the school counsellor. The school counsellor is great! She wanted to see my transcripts from École secondaire Des Ponts. I had remembered to add my letters of recommendation to my transcripts. She examined my transcripts carefully and smiled as she read the letters of recommendation. She also asked me questions about the subjects I wanted to take this year. She worked on the computer for 15 minutes, and then she printed my schedule. I thanked the school counsellor and the secretary, and then joined my parents. My parents and I liked my new school. We walked to the school door together. They walked home, and I walked to my 9:15 class.

I will tell you more about my classes and teachers in my next letter.

Your friend,

Josef

Activity 1, Part 3

Rewrite the following sentences about Josef's first day at school in the simple past tense. Underline all the verbs in the simple past tense.

Example: Josef's father calls the school and arranges for an interview. (2 changes)
Josef's father <u>called</u> the school and <u>arranged</u> for an interview.

1. Josef's mother prepares a special breakfast. (1)

   ____.

2. They finish their breakfast and walk to Josef's school. (2)

   ____.

3. They arrive early. (1)

   ____.

4. First they talk to the secretary, and then they follow the secretary to the principal's office. (2)

   ____.

5. The principal interviews Josef and asks many questions about Canadian schools. (2)

   ____.

6. Josef and his parents return to the school office and complete the school registration form. (2)

   ____.

7. Josef shows his transcripts to the school counsellor before they work on his schedule. (2)

   ____.

8. The computer prints Josef's schedule. (1)

   ____.

9. Josef thanks the school counsellor and secretary before he walks to his next class. (2)

   ____.

Activity 1, Part 4

What do you think? Circle the correct word(s).

1. Josef (likes) (doesn't like) to receive letters from Canada.
2. Josef's interview was (long) (short).
3. When he has an interview, Josef feels very (nervous) (comfortable).
4. Josef's interview was (difficult) (easy).
5. The principal asked (some) (many) questions about Canadian schools.
6. Josef was (happy) (sad) about his schedule.
7. The teachers at École secondaire Des Ponts (miss) (don't miss) Josef.
8. Josef is (nervous) (comfortable) when he talks to his school counsellor.
9. Josef's parents are (happy) (sad) about his new school.
10. The school counsellor and Josef hope that his school schedule is (temporary) (permanent).

Activity 1, Part 5
Rewrite the following sentences in the simple past tense.

Example: I **am going to use** your dictionary **tomorrow.**
I **used** your dictionary **yesterday.**

Future	Past
in (2 days)	(2 days) ago
next (week)	last (week)
tomorrow/today	yesterday
tonight	last night
this (week)	last (week)

1. I **am going to call** you next week. (2)

____.

2. He **is going to arrive** in Toronto **next month.** (2)

____.

3. They **are going to try** the new calculator **tonight.** (2)

____.

4. She **is going to finish** her picture **tomorrow.** (2)

____.

5. We **are going to adopt** two cats and a bird **next year.** (2)

____.

6. They **are going to print** their project **tomorrow.** (2)

____.

7. The children **are going to receive** their tests **in five minutes.** (2)

____.

Activity 1, Part 6
Rewrite the following sentence in the simple past tense.

to be ➜ was or were	to have ➜ had
I am ➜ I was you are ➜ you were he/she/it is ➜ he/she/it was we are ➜ we were they are ➜ they were	I have ➜ I had you have ➜ you had he/she/it has ➜ he/she/it had we have ➜ we had they have ➜ they had

1. The man is very nervous.

____.

2. The students have homework on the weekend.

____.

3. His students are very happy, but your students are sad.

____.

4. You have three telephone calls.

____.

5. They are in the computer room.

____.

6. He has many paragraphs to write, but they are easy.

____.

7. Their lawyers have a difficult job.

____.

8. She is at the school office.

____.

9. The computer programmers have many projects.

____.

10. We have time for a long lunch.

____.

11. Hamid is in the library.

____.

12. The man has a lot of work to do.

____.

13. You and your friend are in my APD class.

____.

Activity 1, Part 7

How do you change a regular verb to the simple past tense? **C = consonant**
V = vowel

– verb + ed: add "ed"	→ talk	→ talked
– verb that ends with a silent "e": add "d"	→ change	→ changed
– verb that ends with a C V C: double the C and add "ed"	→ stop	→ stopped
– verb that ends with a C C and "y": change the "y" to "i" and add "ed"	→ try	→ tried

The simple past tense of regular verbs ends with "ed". Write the simple past tense of the following verbs in the correct columns.

add	ask	end	enter	finish	hyphenate
imagine	immigrate	interview	join	look	match
miss	print	return	show	sound like	talk

Verbs Ending with "d" sound	Verbs Ending with "t" Sound	Verbs Ending with "id" Sound
______	______	______
______	______	______
______	______	______
______	______	______
______	______	______
______	______	______

Activity 1, Part 8

Fill in the blanks with the simple past tense of the verbs listed on the left. Use each verb only once.

complete
end
marry
play
point
promise
receive
remember
stop
study
try

Example: I **played** the video game for two hours.

1. The small children ______________________ at the NBA player.
2. My brother ______________________ for his science test for eight hours!
3. I ______________________ to bring my dictionary to class today.
4. The DJ ______________________ the music on the radio every hour for the news broadcast.
5. My brother ______________________ a very special person. Now I have a very nice sister-in-law.
6. The children ______________________ to be good in the park.
7. I ______________________ two letters from my friends last week.
8. I ______________________ to draw a picture of my friend in art class, but it doesn't look like my friend.
9. We ______________________ the exercise before the class ______________________.

Activity 1, Part 9
Josef writes a paragraph about his first day at his new school.

Use the correct simple past tense of the verbs "to be" and "to have" in his paragraph.

I (1) ________________ very nervous this morning. My parents and I (2) ________________ an appointment with the principal at 8:00. We walked to school together. We (3) ________________ early because we arrived at 7:45. I (4) ________________ ready. I (5) ________________ all my transcripts and letters of recommendation with me. The secretary (6) ________________ very friendly and kind. She answered many of our questions. It (7) ________________ 8:00, and my parents and I (8) ________________ ready to meet the principal. The principal opened his office door and asked us to sit down. He (9) ________________ many questions to ask me about Canadian schools. My parents (10) ________________ interested in his questions and my answers. They learned a lot about ESDP that day. When the interview ended, I followed the secretary to the school counsellor's office. My parents (11) ________________ very happy with the new school. They waved goodbye and returned home. The school counsellor and I worked on my schedule. When we finished the schedule, we (12) ________________ very pleased. I registered for all the courses I wanted. I (13) ________________ excited about meeting my new teachers and classmates. It is now 3:00 p.m., and I feel I (14) ________________ an excellent first day!

Activity 2, Part 1
Use the correct subject pronouns for the proper names and nouns that are underlined in the following sentences. Pretend that your name is Danny (short for Daniel or Danielle).

Example: <u>Suzanne</u> and <u>Danny</u> enjoy art class. ➜ **She** and **I** enjoy art class.
<u>My father</u> and <u>Danny</u> like to walk slowly. ➜ **He** and **I** like to walk slowly.

1. <u>Henry</u> and <u>Danny</u> like soccer.

   ____

2. You and <u>Danny</u> study different languages.

   ____

3. <u>My parents</u> and <u>Danny</u> like to walk on the weekend.

   ____

4. <u>My brother</u> and <u>Danny</u> help our mother on the weekend.

   ____

5. <u>My sister</u> and <u>Danny</u> talk on the telephone for hours!

   ____

Activity 2, Part 2

Use the correct expression "How many", "What", "When", "Where", "Whom", or "Who" to complete the following interview questions.

Example: How many classes did you have last year? (number)

1. ______________________________ is your family name? (noun)
2. ______________________________ was your principal last year? (person)
3. ______________________________ brothers do you have? (number)
4. To ______________________________ did you talk at the school office? (person)
5. ______________________________ did you move to Argentina? (time)
6. ______________________________ do you live? (place)
7. ______________________________ sisters do you have? (number)
8. ______________________________ is your favourite basketball player? (person)
9. ______________________________ did you begin to learn French? (time)
10. ______________________________ is your favourite subject at school? (noun)
11. ______________________________ is your sister's school? (place)
12. ______________________________ did you begin to learn English? (time)
13. ______________________________ sports do you play after school? (number)
14. ______________________________ classes did you have in Canada every day? (number)
15. ______________________________ is your favourite TV program? (noun)
16. ______________________________ are your transcripts? (place)
17. ______________________________ did you call the school? (time)
18. ______________________________ do you want to study later? (noun)
19. ______________________________ do you want to work in ten years? (place)
20. ______________________________ welcomed you to our school this morning? (person)

Activity 2, Part 3

Fill in each blank with the correct adjective or adverb.

careful	clear	permanent	slow	temporary
carefully	clearly	permanently	slowly	temporarily

1. The radio is new. Its sound is very ______________________________.
2. His schedule is ______________________________. He will have this schedule for the year.
3. Their address is ______________________________. They will live there for only two months.
4. He is an excellent student. He listens ______________________________.
5. When she has a lot of time, she likes to work ______________________________.

Activity 2, Part 4

Chantal's Weekend

Chantal plays with her ten-year-old brother for ten minutes and talks to her mother for half an hour after she returns from school on Friday. On Saturday morning, she and her family walk to her grandmother's house for a nice Saturday lunch. In the afternoon, she studies for her history test and finishes her homework. In the evening, she stops working and calls her friends on the telephone. Her friends promise to come to her house at 7:30. After they arrive, they listen to their favourite music in Chantal's room. On Sunday, Chantal works on her art project all day. In the evening, she waters the plants in the house and helps her brother with his homework.

Toni's Weekend

Toni plays soccer on Friday afternoon in the school gym. On Saturday morning, she works on her science project. She finishes her project at around 7:00 in the evening. In the evening, she listens to music. On Sunday, she, her sister, brothers and father join a sports club on their street. Her sister and father play volleyball, and she and her brothers play basketball. After they finish, they return to their mother's home. They arrive at about 2:30 in the afternoon. Toni studies for her two tests. She finishes at about 8:00 in the evening. Before she prepares her school lunch for Monday, she talks with her friends on the telephone.

Activity 2, Part 5
What did Chantal do on the weekend? Change the paragraph on Chantal's weekend to the simple past tense.

____

____

____

____

____

____

____

Activity 2, Part 6
Use the simple past tense to answer the following questions about Toni's weekend.

1. When did Toni play soccer?

   ____.

2. Where did Toni and her family play sports?

   ____.

3. With whom did Toni play basketball?

____.

4. What did Toni and her family join on Sunday afternoon?

____.

5. When did Toni return home to study for her tests?

____.

6. Where did Toni play soccer?

____.

7. With whom did her sister play volleyball?

____.

8. What did Toni prepare on Sunday night?

____.

9. To whom did Toni talk on the telephone?

____.

10. When did Toni talk on the telephone?

____.

Activity 2, Part 7

Read the paragraph about Toni's weekend and answer the following questions, using "Yes, she did" or "No, she didn't."

Example: Did Toni talk on the telephone before she prepared her lunch?
"No, she didn't. She talked on the telephone after she prepared her lunch."

*****Use the correct subject pronouns.**

1. Did Toni play soccer on Friday afternoon?

____.

2. Did Toni and her family play sports on Saturday?

____.

3. Did Toni and her sister play basketball?

____.

4. Did Toni and her family join a sports club on Sunday afternoon?

____.

5. Did Toni return home to study for her tests?

____.

6. Did Toni play soccer at the sports club?

____.

7. Did her sister play volleyball at the school gym?

____.

8. Did Toni prepare her lunch (for Monday) on Sunday night?

____.

9. Did Toni's father play volleyball on Sunday?

____.

Activity 2, Part 8

Answer the questions below about your weekend. Use a dictionary if necessary.

1. What sport did you play on Saturday morning?

____.

2. Where did you walk on Saturday afternoon?

____.

3. To whom did you talk on the telephone on the weekend?

____.

4. When did you study for your test?

____.

5. Where did you play (a sport)?

____.

6. What did you do with your friends or family?

____.

Unit II - Text 12

Surprise!

Activity 1, Part 1
Listen carefully and write the letter A or E in each blank as your teacher says each word. Some words end with a silent E.

1. M___D M___D___
2. F___D F___D F___D___
3. P___N P___N P___N___
4. M___N M___N M___N___
5. P___T P___T P___T___

Activity 1, Part 2
Listen carefully and write the letter I, O, or E in each blank as your teacher says each word. Some words end with a silent E.

1. R___B R___B___ R___B
2. B___D B___D___ B___D___
3. T___M T___M___ T___M
4. D___M D___M___
5. P___T P___T

Activity 1, Part 3
Listen carefully and write the letter A, E, I, or O in each blank as your teacher says each word. Some words end with a silent E.

1. B___G B___G B___G B___G
2. P___T P___T P___T P___T P___T___
3. T___N T___N T___N T___N T___N___
4. D___N___ D___N D___N D___N D___N
5. M___SS M___SS M___SS M___SS

Activity 1, Part 4
Listen carefully and write the letter O or U in each blank as your teacher says each word. Some words end with a silent E.

1. N___T N___T N___T___
2. C___B C___B C___B___
3. C___D C___D C___D___
4. C___T C___T C___T___
5. M___M M___M
6. D___G D___G
7. G___T G___T

Activity 1, Part 5

Listen carefully and write the letter A, E, I, O, or U in each blank below as your teacher says each word. Some words end with a silent E.

1. C___T   C___T   C___T___   C___T   C___T___
2. H___M   H___M   H___M   H___M   H___M___
3. H___T   H___T   H___T___   H___T   H___T
4. B___T   B___T   B___T___   B___T   B___T
5. B___N   B___N   B___N   B___N___   B___N

Activity 1, Part 6

Listen carefully and write the correct vowel in each blank as your teacher says each word. Some words end with a silent E.

1. H___T___	11. D___N	21. B___T	31. P___N
2. H___T	12. C___D	22. B___T	32. P___N
3. P___T	13. C___D	23. B___T___	33. P___N
4. P___T	14. T___B	24. P___T	34. N___B
5. D___M	15. T___B___	25. B___D	35. N___B
6. D___M___	16. D___M	26. B___D___	36. L___D
7. H___P___	17. H___M	27. H___P	37. L___D
8. H___P	18. H___R___	28. C___T___	38. P___D
9. C___P	19. H___N	29. P___N___	39. W___D
10. C___P	20. D___N	30. P___N___	40. L___N___

Activity 1, Part 7

Dictation: Write A, E, I, O, or U to complete the words below. Some words end with a silent E.

1. The c___t___ c___t s___t ___n the r___d m___t.
2. The m___d c___b r___n to the b___g bl___ck h___t h___r___.
3. P___t g___t the m___n a p___t of h___t d___gs.
4. The b___g r___t ___n the h___t ___nd the c___t___ b___d d___g ___n the d___n m___d___ a b___g m___ss ___n the c___t gr___ss.
5. P___m s___t by the h___t t___b ___n h___r c___t___ r___d r___b___.

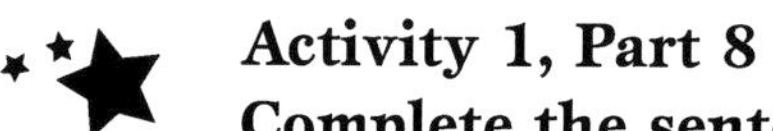

Activity 1, Part 8
Complete the sentences below with compound words.

The words "any", "every", "no" and "some" are used to form compound words.

<table>
<tr><td colspan="2">1. any: ____________________
2. every: ____________________
3. no: ____________________
4. some: ____________________</td><td>1. "any"
any + one = anyone
any + place = anyplace
any + thing = anything
any + where = anywhere</td></tr>
<tr><td>2. "every"
every + one = everyone
every + place = everyplace
every + thing = everything
every + where = everywhere</td><td>3. "no"
no + thing = nothing
no + where = nowhere
exceptions:
no one
no place</td><td>4. "some"
some + one = someone
some + place = someplace
some + thing = something
some + where = somewhere</td></tr>
</table>

Add "any", "every", "no", and "some" to "one".

1. He wants to play basketball with ____________________ (all the students).
2. He wants to play basketball with ____________________ (only one student).
3. He wants to play basketball with ____________________ who wants to play for one hour.

Add "any", "every", "no", and "some" to "thing".

4. He doesn't want a present. He wants ____________________ for his birthday.
5. He wants ____________________ very special for his birthday.
6. He wants ____________________ on this long list for his birthday.
7. He wants ____________________ (you can decide which thing) from this list for his birthday.

Add "any", "every", "no", and "some" to "place".

8. He wants to go ____________________ very special on his birthday.
9. He wants to go ____________________ on this long list for his birthday. He wants to have fun for one week.
10. He wants to go ____________________ (you can decide where from this list) on his birthday.

Add "any", "every", "no", and "some" to "where".

11. They looked here, there, and ____________________ for the small child.
12. The child was ____________________ in the park. He was not in the park.
13. I think we will look again. He must be ____________________!
14. Where do you want me to look? I will look ____________________ you want me to.

Activity 1, Part 9

Write the antonym of the words listed on the left by using the appropriate prefixes ("un-", "im-", or "in-"), and then fill in each blank with the correct word. Use each word only once.

Antonyms		
1. "un-" = "not"	**2. "im-" = "not"**	**3. "in-" = "not"**
clear ➔ unclear	polite ➔ impolite	correct ➔ incorrect
comfortable ➔ uncomfortable	patient ➔ impatient	complete ➔ incomplete
complicated ➔ uncomplicated	possible ➔ impossible	
exciting ➔ unexciting	perfect ➔ imperfect	
friendly ➔ unfriendly		
happy➔ unhappy		
important ➔ unimportant		
interesting ➔ uninteresting		
usual ➔ unusual		

clear comfortable complete complicated correct exciting friendly happy **important** interesting patient perfect polite possible usual	**Example:** This paper is **unimportant**. Don't keep it. Recycle it! 1. The math question was simple. It was ____________________. 2. Wow! Green ice cream? That's very ____________________! 3. This child is sad. He is ____________________. 4. We didn't like the book. It was ____________________. 5. The score was 0-0. The soccer game was ____________________. 6. I cannot understand your answer. It is ____________________. 7. The child never says "Thank you" or "Please". He is ____________________. 8. This is not the answer. Your answer is ____________________. 9. Young children don't like to wait. They are ____________________. 10. I didn't finish my homework. My homework is ____________________. 11. It is ____________________ to walk to Australia from Canada. 12. I cannot sit in this chair. It is very ____________________. 13. The new student doesn't like to meet other students. She is ____________________. 14. We all make mistakes. We are all ____________________.

Activity 1, Part 10
Read the following conversation twice, once without contractions and once with contractions.

Contractions are used in conversation. As you read, underline the words where you can use contractions.

Example: That is a great idea. ("That is" can be replaced by "that's".)

I will eat ➜ I'll eat you will drink ➜ you'll drink he/she/it will play ➜ he/she/it'll play we will walk ➜ we'll walk they will plan ➜ they'll plan (subject pronoun) will not ➜ won't	I am (going to...) ➜ I'm (going to....) you are (going to...) ➜ you're (going to...) he/she/it (is going to...) ➜ he/she/it's (going to...) we are (going to...) ➜ we're (going to...) they are (going to...) ➜ they're (going to...) (I am, you, we, they) are not ➜ aren't (he, she, it) is not ➜ isn't
I have ➜ I've you have ➜ you've he/she/it has ➜ he/she/it's we have ➜ we've they have ➜ they've (I, you, we, they) have not ➜ haven't (he, she, it) has not ➜ hasn't	let us ➜ let's that is ➜ that's does not ➜ doesn't do not ➜ don't did not ➜ didn't

Tina: Where are you going?
Toni: (*looks at the clock in the corridor*) It is lunch time. I am going to eat lunch.
Hamid: Where are you going to eat today?
Chantal: I am going to the school cafeteria.
Tina: And you, Toni?
Toni: (*Toni points to Keiko.*) We are going to the cafeteria too.
Hamid: I have a good idea. Let us eat together.
Omar: Okay!

The students talk as they walk to the cafeteria.
Tina: What are you going to have for lunch?
Keiko: I think I am going to eat pizza.
Toni: (*Toni points to Omar and smiles.*) We will have spaghetti, as usual.
Hamid: I do not want pizza or spaghetti. I will have salad.
Tina: I did not eat salad yesterday. I think I am going to eat salad also.
Chantal: Look at the students there. They are eating hamburgers and french fries. I am going to eat a hamburger and french fries too.

Twenty minutes later.
Tina: What classes do you have after lunch?
Chantal: I have a français class.
Tina: And you, Toni?
Toni: (*Toni points to Keiko.*) We have computer science class.
Hamid: It is a beautiful day and we have a lot of time before the bell rings. Let us go to the gym and play basketball!
Omar: That is a great idea.

Activity 1, Part 11
Reread the above conversation silently and underline the words that were not contracted.

How many "possible" contractions did you find? I found _______ possible contractions.

Activity 1, Part 12
Write the correct question tag and punctuate each sentence correctly.

Example: He **has** math class on Thursday mornings, **doesn't he**?
She **doesn't** have math class on Thursday mornings, **does she**?

1. Hamid wants everyone to eat together, ________________
2. Chantal doesn't have a history class today, ________________
3. Hamid eats salad, ________________
4. Tina doesn't want to eat spaghetti, ________________

Example: We **have** math class on Thursday mornings, **don't we**?
They **don't have** math class on Thursday mornings, **do they**?

5. The students bring their lunches to the table, ________________
6. Toni and Keiko have computer science class today, ________________
7. Mr. Perreault's students play basketball, ________________
8. The students don't talk as they walk, ________________

Example: He **isn't** in your math class on Thursday mornings, **is he**?
She **is** in your math class on Thursday mornings, **isn't she**?
This ice cream **is** very good, **isn't it**?

9. Chantal is going to the school cafeteria, ________________
10. Keiko isn't going to eat pizza, ________________
11. That is a great idea, ________________
12. That isn't sausage pizza, ________________

Example: They **are** going to their math class, **aren't they**?
We **aren't** in the same class, **are we**?

13. Toni and Keiko are going to the cafeteria, ________________
14. You are going to eat lunch now, ________________
15. They aren't eating hamburgers, ________________
16. They aren't going home after lunch, ________________

Example: They **will** go to their math class, **won't they**?
You **won't** be in the same group, **will you**?

17. Toni and Omar will have spaghetti, ______________________________
18. Toni and Omar won't have spaghetti, ______________________________
19. Hamid will have salad, ______________________________
20. Hamid won't eat spaghetti, ______________________________

Example: They **walked** to their math class, **didn't they**?
You **didn't** join the same group, **did you**?

21. Hamid wanted everyone to eat together, ______________________________
22. The students didn't finish their lunches at the same time, ______________________________
23. Hamid had salad, ______________________________
24. Hamid didn't eat spaghetti, ______________________________

Activity 2, Part 1

Add the suffix "-ful" or "-less" to "beauty", "care", "cheer", "colour", "help", "hope", "rest", "use", or "wonder", and then fill in the blanks with the correct adjective.

	"-ful" = full of...	"-less" = without...
beauty	beauty ➜ beautiful: (having qualities of beauty)	care ➜ careless: (not taking enough care)
		cheer ➜ cheerless: (lacking cheer)
care	care ➜ careful: (taking care)	colour ➜ colourless: (lacking colour)
cheer	cheer ➜ cheerful: (full of cheer)	help ➜ helpless: (unable to act without help)
colour	colour ➜ colourful: (full of colour)	
help	help ➜ helpful: (providing help)	hope ➜ hopeless: (without hope)
hope	hope ➜ hopeful: (full of hope)	rest ➜ restless: (lacking rest)
rest	rest ➜ restful: (quiet, at rest)	use ➜ useless: (not able to be used)
use	use ➜ useful: (capable of being put to use)	
wonder	wonder ➜ wonderful: (causing wonder)	

1. I like this poster. It is so ____________________.
2. I am very tired. I had a ____________________ night.
3. This secretary is very ____________________. She will answer all your questions!
4. This work is incomplete. The student is very ____________________.
5. This old computer doesn't work. It is ____________________.
6. He is so friendly and ____________________. I like to spend time with him.
7. They don't think he will live. The doctors say it is ____________________.

Activity 2, Part 2
Write the definition of the words and expressions that are new to you.

Vocabulary List

I. Nouns

1. bed: ____________
2. bedroom: ____________
3. copy: ____________
4. dinner: ____________
5. experience: ____________
6. gift: ____________
7. group: ____________
8. guide: ____________
9. hall: ____________
10. hamburger: ____________
11. idea: ____________
12. juice: ____________
13. kitchen: ____________
14. life: ____________
15. mail: ____________
16. market: ____________
17. opportunity: ____________
18. package: ____________
19. room: ____________
20. rules: ____________
21. salad: ____________
22. spaghetti: ____________
23. stairs: ____________
24. store: ____________
25. surprise: ____________
26. transportation: ____________
27. voice: ____________
28. wall: ____________

II. Adjectives

1. alone: ____________
2. late: ____________
3. lonely: ____________
4. pleased: ____________
5. possible: ____________
6. tired: ____________
7. young: ____________

III. Homonyms

a. male: ____________
b. mail: ____________

IV. Adjective + "ly" ➔ adverb

1. friendly: ____________
2. patiently: ____________
3. politely: ____________
4. quietly: ____________
5. quickly: ____________
6. shyly: ____________
7. softly: ____________
8. usually: ____________

V. Verbs

1. to agree: ____________
2. to check: ____________
3. to hate: ____________
4. to insist: ____________
5. to love: ____________
6. to open: ____________
7. to rest: ____________
8. to wrap: ____________

VI. Expressions	8. meet ➜ met
I don't think so.: ____________	9. put ➜ put
Sorry.: ____________	10. see ➜ saw
That's all right.: ____________	11. spend ➜ spent
VII. Irregular Simple Past Tense	**VIII. Questions and Answers**
1. bring ➜ brought	Where? a. here: ____________
2. begin ➜ began	b. there: ____________
3. come ➜ came	Which? a. this: ____________
4. find ➜ found	b. that: ____________
5. forget ➜ forgot	When? a. now: ____________
6. know ➜ knew	b. later: ____________
7. make ➜ made	

Activity 2, Part 3
Compare the following.

Example: new: this/that pencil — This pencil is newer than that pencil.
cute: this/that poster — This poster is cuter than that poster.
easy: this/that exercise — This exercise is easier than that exercise.

1. slow: this/that clock

   ____.

2. gentle: this/that child

   ____.

3. short: this/that baby

   ____.

4. late: this/that class

   ____.

5. lonely: this/that child

   ____.

6. sharp: this/that pencil

   ____.

7. nice: this/that song

____.

8. friendly: this/that teacher

____.

9. young: this/that woman

____.

10. unhappy: this/that student

____.

11. soft: this/that music

____.

12. old: this/that desk

____.

Activity 2, Part 4
Compare the following.

Example: difficult: this/that exercise
This exercise is more difficult than that exercise.

1. colourful: this/that picture

____.

2. patient: this/that principal

____.

3. uncomfortable: this/that chair

____.

4. helpful: this/that secretary

____.

5. cheerful: this/that nurse

____.

Activity 2, Part 5
Text 12: Surprise!

Josef opened the door and walked into the house slowly and quietly. Angelica, Josef's younger sister, looked at the clock in the hall. It was 4:30. That was the usual time for Josef to return from school. He was never late. He was always home between 4:30 and 4:45. In Canada, he was always late because he was always busy. He was busy with his friends; he was busy with his sport teams; he was busy with his after-school projects and activities. But not here. In Argentina, he came home after his last class, and all of his classes finished at 4:00 every day.

Josef started to go to his new school more than a month ago. His first day at school was very nice. He met many students and teachers. Everyone was helpful. Everyone was friendly. Everyone was polite. But Josef was a shy and quiet student, and all the students at his new school had their group of friends. He didn't make any new friends at all! He missed his weekends in Canada. He also missed the time he spent with his special friends at ESDP. Josef tried to be patient. He knew it was difficult to make new friends. It was even more difficult to make new friends in another country. Everything was different. The city was different. The transportation was different. The school was different. The rules were different. The teachers and students were different. Everything was different! And now it was Friday. Another weekend and nothing to do! Another weekend and nowhere to go!

"Hi, Josef!" It was Angelica's cheerful voice. Angelica was 12 years old and she loved Josef. She hated to see him so unhappy and lonely. "Come to the kitchen, Josef. I made something special for you."

Josef didn't want to speak to anyone! He didn't want to sit down and talk about his day. He wanted to be alone in his bedroom. "No thanks," he said. "Is there any mail for me?"

"I don't think so. Sorry."

"That's all right. I'll just go to my room and rest. I promise I'll come down in ten or fifteen minutes." Josef walked slowly up the stairs to his bedroom. He looked very tired and sad.

Angelica smiled. She knew he didn't want to sit down and talk. That is why she had prepared a surprise for him. She arrived earlier because she wanted to check the mail. There was something for Josef. She knew it was from Josef's friends because all of their names were on it. But this was not just a letter. It was bigger. It was a package! She was very pleased.

She took some colourful paper and wrapped the package. Now it looked like a gift! She put it on Josef's bed and came down the stairs to wait for him in the kitchen.

When Josef saw the gift on his bed, he was very surprised and pleased. He loved surprises. He opened the package quickly. It contained a letter and a small booklet. Josef began to read the letter.

October 29, 20_____

Dear Josef,

How are you? We hope that everything is going well for you. Here, everyone is fine, but we do miss you.

In one of your letters, you said we forgot to explain the details of our class project with Mr. Perreault. You asked Omar to write about the project, but we decided not to tell you anything about it. That's because we wanted to send a copy of the project to you. We started to work on the project about five weeks ago. You are right! It was a lot of fun, but it was also a lot of work.

This is how the project started. It was all Tina's fault!

As you know, Tina joined the "Welcoming Committee". She was very excited about welcoming David to ESDP. Mr. Perreault asked her to make a short presentation about her day as a member of the Welcoming Committee. Tina described everything she and David did that day. She said she and David had a wonderful day, but at the end of the presentation she added that she was a little worried about David and his family. She said they were new in Canada and they had a lot to learn about life here.

Then we started to talk about last year and how difficult it was for all of us and our families. We explained that it was difficult to be in a new city and a new school! Mr. Perreault agreed. As you know, he is new in Doveside too.

Suddenly, Mr. Perreault stood up and smiled. "Students, I have a great idea! You are going to write a guide! It will be a guide for all the new students and their families who move to our town and come to our school."

Of course, we all said that it was impossible. But Mr. Perreault insisted. He said we were experts on ESDP. He said this was the perfect opportunity to share our knowledge and experience.

Well, here it is. This is a copy of our Guide to Doveside and ESDP. It is also your birthday present. Happy Birthday! We know it is a little late because your birthday was at the end of September, but we hope you like your gift. All the new students will receive this guide on their first day at our school.

We miss you.

Your friends,
Tina, Omar, Hamid and Chantal

Activity 2, Part 6
Answer the following questions with

"Yes, (he/she/it) was" or "Yes, (he/she/it) did" or
"No, (he/she/it) wasn't" or "No, (he/she/it) didn't."

1. Did Josef walk into the house slowly and quietly? ______________________.
2. Was it 5:30 when Josef opened the door? ______________________.
3. Was 5:30 the usual time for Josef to return from school? ______________________.
4. Was Josef always home between 4:30 and 4:45? ______________________.
5. Was he always busy after school when he lived in Canada? ______________________.
6. Did Josef make many new friends on his first day at school? ______________________.
7. Was everyone helpful, friendly and polite? ______________________.
8. Was Angelica sad because Josef was lonely at his new school? ______________________.
9. Did Angelica make something special for Josef? ______________________.
10. Did Josef want to speak to Angelica? ______________________.
11. Did Josef want to be alone in his bedroom? ______________________.
12. Did Josef go to his room to call his friends? ______________________.
13. Was Josef very tired and sad? ______________________.
14. Was Angelica pleased to see Josef go up to his room? ______________________.
15. Did Angelica do her homework after she returned home? ______________________.
16. Did Angelica know who sent the package? ______________________.
17. Did she wrap the package? ______________________.
18. Was Josef surprised and pleased when he saw the gift on his bed? ______________________.
19. Did Josef open the package slowly? ______________________.
20. Was the letter from Josef's American friends? ______________________.
21. Did the letter describe Mr. Perreault? ______________________.
22. Was the project a lot of work? ______________________.
23. Did Tina join the "Green Committee"? ______________________.
24. Was the booklet a guide for new students at ESDP? ______________________.
25. Was the guide also Josef's birthday present? ______________________.

Activity 2, Part 7

Identify the part of speech and place each word in the correct column.

	Noun	Verb	Adjective	Adverb
friend				
friendly				
colour				
to colour				
colourless				
polite				
politely				

Activity 2, Part 8

Answer the questions below in the negative, and then in the affirmative.

Example: Did you walk to the supermarket last night?
No, I didn't walk to the supermarket last night.
Yes, I walked to the supermarket last night.

1. Did you look at this book last Saturday?

   No, ______________________________ last Saturday.

   Yes, ______________________________ last Saturday.

2. Did you like the pictures on the posters yesterday?

   No, ______________________________ yesterday.

   Yes, ______________________________ yesterday.

3. Did you enjoy the juice?

   No, ______________________________.

   Yes, ______________________________.

4. Did you return to New York a year ago?

   No, ______________________________ a year ago.

   Yes, ______________________________ a year ago.

5. Did you prepare the dinner?

   No, ______________________________.

   Yes, ______________________________.

6. Did you have homework last weekend?

   No, ____ last weekend.

   Yes, ____ last weekend.

7. Did you do your homework?

   No, ____.

   Yes, ____.

8. Did you come to school last Thursday?

   No, ____ last Thursday.

   Yes, ____ last Thursday.

9. Did you wave "Hello" to the new gym teacher?

   No, ____.

   Yes, ____.

10. Did you bring juice for the children?

   No, ____.

   Yes, ____.

Activity 2, Part 9
Rewrite the following sentences in the past tense.

Example: I am going to begin my project tonight.
I began my project last night.

Future	Past
in (2 days) next (week) tomorrow/(later) today tonight this (week)	(2 days) ago last (week) yesterday last night last week

1. I am going to bring flowers next week.

   ____.

2. He is going to come to Ottawa next month.

   ____.

3. They are going to spend some time with my grandparents today.

____.

4. She is going to make a poster tomorrow.

____.

5. We are going to meet her parents in half an hour.

____.

6. They are going to see Niagara Falls in three days.

____.

7. The children are going to do their homework tonight.

____.

8. I am going to be in the video store in two hours.

____.

9. They have two computer science teachers this year.

____.

10. I am going to put this poster on the wall in a few minutes.

____.

11. I will know the question next time.

____.

12. I will find my dictionary tonight.

____.

Unit II - Text 13

To Buy or to Rent?

Activity 1, Part 1
Write the definition of the words and expressions that are new to you.

Vocabulary List

Where Do You Live?

1. apartment: ______________________
2. bungalow: ______________________
3. condominium: ______________________
4. a. detached: ______________________
   b. single-family home: ______________________
5. duplex: ______________________
6. townhouse: ______________________
7. downtown: ______________________
8. suburb: ______________________

Parts of a House or Apartment

1. living room: ______________________
   a. fireplace: ______________________
2. dining room: ______________________
   a. dining area: ______________________
3. a. bedroom: ______________________
   b. master bedroom: ______________________
      1. closet: ______________________
      2. walk-in closet: ______________________
4. a. kitchen: ______________________
   b. appliances: ______________________
      1. dishwasher: ______________________
      2. refrigerator: ______________________
      3. stove: ______________________
   c. eat-in kitchen: ______________________
5. a. bathroom: ______________________
      1. bathtub: ______________________
      2. shower: ______________________
      3. sink: ______________________
      4. toilet: ______________________
   b. powder room: ______________________
6. other rooms
   a. den: ______________________
   b. family room: ______________________
   c. guest room: ______________________
7. hallway: ______________________
8. a. garage: ______________________
   b. parking: ______________________
9. laundry room: ______________________
   a. washing machine: ______________________
   b. dryer: ______________________
10. floors: ______________________
    a. carpet (carpeted): ______________________
    b. hardwood: ______________________
    c. rug: ______________________
11. storage room: ______________________
12. a. garden: ______________________
    b. yard: ______________________
13. utilities: ______________________
    a. electricity: ______________________
    b. heat: ______________________
    c. water: ______________________

Activity 1, Part 2
Answer the following questions in point form, and then ask your classmates the questions, noting their answers as well.

1. Do you live in an apartment, a bungalow, a condominium, a single-family house, a duplex, or a townhouse?

   ______________________________.

2. Do you live downtown or in the suburbs?

   ______________________________.

3. Does your living room have a fireplace?

   ______________________________.

4. Do you have a dining room, dining area, or eat-in kitchen?

   ______________________________.

5. How many bedrooms are there where you live?

   ______________________________.

6. Does your bedroom have a regular closet or a walk-in closet?

   ______________________________.

7. Is there a den or family room where you live?

   ______________________________.

8. Do you have a guest room?

   ______________________________.

9. Do you have a walk-in closet in your hallway?

   ______________________________.

10. a. How many appliances are there in your kitchen? ______________________________.

    b. What are the appliances? ______________________________.

11. Is there an "eat-in" area in your kitchen?

    ______________________________.

12. How many bathrooms are there where you live?

    ______________________________.

13. Do you have a bathroom with a bathtub and shower?

____.

14. Is there a powder room where you live?

____.

15. Do you have a garage, or is there parking where you live?

____.

16. Do you use your laundry room or the laundry room in your building?

____.

17. Do you have carpeted or hardwood floors?

____.

18. Do you have a storage room in your apartment or house?

____.

19. Do you have a yard or garden that belongs to you and your family?

____.

Activity 1, Part 3
Write the definition of the words and expressions that are new to you.

Vocabulary List

I. Real Estate Nouns	**II. People in Real Estate**
1. area: ______________	1. agent: ______________
2. lease: ______________	2. buyer: ______________
3. mortgage: ______________	3. landlord: ______________
4. payment: ______________	4. tenant: ______________
5. property: ______________	5. manager: ______________
6. real estate: ______________	6. a. seller: ______________
7. sale: ______________	b. vendor: ______________
8. sign: ______________	
9. vacancy: ______________	

III. Nouns

1. advantages: ____________________
2. advertisement/ad: ____________________
3. air conditioning: ____________________
4. artist: ____________________
5. bank: ____________________
6. decision: ____________________
7. furniture: ____________________
8. garbage: ____________________
9. K = thousand: ____________________
10. money: ____________________
11. noise: ____________________
12. newspaper: ____________________
13. paperwork: ____________________
14. piece: ____________________
15. pet: ____________________
16. race: ____________________
17. responsibility: ____________________
18. right: ____________________
19. section: ____________________

IV. Adjectives

1. clean: ____________________
2. hot: ____________________
3. large: ____________________
4. legal: ____________________
5. loud: ____________________
6. modern: ____________________
7. safe: ____________________
8. tall: ____________________

V. Real Estate Verbs

1. to buy: ____________________
2. to offer: ____________________
3. to own: ____________________
4. to renovate: ____________________
5. to rent: ____________________
6. to sell: ____________________
7. to sign: ____________________

VI. Other Verbs:

1. to accept: ____________________
2. to borrow: ____________________
3. to classify: ____________________
4. to damage: ____________________
5. to decide: ____________________
6. to detach: ____________________
7. to disappoint: ____________________
8. to furnish: ____________________
9. to include: ____________________
10. to learn: ____________________
11. to need: ____________________
12. to paint: ____________________
13. to pay: ____________________
14. to protect: ____________________
15. to refuse: ____________________
16. to repair: ____________________
17. to replace: ____________________
18. to understand: ____________________

Irregular Simple Past Tense

say ➜ said

VII. Expressions

1. How can I help you?: ____________________
2. What kind?: ____________________
3. I would like to...: ____________________
4. Would you like to...?: ____________________

Activity 1, Part 4
Text 13A: To Buy or To Rent? (Entry 1)

Where do the people of Doveside live? Do they buy houses? Do they rent apartments or houses? Do they buy condominiums? The people of Doveside think carefully and make many decisions before they finally decide where to live. They know that each choice has its advantages and its disadvantages.

Many people in Doveside decide to buy a house. Once they decide to buy a house, they have many decisions to make. Do they want a small house or a big house? Do they want a house downtown or a house in the suburbs? What kind of house do they want? There are many different kinds of houses in Doveside! Do they want to live in a bungalow, a single-family house, a duplex or a townhouse?

People who want to buy a house usually use a real estate agent. Real estate agents show buyers many houses. When the buyers want to buy one of the houses they have seen, they make an offer to the people who are selling the house. If the vendors accept the offer, the buyers usually borrow money from the bank. They use this money to pay for the house. The buyers arrange a monthly mortgage with the bank. The mortgage is the money they will pay the bank each month until all the money they borrowed has been paid back. Once the mortgage has been arranged, the buyers, real estate agents and lawyers complete the legal paperwork. The house belongs to the bank until the buyers have paid off the entire mortgage. Mortgages are usually twenty or thirty years long. Some mortgages are even longer!

Other people in Doveside decide to rent a place to live. They have many decisions to make too. Do they want to rent an apartment or a house? Do they want to rent a furnished or unfurnished apartment or house? They can use a real estate agent if they want, but they can usually find a place to rent without the help of a real estate agent. They can look for "For Rent" signs on apartment buildings or on houses. They can also look in the Classified section of the newspaper, which contains various kinds of advertisements. There are usually many advertisements in the classified section under "Real Estate". In every advertisement, there is a telephone number to call for more information. After they find a place they want to rent, they visit it, and then they sign a legal lease with the landlord or property manager.

Still other people in Doveside want to buy a place that has the advantages of renting an apartment, but not the disadvantages of owning a house. These people decide to buy a condominium. Some condominiums are in tall buildings like apartment buildings. Other condominiums look like townhouses or detached houses.

What do you think? Is it better to buy or to rent?

Activity 1, Part 5

Answer the following questions using complete sentences. Refer to the text *To Buy or to Rent?*

1. What is the job of a real estate agent?

   ____.

2. Where does the money to pay for a house (usually) come from?

   ____.

3. How does the buyer return the money he or she has borrowed?

   ____.

4. When does the house belong to the buyer?

   ____.

5. Who owns the house until the buyer has repaid all the money borrowed?

   ____.

6. List two other things people buy using "monthly" payments.

   ____.

Activity 1, Part 6

Leases are documents that explain the rights and responsibilities of landlords and tenants. Remember that leases can vary. Write "true" or "false" for the following rules and regulations that might appear in a lease.

1. ________ Tenants can leave garbage in the yard.
2. ________ Tenants can keep any pet they want.
3. ________ Tenants can pay the rent late.
4. ________ If children or pets cause damage, tenants have to pay for repairs.
5. ________ Tenants have to repair or replace appliances that are damaged by careless use.
6. ________ A landlord must paint the apartment when (reasonably) necessary.
7. ________ A landlord doesn't have to replace or repair appliances that are out of order.
8. ________ A landlord can turn off the tenant's heat and water.
9. ________ A landlord can enter a tenant's apartment whenever he or she wants to.
10. ________ A landlord must keep the apartment building clean (no pests, e.g., cockroaches) and safe.
11. ________ Tenants can listen to loud music and make loud noises whenever they want to.
12. ________ A landlord can refuse to rent to a tenant who does not have good references.
13. ________ A landlord can refuse to rent to tenants because of their nationality or race.
14. ________ Tenants must keep their apartments or houses reasonably clean.
15. ________ A landlord can refuse to rent to "joint tenants" [tenants who want to share the house or apartment].

Activity 1, Part 7
Use the following homonyms correctly in each of the sentences.

for/four	hear/here	hour/our	knew/new	know/no
right/write	son/sun	their/they're	to/two/too	

Example: I want **to** eat **two** hamburgers **too**.

1. The young child ______________ the address of his ______________ school.
2. Please ______________ the ______________ answers in the following sentences.
3. ______________ class will begin in one ______________.
4. I brought ______________ colouring pencils ______________ this exercise.
5. My sister says she likes ______________ play basketball with her ______________ friends.
6. "______________," I said, "I don't ______________ the name of the new teacher."
7. My daughter likes the moon; my ______________ likes the ______________.
8. ______________ going to return to ______________ house in five minutes.
9. I think if I stand ______________, I will______________ the song better.
10. I looked everywhere. It's ______________ where! I don't ______________ where it is.
11. His ______________ likes to play with my boy when the ______________ is shining.
12. If your answer is not ______________, please erase it and ______________ the correct answer.
13. There are ______________ books on my desk ______________ the new students.
14. In one ______________, we will see ______________ favourite singer.

Activity 1, Part 8
Write <u>must</u> or <u>has/have to</u> or <u>should</u> in the sentences below.

must or **has/have to:**	very important necessary no choice	**should:**	a good idea a choice

1. You ____________________ eat to live.
2. You ____________________ exercise three times a week.
3. You ____________________ do your homework every night.
4. You ____________________ study if you want to go to university.
5. Students in Canada ____________________ go to school until they are 16 years old.
6. Parents ____________________ encourage their children to study.
7. Students ____________________ help new students.
8. You ____________________ have oxygen to live.
9. We ____________________ stop pollution.
10. We ____________________ drink water to live.

Activity 1, Part 9

a. Use the following words to fill in the blanks.

b. Identify the part of speech of each word by indicating if it is a noun, verb, or adjective.

Example: a. The owners **decide** to sell their home. (verb)
b. They have a **decided** look on their faces. (adjective)

advertise	decide	disappoint	furnish	renovate
advertised	decided	disappointed	furnished	renovated
advertisement	decision	disappointment	furniture	renovation

1. a. People who want to sell their houses can ____________________ in the newspaper. (______)
   b. I saw an ____________________ for that house. (______)

2. a. I saw two apartments I liked on the weekend. I cannot____________________ which apartment I like more. (______)
   b. I must make my ____________________ before 10:00 a.m. on Monday. (______)

3. a. I am looking for an apartment that has ____________________, because I don't have time to go to stores and buy tables, chairs and other things. (______)
   b. I am looking for a ____________________ apartment. (______)

4. a. They wanted to ____________________ their kitchen last year. (______)
   b. Now their house has a ____________________ kitchen. (______)

5. a. Parents don't like to ____________________ their young children. (______)
   b. It is difficult for parents to see ____________________ on the faces of their children. (______)

Activity 1, Part 10

a. The prefix "dis-" changes a word into its antonym.
Add the prefix "dis-" to the words in the list and complete the sentences below.

advantage agree like belief	1. It happened so fast I was in total ____________________. 2. There are many "health" ____________________s to doing no exercises. 3. I ____________________ this artist's works because they are not very colourful. 4. Our opinions are different. I ____________________ with your opinions.

b. The suffix "-er" or "-or" changes a verb into a noun.

Example: play + er ➜ player: a. a person ➜ basketball player
b. a thing ➜ cassette player

renovat(e) + or ➜ renovator

Add "-er" or "-or" to the verbs in the list and fill in the blanks with the correct verb.
Use a dictionary to help you spell the words correctly.

begin
call
decorate
erase
keep
manage
move
own
print
research
sell
send
sing
teach
wait
write

Example: I like the new song by this **singer**.

1. When I find a new apartment, I will need a ________________ to help me move all my furniture.
2. After I write my essay on the computer, I use the ________________.
3. I like to use a pencil because, when I make a mistake, I can use the ________________.
4. The person who telephones is the "________________".
5. A person who works in a laboratory is called a ________________.
6. I started Italian classes last week. I am in the ________________ class.
7. The person who takes care of the zoo is the zoo ________________.
8. Readers love to meet the ________________ of their favourite book.
9. Small children like to have a friendly and helpful ________________.
10. The name of the ________________ is on the envelope of the letter.
11. The ________________ of this apartment building is very nice and helpful.
12. Another name for the vendor of a house is the "________________".
13. This ________________ works in my favourite restaurant. He is very patient.
14. This is my house. I am the ________________ of this house.
15. I have a new apartment, but I need a ________________ to help me make my apartment look beautiful.

Activity 1, Part 11

Write your opinion in response to this question: Is it better to buy or to rent?

Advantages of Owning a House	Disadvantages of Owning a House
____________________	____________________
____________________	____________________
____________________	____________________
____________________	____________________
Advantages of Renting an Apartment	**Disadvantages of Renting an Apartment**
____________________	____________________
____________________	____________________
____________________	____________________
____________________	____________________
Advantages of Owning a Condominium	**Disadvantages of Owning a Condominium**
____________________	____________________
____________________	____________________
____________________	____________________
____________________	____________________

Activity 2, Part 1

Match each word on the right with its abbreviation on the left.

To rent or buy a home listed in the Classified section of the newspaper, you must learn to read real estate abbreviations. Some of the abbreviations consist of the consonants in the words. For example, the abbreviation for "bedroom" is "bdrm". Many of the abbreviations consist of some of the consonants in the words. For example, the abbreviation for "bathroom" is "bth".

1. __F__ bdrm	A. air conditioning
2. _____ liv	B. appliances
3. _____ util	C. balcony
4. _____ K	D. bathroom
5. _____ incl	E. basement
6. _____ bth	**F. bedroom**
7. _____ pkng	G. dining room
8. _____ f/p	H. finished
9. _____ hwd	I. fireplace
10. _____ gar	J. four-piece
11. _____ app	K. garage
12. _____ reno	L. garden
13. _____ din	M. hardwood
14. _____ a/c	N. included
15. _____ lrg	O. large
16. _____ fin	P. living room
17. _____ bsmt	Q. parking
18. _____ gdn	R. renovated
19. _____ 4-pc	S. thousand
20. _____ balc	T. utilities

Activity 2, Part 2

Write abbreviations for the following real estate words and expressions.

1. kitchen: ____________
2. floor: ____________
3. furnished: ____________
4. building: ____________
5. central air conditioning: ____________
6. townhouse: ____________

Check the Real Estate section of your newspaper. Are your abbreviations correct?

Activity 2, Part 3

The following three real estate ads were in the classified section of the *Doveside Daily*. Write the information in full, using complete sentences.

Andrews Blvd/York Ave, 4-bdrm t/h, 3 bath, fin bsmt, lrg liv/din, 2-car gar, $299K, York Real Estate-D Williams (416) 555-1592

Example: A four-bedroom townhouse near Andrews Boulevard and York Avenue is for sale for $299,000. It has a large living room and dining room. It also has three bathrooms, a finished basement, and a two-car garage. For more details, please contact D. Williams at York Real Estate at 416-555-1592.

Murray St/Parkson Rd, 2-bdrm bung, 2 bth, lrg liv rm, f/p, gar, 249K, Jean 416-555-4884

1. ____

____

____

____

____

Carlton Cres/Dale Blvd, 1 bdrm, eat-in kit, 4 appl, pkg, a/c, util incl, $995, Refs, 416-555-1019

2. ____

____

____

____

____

Activity 2, Part 4
Write a classified ad for an imaginary place. Use real estate abbreviations.

Activity 2, Part 5
Text 13B: To Buy or To Rent (Entry 2)

Mr. and Mrs. Davidson see the following ad in the classified section of the Saturday paper.

They like the house because it is big. They also like the house because the Davidsons work in the downtown area. Their two children go to school in the downtown area too. The Davidsons want to know more about the house on Bayside Ave.
Mrs. Davidson telephones Nova Realty from her office early Monday morning.

> 119 Bayside Ave, reno 3 + 1 bdrm, 2 1/2 bth, semi, dntn, 5 appl, f/p, hwd, fin bsmt, gar, util incl, #1999 Nova Realty/Gilles Beaudry 111-555-2345

....

Mrs. Davidson: Good morning. I would like to speak to Mr. Beaudry, please.

Secretary: I'm sorry. Mr. Beaudry is not in now. He is with a client. May I take a message?

Mrs. Davidson: Yes, please. My name is Mrs. Davidson. I am calling about the semi-detached house on Bayside Ave. I saw the ad in the newspaper on the weekend.

Secretary: I'll let Mr. Beaudry know. How can he reach you, Mrs. Davidson?

Mrs. Davidson: He can telephone me at my office between 1:00 and 5:30 p.m. My number is 111-555-8797, extension 210.

Secretary: Thank you, Mrs. Davidson.

2:45 p.m

Mr. Beaudry: Hello, Mrs. Davidson. This is Gilles Beaudry. My secretary said you were interested in the house on Bayside Ave. She said you needed more information. How may I help you?

Mrs. Davidson: Thank you for returning my call, Mr. Beaudry. I have some questions about the ad. What does a 3 + 1 bedroom mean?

Mr. Beaudry: A 3 + 1 bedroom means that the house has three bedrooms and a small den or library. The small room can be used as a bedroom if you need a fourth bedroom.

Mrs. Davidson: Oh, I see. And what is a 1/2 bathroom please?

Mr. Beaudry: A 1/2 bathroom is a powder room that has a toilet and a sink.

Mrs. Davidson: Do the other bathrooms have showers and bathtubs?

Mr. Beaudry: Yes, they do. The other bathrooms are 4-piece bathrooms. That means they have a toilet, sink, bathtub and shower.

Mrs. Davidson: I understand. The ad also says the utilities are included. What does that mean?

Mr. Beaudry: It means that your electricity, water and heat are included in the rent.

Mrs. Davidson: That's good. I like carpeting. Is there any carpeting in the house?

Mr. Beaudry: No, there isn't. All the floors are hardwood floors. They are made of wood, but you can always put rugs or carpets on wooden floors.

Mrs. Davidson: I see. And the basement is finished. Does that mean that we can use it as a family room or guest room?

Mr. Beaudry: Oh, yes. The owners renovated the house three years ago. The bathrooms, kitchen and basement are clean and modern.

Mrs. Davidson: The ad said there are five appliances. What are the appliances?

Mr. Beaudry: Three of the appliances are in the kitchen. They are the stove, refrigerator and dishwasher. As well, there is a washing machine and dryer in the laundry room.

Mrs. Davidson: The house sounds very nice. When can my husband and I go to see it?

Mr. Beaudry: You can go and see the house at 6:30 if you want.

Mrs. Davidson: That sounds very good. We'll see you at 119 Bayside Avenue at 6:30 this evening, if that is convenient for you.

Mr. Beaudry: I'll be there. Bye for now.

Mrs. Davidson: Goodbye, Mr. Beaudry, and thank you very much for your help.

Activity 2, Part 6
Reread the conversation between Mrs. Davidson and Mr. Beaudry and write "true" or "false" for the following sentences. If the sentences are false, correct the information.
Example: Mr. Beaudry works at York Realty. ➜ false: Mr. Beaudry works at Nova Realty.

1. The house is a big house.

   ___________: ____.

2. The house is in the suburbs.

   ___________: ____.

3. The house has two bathrooms and one powder room.

   ___________: ____.

4. The kitchen, bathrooms and basement are old but clean.

   ___________: ____.

5. Mr. Beaudry returned Mrs. Davidson's call at 2:30.

___________: ____.

6. The utilities (electricity, water, heat) are not included in the rent.

___________: ____.

7. Mr. and Mrs. Davidson will see the house on the weekend.

___________: ____.

8. Mr. and Mrs. Davidson want to use the basement as a guest room or a family room.

___________: ____.

9. Mr. and Mrs. Davidson have three children.

___________: ____.

10. Mrs. Davidson is disappointed that there is no carpeting in the house.

___________: ____.

Activity 2, Part 7
Use the present tense or simple past tense of the verbs in the list on the left to complete the paragraph. Use each verb only once.

accept buy decide borrow furnish need offer own paint pay renovate replace repair see sell sign	Last year, my sister Dina said she did not want to live in an apartment anymore because she did not want to (1) ________________ rent. She said she wanted to use her rent money to (2) ________________ a small house in the downtown area. Dina found a very nice real estate agent, and every weekend they looked at houses together. Last weekend, she (3) ________________ a house she liked. She was very excited about the house. I encouraged her to make an offer. The vendor (4) ________________ his house because he wanted to buy a bigger house. After thinking about it carefully, Dina (5) ________________ to buy it. She (6) ________________ the vendor $169,000 for his house. The vendor (7) ________________ her offer. I was very pleased, because I didn't want her to be disappointed. She talked to her bank manager on Tuesday morning. She (8) ________________ $160,000 from the bank. Now she has a 25 year mortgage. That means Dina will

	(9) ________________ the house in 25 years! On Friday afternoon, the vendor, the real estate agent and my sister arrived at the lawyer's office. The vendor and my sister (10) ________________ the legal papers. My sister is very excited. She cannot wait to move into her new house. She plans to move into the house in July. She is making many plans. First she has to (11) ________________ or (12) ________________ the air conditioner because it does not work. She (13) ________________ an air conditioner that works because July is a very hot month in Doveside. In June, Dina plans to choose nice colours for the walls. After she (14) ________________ the walls, she plans to (15) ________________ the house with modern furniture. She wants to buy modern tables, chairs and other things. She also wants to buy some beautiful rugs. When Dina has more money, she plans to (16) ________________ the kitchen and bathroom because they are very old.

Big Cities and Small Cities

Unit II - Text 14

Activity 1, Part 1
Write the definition of the words and expressions that are new to you.

Vocabulary List

I. Words and Expressions

1. How far....?
   a. kilometre: ______
   b. mile: ______
   c. period: ______
2. a. here: ______
   b. there: ______
3. a. inside: ______
   b. indoor: ______
4. a. outside: ______
   b. outdoor: ______
5. a. across from: ______
   b. facing: ______
   c. opposite: ______
6. a. behind: ______
   b. in front of: ______
7. between: ______
8. a. next to: ______
   b. beside: ______
9. a. near: ______
   b. far: ______
10. a. to the left of: ______
    b. to the right of: ______
11. a. north of: ______
    b. south of: ______
    c. east of: ______
    d. west of: ______
12. at the corner of: ______

II. Government Services

1. city hall: ______
2. fire station: ______
3. police station: ______
4. post office: ______
5. tourist office: ______

III. Health Services

1. clinic: ______
2. hospital: ______
3. veterinarian: ______

IV. Transportation

1. airport: ______
2. station: ______
   a. bus: ______
   b. subway: ______
   c. train: ______
3. terminal: ______
   a. bus: ______
   b. subway: ______
   c. train: ______

V. Recreation

1. a. cinema: ____________________
   b. movie theatre: ____________________
2. gallery: ____________________
3. concert hall: ____________________
4. museum: ____________________
5. park: ____________________
6. theatre: ____________________
7. arena: ____________________
8. a. sports centre: ____________________
   b. sports club: ____________________

VI. Other Services

1. bank: ____________________
2. barbershop: ____________________
3. beauty salon/parlour: ____________________
4. dry cleaner: ____________________
5. laundromat: ____________________
6. garage: ____________________
7. gas station: ____________________
8. radio/TV station: ____________________
9. parking lot: ____________________
10. factory: ____________________

VII. Shops and Stores

1. bakery: ____________________
2. butcher shop: ____________________
3. convenience store: ____________________
4. supermarket: ____________________
5. coffee shop: ____________________
6. restaurant: ____________________
7. camera shop: ____________________
8. drugstore: ____________________
9. electronics store: ____________________
10. florist: ____________________
11. jewellery store: ____________________
12. mall: ____________________
13. pet shop: ____________________
14. stationery store: ____________________
15. toy store: ____________________
16. bookstore: ____________________

VIII. Religion

1. church: ____________________
2. mosque: ____________________
3. synagogue: ____________________
4. temple: ____________________

IX. Irregular Simple Past Tense

1. sit ➔ sat
2. stand ➔ stood

Activity 1, Part 2

Fill in the blanks using the words in the list on the left. Use each word only once.

airport arena bakery barbershop beauty salon butcher camera churches city hall clinic club coffee concert hall drugstore dry cleaner electronics fire station florist gallery hospital jewellery station	1. When we want to buy meat, we go to the ____________________ shop on the next street. 2. There is an art exhibition at the art ____________________. 3. When a boy or man wants to have his hair cut, he goes to the ____________________. 4. We buy medicine at the ____________________. 5. When people want to go to a nearby city or town, they often go to the bus ____________________. 6. The man is going to buy diamond earrings for his wife from the ____________________ store. 7. When we want to buy fresh bread, muffins and cakes, we go to the ____________________ on Carlton Avenue. 8. We can buy television sets and computers at the ____________________ store. 9. When we want to get copies of a photograph, we go to the ____________________ shop. 10. I love to buy fresh roses from the ____________________. 11. When I want to travel to China from Toronto, I go to the Air Canada terminal of the ____________________. 12. When people have questions about government services in their city or town, they call their ____________________. 13. When we want to play hockey, we go to the skating rink at the ____________________. 14. People usually see their doctor once a year. Their doctor works at a ____________________. 15. My aunt is in the ____________________. She had a baby girl yesterday. 16. When a woman wants to have her hair cut, she goes to the ____________________. 17. When we want to meet our friends for a cappuccino or cup of tea, we meet at our favourite ____________________ shop. 18. Christian people pray in their ____________________. 19. Many people don't use washing machines and dryers. They take their clothes to the ____________________. 20. When people want to exercise, they can go to a community sports centre or join a private sports ____________________. 21. My favourite group will sing at our ____________________ next week. 22. When I call 911, they contact the police or the ____________________.

Activity 1, Part 3
Use the words on the left to complete the sentences. Use each word only once.

<table>
<tr>
<td>bank
churches
cinema
convenience
garage
gas station
laundromat
mall
mosques
movie theatre
museum
park
pet shop
police station
post office
radio/TV station
restaurant
subway
supermarket
synagogues
temples
theatre
tourist office
toy store
veterinary</td>
<td>1. Some people like to see films. They go to the ____________________.
I like to see real people on stage. I go to the ____________________.
2. Many people buy food for the week at the ____________________.
3. My car doesn't start. I'll take it to the ____________________ today.
4. People often go to a big ____________________ to buy clothes, shoes, gifts and other things.
5. When we forget to buy milk from the supermarket, we often go to a ____________________ store near our home.
6. That ____________________ is showing the new Kung Fu film.
7. Many people and their dogs run in the ____________________.
8. Muslim people pray in their ____________________.
9. I want to buy a game for my 5-year-old cousin at the ____________________.
10. People who want to buy toys for their cats and dogs go to the ____________________.
11. The CBC is Canada's public ____________________.
12. Students often go to the ____________________, where they can see the clothes and other things people used hundreds of years ago.
13. People who own a car usually go to a ____________________ once or twice a week to fill up their fuel tanks.
14. People who live downtown prefer to use the underground train. It is called the ____________________.
15. People who don't have washing machines and dryers go to the ____________________ to wash their clothes.
16. After I write letters, I walk to the ____________________ to mail them.
17. The ____________________ ____________________ will be happy to give you maps of the city.
18. Christians pray in ____________________, but Jewish people pray in ____________________.
19. Cats and dogs have their doctors too, but they don't go to regular clinics; they go to ____________________ clinics.
20. When people need money, they go to their ____________________.
21. Hindus and Buddhists pray in their ____________________.
22. McDonald's? Wendy's? Harvey's? Burger King? Which fast food ____________________ is Canadian?
23. In an emergency, I call 911 and ask to speak to an officer at the ____________________.</td>
</tr>
</table>

Activity 1, Part 4
Text 14: Big Cities and Small Cities

"The City of Toronto" by Hamid Moussa

Ontario is one of the ten provinces of Canada. To the east of Ontario is the province of Quebec and to the west of Ontario is the province of Manitoba. The Territories are to the north of Ontario and the United States are to the south of Ontario. Every province in Canada has a provincial capital. The capital of Ontario is Toronto. How far is the capital of Ontario from Ottawa, the capital of Canada? It is not very far. Toronto is about 450 kilometres from Ottawa.

The municipal offices of the City of Toronto are in an area called Nathan Phillips Square. There are two tall buildings in Nathan Phillips Square that are opposite of each other. They face each other. The two buildings are our City Hall. Many of our municipal offices are inside these two buildings. The area in front of the buildings and between the two buildings is very special too. This area around City Hall is like a big park. There are many outdoor parties, festivals and celebrations there during the year.

Many people can enjoy these activities because we have very good public transportation. There is a subway station near City Hall. Many buses stop beside City Hall, too. And for people with cars, there is also a large parking lot next to City Hall and an underground parking lot under City Hall.

All cities and towns in Canada provide municipal services, health services, education services and transportation services for the people in their communities. The people of the various communities often build places of worship. They also work in stores, shops and businesses that provide various kinds of services.

"Doveside and Its Districts" by Tina Wong

Doveside is a small city in Ontario. There are about 110,000 people who live here. The city is divided into three districts. The districts are Swanville, Nightingale and Larktown. Every district has a small downtown area with its own schools, hospitals, city hall, supermarkets, mall and bus terminals.

There is a mountain 50 kilometres north of Doveside, and there is a beautiful national park 20 kilometres east of the city. There is also a small lake to the south of the city. The small airport and two factories are to the west, outside the city. The factories are the two main industries of Doveside. One factory makes computers, and the other factory makes bicycles.

Doveside is unique because its people are very special! We work together as a community. About nine years ago, we voted to live in a clean and healthy environment. We voted to pay more taxes and make public transportation free in Doveside. We also voted not to permit any cars in the downtown areas. That is why our downtown area is so clean and beautiful. There are flowers and trees everywhere! Our downtown area is for people, not for cars. The only kinds of transportation in the downtown area are buses and bicycles.

Of course, many of us need to come downtown to work, shop and go to school. How do we manage? First, we take buses to the bus terminals in our districts. When we arrive at the bus terminals, we have two choices. Some people choose to continue by bus; other people choose to travel by bicycle. People who want to use a bicycle for the day go to the bicycle office. The bicycle office is like a bicycle library. People borrow a bicycle for the day or for a few hours and return it when they want to go home. It is like borrowing a library book.

Another reason why Doveside is very special is that we enjoy many different recreational activities. Many of us are very active and love fresh air and outdoor activities. We enjoy swimming pools and sports arenas in our community centres, and bicycle paths and walking trails in our parks. In the summer, we like to go camping, canoeing and fishing. In the winter, we go ice skating, skiing, or ice fishing. That is why we spend so much time, energy and money on our beautiful parks! We also enjoy the quiet life in Doveside. We like to visit museums, libraries, theatres, cinemas and many different restaurants. Doveside also has a very large and popular arts centre and concert hall.

Many community services are provided by volunteers. Our volunteers provide free day care for small children and after-school programs for young people in Doveside. The after-school programs are usually sports programs or arts and crafts workshops. There are also many volunteer programs for our senior citizens. Everyone in Doveside is involved in one or two volunteer activities.

Now you know why Doveside is very special. It's special because of its people and community spirit. We like to do things together. We even celebrate many festivals and holidays as a community. Thanksgiving and Canada Day are wonderful, because we plan parades and community fairs. For religious festivals, we plan street carnivals and multicultural dinners. That is why Doveside is the friendliest city in the world. Everyone knows everyone! We do not really live in a city. We live in an extended family!

Here is a small map of one of the nicest parts of Doveside called Swanville. I love this part of Swanville's downtown area because it has so many old trees, water fountains and small gardens. I especially love it in the spring, summer and fall because it is so colourful. When I go to the library, I always try to find time to take a short and relaxing walk. Swanville is so beautiful – just like the rest of Doveside!

You are a tall giant standing here:

Carlton Technical College	Lily Pool Park Swanville City Hall	The Swanville Museum	
		Swan's Fine Arts Centre	Swan's Concert Hall

water fountain

...................Catherine Avenue...................

Garden Clinic	Swanville Library Pool Florist	Coffee-Time Downtown Veterinary Clinic	Giovanni's Italian Restaurant Video Store

X

Activity 1, Part 5
Use words from the vocabulary lists of this activity to solve the crossword puzzle.

DOWN
1. A place to put your money.
2. A type of store that sells office and school supplies.
3. A place to have a baby.
4. A place to buy food for the week.
5. A place for boys and men to get their hair cut.
6. A place for Jewish people to pray.
7. A person who sells fresh meat.
8. A place to buy flowers.
9. A building that has 10-100 stores and shops.
10. A place where we find an ice rink.
11. A place where there are trees, flowers and a playground for children.

ACROSS
12. A place to buy gasoline for your car.
13. A place to learn.
14. A place to park your car for a few hours.
15. A place to see historical objects.
16. A place to buy fresh cakes and bread.
17. A place to borrow books.
18. A place where things like TVs, radios and cars are built.
19. A place for Christian people to pray.
20. A place for Muslim people to pray.
21. A place to learn about your town's laws.
22. You can study here after you finish school.
23. A type of store that is open 24 hours a day.

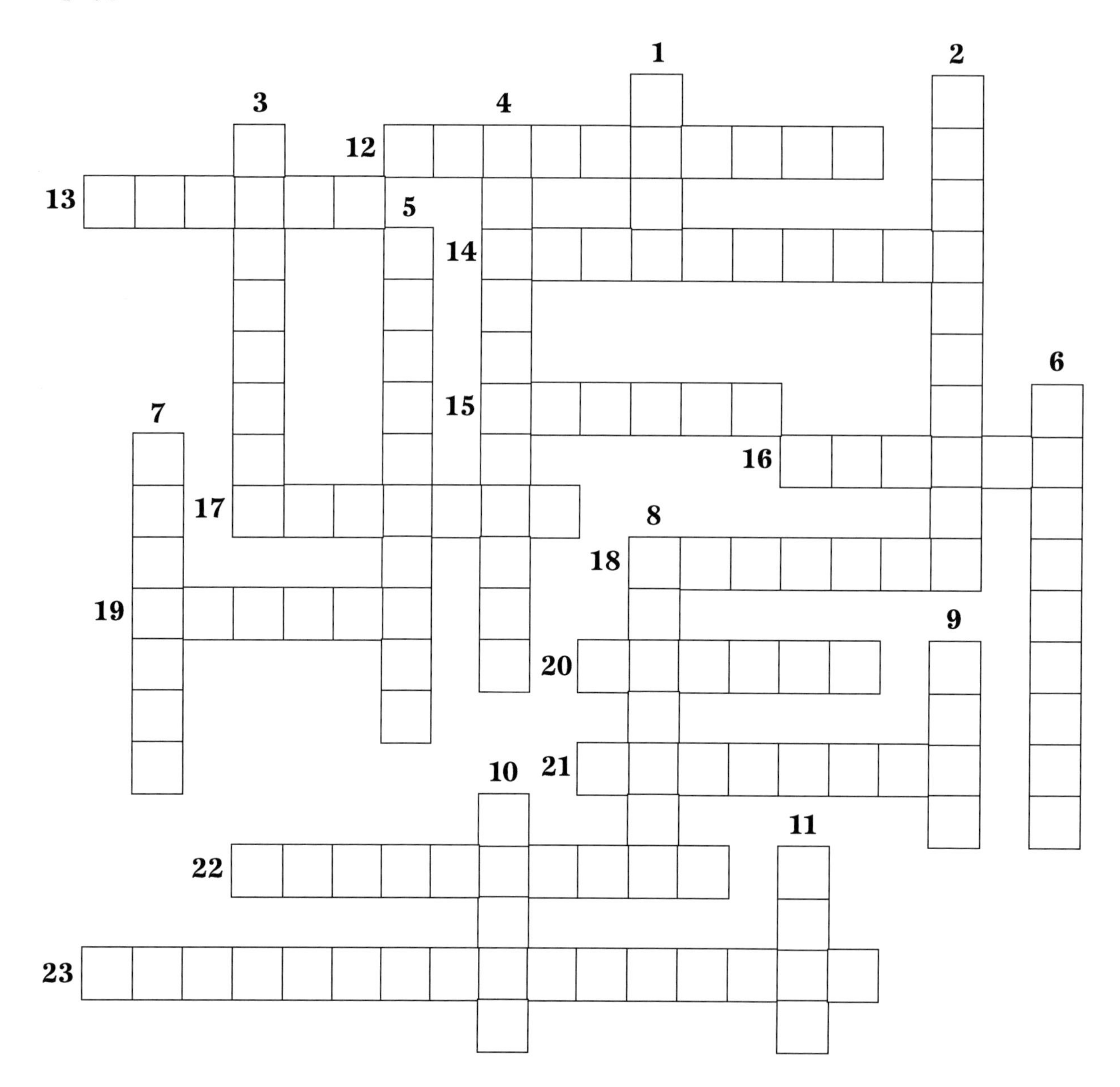

Activity 2, Part 1

There are many words that can be used as both nouns and verbs. Fill in each blank with a word from the column on the left. If you use a word as a noun, write "N"; if you use a word as a verb, write "V".

answer drink end help hope interview knock mail permit plan plant **rent** research shop smile vote walk water work	**Example:** I want to **rent** a two-bedroom apartment. (V) (or) I pay the **rent** on the first day of every month. (N) 1. It is the responsibility of every Canadian to ____________________ when there is an election. (____) 2. The teachers ____________________ the new student's questions. (____) 3. They are completing their ____________________ in that laboratory. (____) 4. I ____________________ my grandparents will come for a visit next summer. (____) 5. You did an excellent job. Good ____________________! (____) 6. My house is at the ____________________ of the street. (____) 7. I like to ____________________ in fruit and vegetable markets. (____) 8. The manager will ____________________ my sister for the job tomorrow. (____) 9. My favourite ____________________ is orange juice. (____) 10. People need to buy a ____________________ before they can go fishing. (____) 11. For exercise, my dog and I take a twenty-minute ____________________ in the park every morning. (____) 12. The doorbell doesn't work. I think if we ____________________ on the door, they will hear us. (____) 13. Please ____________________ the flowers. It's a hot day. (____) 14. I ____________________ to visit my aunt on the weekend. (____) 15. I want to thank you for your ____________________. (____) 16. Children ____________________ when you take their pictures with a camera. (____) 17. I always ____________________ my letters at the post office. (____) 18. The "Green Committee" will ____________________ many trees and bushes. (____)

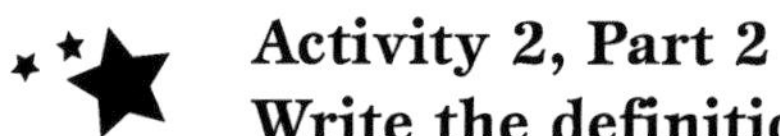

Activity 2, Part 2
Write the definition of the words and expressions that are new to you.

Vocabulary List

I. Community

1. factory: ______________________
2. industry: ______________________
3. district: ______________________
4. population: ______________________
5. carnival: ______________________
6. concert: ______________________
7. craft (show): ______________________
8. daycare: ______________________
9. fair: ______________________
10. festival: ______________________
11. holiday dinner: ______________________
12. parade: ______________________
13. volunteer: ______________________
14. workshop: ______________________

II. Environment

1. fountain: ______________________
2. lake: ______________________
3. mountain: ______________________
4. path: ______________________
5. pool: ______________________
6. trail: ______________________

III. Transportation

1. public: ______________________
2. service: ______________________
   a. (by) air: ______________________
   b. (by) bicycle: ______________________
   c. (by) train: ______________________

IV. Food

1. cheese: ______________________
2. chicken: ______________________
3. fish: ______________________
4. meat: ______________________
5. fruit: ______________________
6. vegetable: ______________________

V. Seasons

1. summer: ______________________
2. winter: ______________________

VI. Nouns

1. adult: ______________________
2. bench: ______________________
3. choice: ______________________
4. clothes: ______________________
5. convenience: ______________________
6. energy: ______________________
7. giant: ______________________
8. photograph: ______________________
9. senior citizen: ______________________
10. spirit: ______________________
11. stranger: ______________________

VII. Adjectives

1. active: ______________________
2. free: ______________________
3. fresh: ______________________
4. healthy: ______________________
5. national: ______________________
6. recreational: ______________________
7. religious: ______________________
8. unique: ______________________

VIII. Recreational Verbs

1. to camp: ______________________
2. a. to canoe: ______________________
   b. to go canoeing: ______________________
3. a. to fish: ______________________
   b. to go fishing: ______________________
4. a. to ice fish: ______________________
   b. to go ice fishing: ______________________
5. a. to skate: ______________________
   b. to go skating: ______________________
6. a. to ski: ______________________
   b. to go skiing: ______________________
7. a. to swim: ______________________
   b. to go swimming: ______________________

IX. Other Verbs

1. to build: ______________________
2. to celebrate: ______________________
3. to fill: ______________________
4. to mail: ______________________
5. to manage: ______________________
6. to permit: ______________________
7. to provide: ______________________
8. to relax: ______________________
9. to run: ______________________
10. to shop: ______________________
11. to travel: ______________________
12. to visit: ______________________
13. to volunteer: ______________________
14. to vote: ______________________

Activity 2, Part 3
Change the verbs on the left into the simple past tense, and then fill in the blanks with the correct verb. Use each verb only once.

am/are/is **come** do forget have know make put say sit see spend stand	When I first (1) **came** to Doveside, I (2) __________________ very sad. For the first few days, I (3) __________________ many hours thinking about my friends and my old school and how much I missed them. However, the next day I needed to go downtown to shop and buy school supplies. I (4) __________________ a city map in my bag and walked to the bus stop near our apartment building. I (5) __________________ not know where to go. I (6) __________________ many questions! Where is Doveside's stationery store? Which bus do I take? Where do I stop? I (7) __________________ at the bus stop for twenty minutes, looking at the map in my hands. Many buses came, but I did not know which bus to take. A young boy (8) __________________ me standing at the bus stop. He walked to me and asked, "Can I help you?" I was very surprised. He looked at the map in my hand and (9) __________________, "I live in Doveside. I know the city very well. Why don't we sit on that park bench, and I'll explain the map to you." I was pleased. Are the people of Doveside friendly and helpful? Do the people of Doveside talk to people they don't know and start a conversation? I decided today was a good day to make a new friend. We (10) __________________ down on the bench, and I asked many questions. He was right! He (11) __________________ the city very well. He answered all of my questions. Soon I (12) __________________ that I was a stranger in Doveside. The young boy and I are good friends now. I will always remember that day as the day when I (13) __________________ my first friend in Doveside.

Activity 2, Part 4
Pretend that you are facing the Pool Florist.
Study the map on page 139 and fill in the blanks using the correct preposition from the list on the left.
Use each preposition only once.

across from behind between in front of left next to opposite right	1. The small coffee shop is to the ____________ of the library. 2. Swan's Fine Arts Centre is ____________ Swan's Concert Hall and City Hall. 3. There is a clinic to the ____________ of the library. 4. City Hall is ____________ the library. 5. The park is ____________ City Hall. 6. Giovanni's Italian Restaurant is ____________ the small coffee shop. 7. The water fountain is ____________ City Hall. 8. The Garden Clinic is ____________ Carlton College.

Activity 2, Part 5

Guide to Doveside

This is the map of Larktown, Doveside's second district. Examine the map closely as you complete the exercise which follows.

1.	2.	3.	**fruit and vegetable store**	4.	5.	6.
school	7.	8.	9.	10.	**convenience store**	11.
12.	13.	**Concert Hall**	14.	15.	16.	**camera shop**
shoe store	17.	18.	19.	20.	**Thai restaurant**	21.
22.	**jean store**	23.	24.	**library**	25.	26.
27.	28.	29.			**pet shop**	30.
fire station	31.	**radio and television station**	32.	33.	34.	35.

You are standing here:
X

Work with a partner to complete the map of Larktown (page 146). As you do this exercise, imagine you are a very, very tall giant standing on the "X". You are facing building 32.

1. The florist is in front of the shoe store and next to the jean store.
2. The shoe store is between the florist and the barbershop.
3. The jewellery store is between the beauty salon and the jean store.
4. The museum is next to the jewellery store and next to the concert hall.
5. The tourist office is next to the jean store. Now the museum is between the tourist office and the concert hall.
6. The bookstore is between the tourist office and the library.
7. The fine arts centre is behind the library.
8. The fine arts centre is between the library and the art gallery.
9. City Hall is to the left of the art gallery and to the right of the concert hall.
10. In the middle of all these buildings there is a small park.
11. The cheese shop is across from City Hall.
12. The bakery is to the right of the cheese shop.
13. The butcher shop is behind the bakery.
14. The supermarket is to the left of the cheese shop.
15. The fruit and vegetable store is between the butcher shop and the fish market.
16. The sports shop is between the school and the supermarket.
17. The sports club is behind the sports shop. It is beside the fish market.
18. The arena is to the left of the sports club and behind the school.
19. The police station is behind the fire station and opposite the florist.
20. The video store is to the right of the police station.
21. The music shop is in front of the video store and next to the radio and television station.
22. The mall is a big building that faces the tourist office, the bookstore and the library.
23. The post office is between the radio and television station and the movie theatre.
24. The card shop is behind the Thai restaurant. It is beside the art gallery.
25. The electronics store is to the right of the Thai restaurant.
26. The electronics store is between the camera shop and the French restaurant.
27. The veterinarian's office is to the right of the pet shop and accross from the French restaurant.
28. The dry cleaner is to the left of the French restaurant.
29. The clinic is in front of the pet shop and next to the movie theatre.
30. The clinic and the hospital are next to each other.
31. The bus terminal is across the camera shop and in front of the train station.
32. The train station is to the right of the ice cream store.

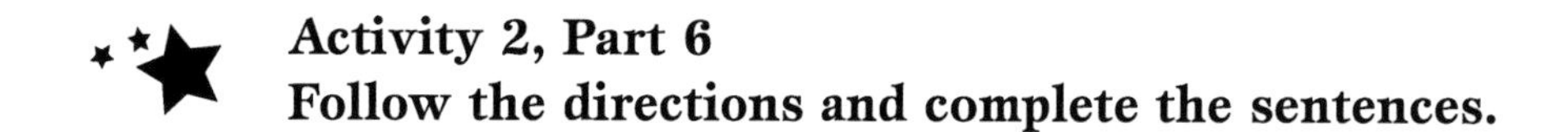

Activity 2, Part 6
Follow the directions and complete the sentences.

Guide to Nightingale

This is a map of downtown Nightingale. Read it carefully and you will find the places you need to go to!

Kennedy Road

cinema 1 | cinema 2 | music store

Churchill Street

laundromat | florist | art store
butcher | park | bookstore
Greek restaurant | coffee shop | ice cream store

Findley Street

pizzeria | Thai restaurant | toy store

Atwood Street

church | temple | mosque

Trudeau Boulevard

pet shop | arena | bicycle shop

museum | supermarket | drugstore
garage | garden | post office
tea house | library | bank

fire station | mall | fruit and vegetable store

synagogue | park | card shop

Terry Fox Avenue

jewellery store | police station

vet's office | City Hall | convenience store
bakery | swimming pool | school

clinic | barber-shop | shoe store

bus terminal | video store | park

Kingston Boulevard

1. You are at the corner of Churchill Street and Terry Fox Avenue.

   a) You cross Findley Street. The building on your right is the ____________________.

   b) After that building, you turn left onto Atwood Street at the end of the block. The second building on your left is the ____________________.

   c) When you exit that place, you go to your left. You turn left again at the corner. The second building on your left is the ____________________.

   d) From there, you turn left and make another left at the corner. The second building on your right is the ____________________.

   e) From that place, you turn right. At the end of the block you turn left. The second building on your right is the ____________________.

   f) After, at the corner, you turn left. The first building on your left is the ____________________. This is the last place to find.

2. You are on Terry Fox Avenue facing the library. The building to your right is the
_________________________ and the building to your left is the
_________________________.

3. What are the four buildings or stores at the corner of Churchill Street and Trudeau Boulevard?

____

____

____

____

4. You are standing at the doors of City Hall, facing the library.

   a) You need to buy a toy for your niece. Explain how you walk to the toy store.

   ____

   ____

   b) You need to buy flowers for your friend's birthday. Explain how you walk to the florist.

   ____

   ____

   ____

   ____

   ____

   c) You need to buy a card for your friend's birthday. Explain how you walk to the card shop.

   ____

   ____

   ____

Activity 2, Part 7
Use complete sentences to answer the following questions on Tina Wong's text about Doveside.

1. What is the population of Doveside?

   ____.

2. How many districts are there in Doveside? What are their names?

   ____.

3. How far is the mountain from Doveside?

   ____.

4. How far is the national park from Doveside?

   ____.

5. What are the two main industries of Doveside?

   ____.

6. When did the people vote to live in a clean and healthy environment?

   ____.

7. Who pays for free public transportation for the residents of Doveside?

   ____.

8. List three reasons why the downtown area is so beautiful.

   ____

   ____.

9. How do people come downtown from the suburbs?

   ____.

10. For what three reasons do people come to the downtown area?

    ____.

11. Some people use the bus when they are in the downtown area. What other means of transportation do people use in Doveside?

    ____.

12. Explain the job of the "bicycle office".

    ____

    ____.

13. List three examples of “winter” activities, “summer” activities and “quiet” activities that the residents of Doveside enjoy.

“Winter” Activities	“Summer” Activities	“Quiet” Activities
1. ____________	____________	____________
2. ____________	____________	____________
3. ____________	____________	____________

14. How do the residents of Doveside celebrate Thanksgiving and Canada Day?

____

15. How do the residents of Doveside celebrate the religious festivals of its residents?

____

16. What two services do volunteers provide for their community?

____

Activity 2, Part 8
Write a paragraph about your first few days at a new school (50-60 words).

____

____

____

____

____

____

____

____

____

____

____

____

Activity 2, Part 9

Do you know your community? Answer the following questions in point form.

1. What is the name of the district where you live? ____________________
2. What is the name of the district where you go to school? ____________________
3. What is the name of the district where your mother works? ____________________
4. What is the name of the district where your father works? ____________________
5. Do you have a community centre in your district? ____________________
6. Are you a member of your community centre? ____________________
7. How much does it cost to participate in your favourite activity? ____________________
8. What are the summer activities that your community centre offers?

   ____
9. What are the winter activities that your community centre offers?

   ____
10. Does your community centre have activities or services for small children? What are they?

    ____
11. Does your community centre have activities or services for young adults? What are they?

    ____
12. Does your community centre have activities or services for adults? What are they?

    ____
13. Does your community centre have activities or services for senior citizens? What are they?

    ____
14. Is your community centre planning activities for the next holiday? What are they?

    ____
15. Which of the following activities does your community or your community centre plan?
    a) carnival: ____________________
    b) concert: ____________________
    c) art and craft show: ____________________
    d) fair: ____________________
    e) festival: ____________________
    f) holiday dinner: ____________________
    g) parade: ____________________
16. Are there any factories in or around your town and city? What do they make?

    ____
17. Are there any industries in your community? What are they?

    ____

Unit II - Text 15

Where Do You Buy Your Groceries?

Activity 1, Part 1
Write the definition of the words and expressions that are new to you.

Vocabulary List

I. Food

1. apple: ______
2. apricot: ______
3. asparagus: ______
4. bagel: ______
5. banana: ______
6. bean: ______
7. beef: ______
8. beet: ______
9. blueberry: ______
10. bread: ______
11. broccoli: ______
12. bun: ______
13. cabbage: ______
14. cake: ______
15. cantaloupe: ______
16. carrot: ______
17. cauliflower: ______
18. celery: ______
19. cereal: ______
20. cheese: ______
21. cherry: ______
22. chick pea: ______
23. cookie: ______
24. corn: ______
25. cracker: ______
26. croissant: ______
27. cucumber: ______
28. fig: ______
29. fish: ______
30. garlic: ______
31. grapefruit: ______
32. grape: ______
33. ice cream: ______
34. lamb: ______
35. lemon: ______
36. lettuce: ______
37. lime: ______
38. macaroni: ______
39. mango: ______
40. milk: ______
41. muffin: ______
42. mushroom: ______
43. noodle: ______
44. orange: ______
45. papaya: ______
46. pasta: ______
47. peach: ______
48. pear: ______
49. pepper: ______
50. pineapple: ______
51. pork: ______
52. potato: ______
53. prune: ______
54. radish: ______
55. raisin: ______
56. raspberry: ______
57. red bean: ______
58. rice: ______
59. soy bean: ______
60. spinach: ______
61. strawberry: ______
62. tangerine: ______
63. toast: ______

64. tofu: ______________________
65. tomato: ______________________
66. watermelon: ______________________
67. yogurt: ______________________
68. dessert: ______________________
69. fish–"catch of the day": ______________________
70. meal: ______________________
71. nut: ______________________
72. oil: ______________________
73. sauce: ______________________
74. spice: ______________________
75. sandwich: ______________________
76. steak: ______________________

II. Nouns

1. cart: ______________________
2. counter: ______________________
3. deli: ______________________
4. grocery: ______________________
5. recipe: ______________________
6. seeds: ______________________
7. soft drink: ______________________
8. a. stone: ______________________
   b. pit: ______________________
9. tulip: ______________________

III. Food Verbs

1. bake: ______________________
2. barbecue: ______________________
3. grate: ______________________
4. grind: ______________________
5. order: ______________________
6. peel: ______________________
7. smell: ______________________
8. taste: ______________________

IV. Other Verbs

1. happen: ______________________
2. invite: ______________________
3. (to be) surprised: ______________________
4. stay: ______________________

V. Adjectives

1. popular: ______________________
2. famous: ______________________
3. a. cold: ______________________
   b. hot: ______________________
4. sunny: ______________________

VI. Synonyms

a. autumn: ______________________
b. fall: ______________________

VII. Other Words

1. during: ______________________
2. even: ______________________
3. most: ______________________
4. several: ______________________
5. still: ______________________

Irregular Simple Past Tense

1. buy ➜ bought
2. can ➜ could
3. choose ➜ chose
4. eat ➜ ate
5. feel ➜ felt
6. get ➜ got
7. give ➜ gave
8. grind ➜ ground
9. go ➜ went
10. mean ➜ meant
11. read ➜ read (pronounced "red")
12. speak ➜ spoke
13. take ➜ took
14. tell ➜ told
15. think ➜ thought
16. write ➜ wrote

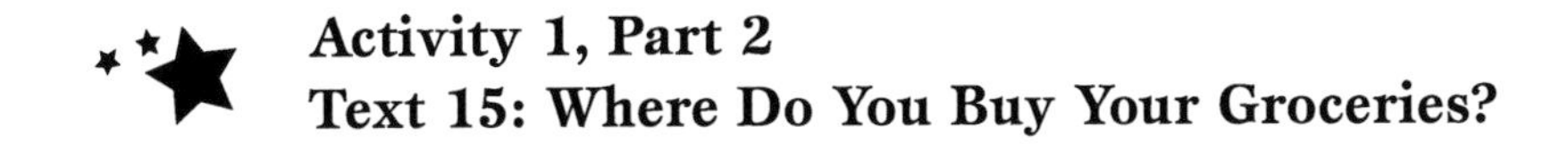

Activity 1, Part 2
Text 15: Where Do You Buy Your Groceries?

"Shopping for Food in Swanville" by Keiko

Families in Doveside buy their groceries from various food stores in Swanville. They usually shop on the weekend and in the evenings. The fresh fruit and vegetable stores in Swanville are very popular, especially during the spring, summer and autumn. Many people who like to barbecue steaks and cook hamburgers buy meat from the butcher. Others who like fresh fish go to the fish market to buy the "catch of the day".

My family does some grocery shopping at the supermarket, but we like to do most of our shopping at the small stores, because we know all the owners.

I went shopping on Saturday. Let me tell you what I did and where I went.

Last Tuesday, my parents invited some friends to come to our house on Saturday for a small dinner party. They often invite friends for Dad's famous spaghetti dinners. I was very excited, because my parents told me to invite two friends. I invited Chantal and Ricardo.

On Saturday morning, after we ate breakfast, I told my parents I wanted to help with the dinner party. My parents were surprised because I usually have a lot of homework to finish on the weekend, but they said I could do the shopping if I wanted. I said yes. I love to go to markets and to fruit and vegetable stores, especially on nice days. Saturday was a very nice and sunny day. My mother and father wrote a list of things they needed for the dinner party, and then they gave me the list. It was long!

I read the list very carefully. There were many things on the list, and that meant I had to go to many places. I took our shopping cart and some money. I was ready!

First, I went to the supermarket. There were only a few things on the list that I wanted to buy from the supermarket. I bought tomato sauce, some spaghetti noodles, oil and soft drinks. I also went to the spice section of the supermarket to get some Italian spices for Dad's spaghetti sauce.

My next stop was the fruit and vegetable store. There were many things I needed to buy there. First, I got some onions, green peppers, mushrooms and garlic. My dad uses a lot of these vegetables in his famous spaghetti sauce. I also got the vegetables my mom uses to make her green salad. I got lettuce, tomatoes, cucumbers, carrots and a few radishes.

I then bought the fruit my mom puts in her delicious fruit salad. I got oranges, apples, pears, grapes, a cantaloupe and a fresh pineapple. I didn't buy any nuts because Mom said we had an unopened package of nuts at home. Mom likes to add nuts to the fruit salad.

I then walked to the cheese store. It is next to the fruit and vegetable store. I got two kinds of grated cheese. We love to add grated cheese to Dad's spaghetti sauce before we begin to eat it. I then had to buy some bread. Our spaghetti dinners always begin with delicious garlic bread. I love to go to the bakery. I love to look at all the loaves of bread, croissants, muffins, bagels, cookies and cakes in the windows. I also love the smell of freshly-baked bread! I chose a loaf of fresh Italian bread for our dinner party.

My last stop was the butcher shop. We always buy the meat last because we want it to stay fresh. I went inside the butcher shop and talked with the butcher for a few minutes. He knows our family. He also knows about my dad's famous spaghetti sauce. I chose two kilos of fresh beef and asked him to grind it. After a few minutes, he gave me the ground beef that Dad needed for his recipe.

I was ready to go home when I saw some beautiful flowers in the flower market. Flowers were not on the list, but I thought of my mom. I decided to buy some fresh yellow tulips because yellow is her favourite colour. I then checked the list carefully. Everything on the list was in my shopping cart and it was only 1:30. I felt great! I had helped my parents with the shopping, and I still had lots of time to finish my homework before Saturday's dinner party.

"Shopping at the Supermarket" by Hamid Moussa

Most of the people who live in Nightingale shop for groceries only once a week. We feel we can save time by shopping in only one store. That is why our modern and clean supermarkets are very popular. At our supermarkets, we can buy more than just food. We can buy almost everything on our weekly shopping list!

Our supermarkets are divided into sections and aisles. The sections have names and the aisles have numbers. Above each aisle there is a sign listing the things we can find on the different shelves.

There are usually eight sections in every supermarket. The most popular section is usually the Delicatessen. People often call it the Deli. It is another reason why our supermarkets are special. They are famous for their delis. That is the section where we can buy fresh food that is already prepared. There, we can buy prepared cold or hot meals and salads. That is why the section is divided into the hot deli and the cold deli. The hot deli section is where we can buy foods like hot barbecued chicken or other meals and dishes that are "ready to eat". The cold deli section is where we can buy things like sandwich meat, cheese and salad.

The busiest section of our supermarket is usually the Fresh Produce Section. That is the section where we can buy fresh fruit and vegetables. Many people say it is the most colourful section of the supermarket because it is full of fruit and vegetables. In the summer, it is very colourful because it is full of strawberries, blueberries, melons, apricots and fresh corn on the cob.

Another section of the supermarket is the Meat and Seafood Section. That is where we can buy poultry, like chicken or turkey. We can also buy different kinds of fresh beef in that section. People buy fresh steaks, stewing beef, roasts, or ground beef there. Sometimes people buy fresh pork or lamb. There are also many people in Nightingale who love fresh seafood. They always buy their fresh fish and other kinds of seafood in that section of the supermarket.

The Frozen Food Section is where we can buy many different things. There, we can buy frozen vegetables and frozen meals. Frozen pizzas, lasagna and other meals are very useful for families who don't always have time to cook meals. That section has frozen juices also. But the reason that section is one of the most popular places in the supermarket for many young children is the ice cream. That is the section where we can choose our favourite kinds of ice cream.

Another very important section of the supermarket is called the Dairy Food Section. That is where we buy milk products like butter, yogurt, cheese and milk, as well as eggs. In some of our supermarkets there are more than thirty different kinds of cheese!

One large section of the supermarket that is divided into several aisles is the Home Section. In that section, we can find beauty and health products like shampoo, toothpaste, soap and many other home supplies. In the other aisles, we can find toilet paper, paper towels, tissue paper and cleaning supplies like laundry detergent and dishwashing liquids. The section has many popular brands.

In all our supermarkets, there is a Bakery where we can buy freshly baked bread, cakes, cookies, muffins and bagels. Some people order birthday cakes and special holiday cakes from the bakery in their favourite supermarket.

Of course, the most beautiful sections of the whole supermarket is the Flower Section. That section is usually full of different, colourful flowers and plants. There, we can buy our favourite fresh flowers and plants twelve months a year.

To find other food or home supplies, we have to read the signs above each aisle. (In some supermarkets, the signs are at the beginning or end of every aisle.) The signs tell us what we can find on the shelves. For example, if we are looking for pet food, canned foods, spices, drinks, cereal, pasta, snacks and other things, we read the signs. The signs can save us a lot of time when we are shopping.

Finally, it is always a lot of fun to choose our favourite magazines or newspapers when we are waiting to pay the cashier for all the food and supplies we have in our shopping cart.

Now you know why supermarkets are popular. We can buy everything there, even things we don't need!

Activity 1, Part 3

Reread Keiko's text, *Shopping for Food in Swanville,* and answer the following questions in complete sentences (except for questions 7, 8 and 9).

1. What are two reasons why the people in Swanville like to shop at small stores?

   ____

   ____.

2. Why are the dinner parties at Keiko's house so popular?

   ____.

3. Why does Keiko take the shopping cart with her?

   ____.

4. What three vegetables does Keiko's dad add to the ground meat when he makes the spaghetti sauce?

   ____.

5. What dessert are they planning to have after dinner? Who is going to make it?

   ____.

6. What do Keiko and her family like to put on the sauce before they begin to eat their spaghetti dinner?

   ____.

7. List the items that Keiko's parents asked her to buy. (There are 24 things on the list.)

   ________ ________ ________ ________

   ________ ________ ________ ________

   ________ ________ ________ ________

   ________ ________ ________ ________

   ________ ________ ________ ________

   ________ ________ ________ ________

8. Keiko went to many stores and shops to buy the things on the list. List the stores and shops below.

   ____________ ____________ ____________

   ____________ ____________ ____________

   ____________ ____________ ____________

9. What did Keiko buy that was not on the list?

   ____

Activity 2, Part 1
Write the definition of the words and expressions that are new to you. (Words that look or sound like French words are marked with an asterisk.)

Vocabulary List

I. Supermarket
1. aisle: ____________
2. shelf: ____________
3. check-out counter: ____________

II. Sections of the Supermarket
1. bakery: ____________
2. beauty products: ____________
   a. shampoo: ____________
   b. toothpaste: ____________
   c. soap: ____________
3. dairy: ____________
   a. butter: ____________
   b. eggs: ____________
   c. milk: ____________
4. fresh produce: ____________
5. frozen foods: ____________
6. household products: ____________
   a. toilet paper: ____________
   b. paper towels: ____________
   c. tissue paper: ____________
   d. laundry detergent: ____________
   e. dishwashing liquid: ____________
7. meat and seafood: ____________
   a. poultry: ____________
      chicken: ____________
      turkey: ____________
   b. lamb: ____________
   c. pork: ____________
      pork chops: ____________
      sausage: ____________
   d. beef: ____________
      roast: ____________
      stew: ____________
      ground/minced beef: ____________

III. Packaging
1. bag: ____________
2. bottle: ____________
3. box: ____________
4. can: ____________
5. carton: ____________
6. case: ____________
7. container: ____________
8. jar: ____________
9. package: ____________
10. roll: ____________
11. sack: ____________

IV. Verbs
1. cook: ____________
2. heat: ____________
3. prefer: ____________
4. save: ____________

V. Preposition
above: ____________

VI. Nouns
1. brand: ____________
2. dish: ____________
3. jam: ____________
4. magazine: ____________
5. product: ____________
6. snack: ____________

VII. Other Words/Expressions
1. almost: ____________
2. already: ____________
3. as well as: ____________

Activity 2, Part 2

Reread Hamid's *Shopping at the Supermarket* and answer the following questions in complete sentences.

1. Why do people in Nightingale prefer to shop at supermarkets?

   ____.

2. Why are delis at the supermarkets so popular?

   ____.

3. Why do young children love the Frozen Food Section?

   ____.

4. What is the name of the section where you buy milk, cheese and butter?

   ____.

5. Where do people of Nightingale order their cakes for special occasions?

   ____.

6. What is Hamid's favourite section in the supermarket?

   ____.

7. Even waiting to pay the cashier is fun for Hamid. Why?

   ____

   ____.

Activity 2, Part 3

1. List two items of food in each box.

a bag of...	a bottle of...	a box of...	a bunch of...
sugar ________	________ ________	________ ________	________ ________
a can of...	**a carton of...**	**a container of...**	**a jar of...**
________ ________	________ ________	________ ________	________ ________
a package of...	**a roll of...**	**a sack of...**	**a case of...**
________ ________	________ ________	________ ________	________ ________

2. List three items of food you can buy in each of the following sections.

Bakery	Dairy	Deli	Florist
______	______	______	______
______	______	______	______
______	______	______	______
Fresh Produce	**Frozen Food**	**Home and Beauty**	**Meat and Seafood**
______	______	______	______
______	______	______	______
______	______	______	______
Canned Goods	**Pet Products**	**Snack Foods**	**Soft Drinks**
______	______	______	______
______	______	______	______
______	______	______	______

3. List two other aisles or sections in a supermarket and two things you can find in each.

Aisles or Sections	Products	Products
______	______	______
______	______	______

4. There are advantages to shopping in large supermarkets and in small stores. List three advantages for each.

Advantages: Supermarkets	Advantages: Small Stores
1. ______	1. ______
2. ______	2. ______
3. ______	3. ______

Activity 2, Part 4

Use the following words to complete Omar's paragraph below. Use the plural form if needed. Use each word only once.

bag bakery bottle box	brand can carton case	check out counter container dairy delicatessen	dozen fresh produce frozen food jar	meat and seafood package roll sack

"Come Shopping With Me!"

When I go to the supermarket, I always have my weekly shopping list with me. First, I go to the (1) ________________ section to buy a hot barbecued chicken and some vegetable rice. I also buy some macaroni salad and salami for our school lunches. I then go to the (2) ________________ section. That's where I get a (3) ________________ (twelve) eggs, a (4) ________________ of margarine and four small strawberry yogurts. I also pick up a one litre (5) ________________ of milk. I never forget to buy a (6) ________________ of bottled water and an extra-large (7) ________________ of club soda. I walk to the (8) ________________ section where I buy some chicken legs and ground beef. I cook chicken every Tuesday night and my brother cooks ground beef on Wednesdays. He loves to make meatballs. I also get a large (9) ________________ of tomato sauce. My next stop is the pasta section where I buy a (10) ________________ of long spaghetti noodles. I then go to the (11) ________________ and get some fresh whole wheat bread. I look at my list. I need some things from the Home section. I go there and I pick up a (12) ________________ of laundry detergent, a bottle of dishwashing liquid and three (13) ________________ (s) of paper towels. Then I walk slowly to my favourite section of the supermarket. I want to bake a cake for dessert. There are so many kinds of cakes! I take a box of Ms. Yummy's Chocolate Cake Mix because the recipe is very easy. All I have to do is add eggs and water and bake it in the oven at 350°F for 35 minutes. The next shelf is full of jams, jellies and peanut butter. I take a (14) ________________ of strawberry jam for my dad. He loves to have toast and jam for breakfast. I also remember to take a small (15) ________________ of sugar. My mom loves to drink her tea with a lot of sugar.

I then go to the most colourful section of the store. I go to the (16) ____________________ section. Everything looks so delicious! I choose six oranges, a bunch of bananas, one cantaloupe, celery, tomatoes, mushrooms and two cucumbers. I also select some nice apples and pears. They are delicious and healthy snacks. I look for a big (17) ____________________ of potatoes. My brothers love french fries. Next, I walk to the (18) ____________________ section where I examine all the meals. I decide to buy a frozen lasagna for the following week. I read the instructions. If I bake the lasagna in a hot oven, it will be ready in 45 minutes. And now for my favourite dessert, I choose Delix, my favourite (19) ____________________ of vanilla ice cream. I like to eat some Delix vanilla ice cream with Ms. Yummy's Chocolate Cake. On my way to the cashier, I examine this week's magazines. I take two because I cannot decide which one to buy. I also check my shopping list. Good! I bought everything on the list. Well, I am now at the (20) ____________________. I push my cart and line up to pay.

Activity 2, Part 5
Classify the following food items by placing each one in the correct section or food group.

apricot	cabbage	cracker	lime	pineapple	steak
asparagus	cantaloupe	cucumber	macaroni	pork	strawberry
bagel	carrot	egg	mango	potato	tangerine
bean	cauliflower	fig	milk	prune	tofu
beef	celery	fish	muffin	raisin	tomato
beet	cereal	grapefruit	onion	raspberry	turkey
blueberry	cheese	grape	orange	red beans	watermelon
bread	cherry	ice cream	papaya	rice	yogurt
broccoli	chick pea	lamb	pasta	soybean	
bun	chicken	lemon	peanut butter	spaghetti	
butter	corn	lettuce	pear	spinach	

I. Fruit		II. Vegetables	
III. Grain Products		**IV. Meat and Meat Alternatives**	
V. Milk Products (5)			

Unit II - Text 16

What's the Weather Like in Doveside?

Activity 1, Part 1
Write the definition of the words and expressions that are new to you.

Vocabulary List

I. Seasons

1. a. autumn: ____________
   b. fall: ____________
2. spring: ____________
3. summer: ____________
4. winter: ____________

II. Weather Descriptions

1. cloud ➜ cloudy: ____________
2. fog ➜ foggy: ____________
3. ice ➜ icy: ____________
4. storm ➜ stormy: ____________
5. sun ➜ sunny: ____________
6. wind ➜ windy: ____________
7. (to) rain ➜ rainy ➜ raining: ____________
8. (to) snow ➜ snowy ➜ snowing: ____________

III. Weather Words

1. blizzard: ____________
2. clear: ____________
3. dry: ____________
4. flake: ____________
5. hail: ____________
6. humid: ____________
7. a. light (adj.): ____________
   b. heavy: ____________
8. lightning: ____________
9. moon: ____________
10. partly sunny: ____________
11. rainbow: ____________
12. a. report: ____________
    b. forecast: ____________
13. shower: ____________
14. sky: ____________
15. snowflake: ____________
16. star: ____________
17. thunder: ____________
18. weather: ____________
19. temperature: ____________
20. thermometer: ____________

IV. Temperature

1. degree: ____________
   a. It's 5 degrees above zero.
   b. It's plus 5.
   c. It's 5 degrees below zero.
   d. It's minus 5.
2. Fahrenheit (F): ____________
3. Celsius (C): ____________

V. Temperature

1. below freezing: ____________
2. freezing: ____________
3. chilly: ____________
4. cool: ____________
5. warm: ____________
6. mild: ____________
7. hot: ____________

VI. Expressions

1. three months long: ______________________
2. all year long: ______________________

VII. Nouns

1. contest: ______________________
2. farmer: ______________________
3. leaf ➔ leaves: ______________________
4. night: ______________________
5. parade: ______________________
6. picnic: ______________________
7. play: ______________________
8. problem: ______________________
9. shop: ______________________
10. vacation: ______________________
11. snowman: ______________________

VIII. Verbs

1. to close: ______________________
2. to complain: ______________________
3. to cover: ______________________
4. to go fishing: ______________________
5. to go camping: ______________________
6. to joke: ______________________
7. to last: ______________________
8. to remind: ______________________
9. to ride: ______________________
10. to shine: ______________________
11. to swim: ______________________
12. to watch: ______________________
13. to win: ______________________
14. to worry: ______________________

IX. Colours

1. black: ______________________
2. blue: ______________________
3. brown: ______________________
4. grey: ______________________
5. orange: ______________________
6. pink: ______________________
7. purple: ______________________
8. red: ______________________
9. white: ______________________
10. yellow: ______________________

X. Adjectives

1. bright: ______________________
2. a. dark: ______________________
   b. light: ______________________

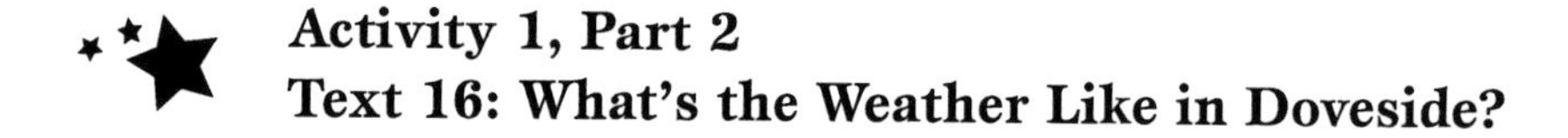

Activity 1, Part 2
Text 16: What's the Weather Like in Doveside?

"A City of Four Seasons" by Chantal Leclerc

Doveside has four seasons, but it doesn't have long winters and short springs like many of the other cities in Ontario. The seasons are about three months long. And we enjoy all the seasons! It is difficult for us to decide which season we like the best, because all seasons are special.

Some people like the white winters of Doveside. Doveside is usually covered with beautiful, clean white snow for the three months of winter. Many of the people who love winter love winter sports too. Many people say Doveside is the perfect city for skiing. Of course, it has the perfect weather for ice skating and playing hockey.

Snow is never a problem for the people of Doveside because we don't worry about ice or snow on the roads. Most of us take public transportation all year long. The weather is cold only at night when the temperature is below freezing. During the day, the temperature is usually mild. That is because it is not very windy in Doveside, thanks to the mountain and the lake.

I like the winter skies of Doveside. They are bright blue, and the sun shines on most days, even when it is snowing. The only bad days happen during the winter storms. Sometimes the snowstorms last for three or four days, but even that is fun because all the schools are closed!

Spring is a very busy time for the people of Doveside. The people who work in the Parks and Recreation Department begin to plant flowers, bushes and trees. They make things ready for our Tulip Festival. It is like the tulip festival in Ottawa except it is much smaller.

The people of Doveside are very busy in spring because they plant their gardens too. They say they spend a lot of time, money and energy on their gardens because they want to win the garden contest. We know they are joking, but it is true. We vote for the nicest garden on July 1, when we celebrate Canada Day.

I don't like spring in Doveside very much because we have many cloudy and rainy days. We even have some rain storms with lots of thunder and lightning. When I complain about the humid spring weather, everyone reminds me that "April showers bring May flowers!" I agree. The rain makes our gardens and our parks look green and beautiful, especially during the summer and fall.

But there are also many warm and sunny spring days. That's when the people of Doveside love to ride their bicycles or go for walks. It is also a time for barbecue parties after three months of winter!

The summer days of Doveside are usually hot and dry. The nights are comfortable, warm and beautiful, especially when the moon and the stars are shining in the sky. There are very few cloudy or rainy days during June, July, or August. Summer is a special season for other reasons too. There are many things to do during the summer. It is the time of year when there are many fairs, carnivals and parades. Many people go on picnics and enjoy concerts or plays in the park. Of course, all of us enjoy shopping at the popular outdoor Farmer's Market.

People who love outdoor summer activities say that summer is their favourite season of the year. They go camping and play many outdoor sports. Many go swimming in the lake. Some even go fishing. It is always difficult to say goodbye to summer and summer vacation, but it is always nice to welcome autumn.

The people of Doveside love autumn because they love the autumn colours. There are many trees in our parks and gardens. We love to watch the leaves on the trees as they begin to change colour. In late October and early November, everywhere we look, we see orange, red, yellow and brown leaves. People also enjoy the change in weather. After three months of hot sunny days, we enjoy the cool days and foggy mornings of fall.

Doveside is a wonderful city. And the beautiful seasons of Doveside really add beauty to our lives!

"My First Winter Morning in Doveside" by Toni Garboni

On Sunday, when I woke up, I looked at the clock near my bed. It was only 7:00 in the morning. It is usually dark at 7:00 in the morning, but not that day. My room was bright, and light was coming through the window. I got out of bed and looked out the window. The whole world was white! The whole world was covered with a white blanket of snow. When I went to bed the night before, it was autumn, and when I woke up the next morning, it was winter!

I ran to the closet and put on my snowsuit, boots, scarf, thick gloves and hat. I felt like an astronaut. I couldn't walk! I went to the front door and opened it quietly to look at my first winter. The cold refreshing air hit my face. I took several deep breaths. The cold air burned my nose and eyes as I breathed. Now I was completely awake.

I looked around me. Everywhere I looked, I saw mountains and blankets of snow. I was surrounded by beauty. I noticed the bright, cloudless sky. The snow began to reflect the sunshine, and it started to look even whiter. The blanket of snow was so bright that it looked blue. I stayed there for a few minutes and did not move a muscle. I wanted to enjoy that moment for as long as possible. Soon, I became very curious and impatient. I had never walked in snow. I had never touched snow. I lifted my leg and took my first step. I was very surprised. The snow was not hard. It was soft. I saw my boot sink into the snow. My first step made a deep hole in the white blanket. It also made a soft sound. I walked slowly to the sidewalk and looked back. There were deep holes where I walked. And now I was near the street, but it was impossible to see where the sidewalk ended and the street began. Everything was white. Even the cars looked like white hills. The trees looked like they were covered with new white blossoms. Every tree looked like an apple tree in bloom.

I took off my gloves and put them in my pocket. I could now feel the tingling cold in my fingers, but I didn't care. I bent down and gently touched snow for the first time in my life. It was so soft, so light! It was like touching bubbles of soap. I picked up some snow and held it close to my face. I blew on the snow and watched the small flakes fly up in the air. They flew around for a few seconds and landed gently at my feet. I put some more snow in my hands and held it tightly this time. The snow in my hands became smaller and smaller until it became a ball. I threw the ball at a tree and a shower of snow flakes fell gently to the white ground. My hands were freezing now. I put my gloves on and walked back to the house. That moment was very special! I had to wake up the rest of the family and share my first winter morning with them!

"Shopping for Clothes in Doveside" by Tina Wong

With every new season comes a new season of fashion, and the people of Doveside love to be fashionable. They go shopping for clothes all the time. There are many popular men's, women's and children's stores in our three districts, but the three most popular clothing stores are in Swanville. They are The Peahen, The Peacock and The Peachick. The Peahen is the store for women; The Peacock is the store for men; and The Peachick is the store for babies and children. The stores are near each other. That means that the whole family can shop for clothes on the same day.

The Peahen sells women's dresses, blouses, skirts, sweaters, coats, jackets and shoes. In its lingerie department you can buy bathrobes, nightgowns, underwear and slippers. The best part of the store is the accessories and jewellery section. In the accessories section you can buy purses, scarves, gloves and hats. In the jewellery section you can buy beautiful earrings, rings, brooches, bracelets and necklaces. You can even buy gold and silver jewellery.

The Peacock is the store for fashionable men. You can buy men's coats, raincoats, shirts, suits, jackets, trousers, sweaters and shoes there. In the sports department, you can buy T-shirts, jeans, swimsuits, jogging suits, shorts, shoes and running shoes. If you want to buy a present for a man, the best place to visit is the accessories department. There, you can buy ties, pyjamas, socks, belts, key chains and men's jewellery.

My favourite store is The Peachick. I love to look at baby clothes. I especially like the little dresses! In this store you can also buy children's toys.

Where do the teenagers of Doveside shop? Many people say teenagers don't shop at all because they always wear jeans, sweatshirts, T-shirts and caps, but that's not true. Many of the teenagers of Doveside are very interested in fashion, and they love to shop in different stores. They prefer to shop at their favourite malls, where they can spend the whole day with their friends, shopping, eating and even watching movies.

Activity 1, Part 3
Use weather words from the vocabulary list in Activity 1, Part 1 to solve the crossword puzzle.

DOWN:

1. A big noise during a storm is called __ __ __ __ __ __ __.
2. There are four __ __ __ __ __ __ __ in a year.
3. Every snow __ __ __ __ __ is different.
4. The leaves on the trees move because it is __ __ __ __ __.
5. Water from the sky is called __ __ __ __.
6. When it is below zero degrees, we say it is below __ __ __ __ __ __ __ __ __ __ __.
7. Another word for "autumn" is __ __ __ __.
8. Sometimes you cannot see the sun because there are too many __ __ __ __ __ __.
9. In the winter, children like to build a __ __ __ __ man that has a hat, nose, eyes and mouth.
10. In the desert, the weather is hot and __ __ __.

ACROSS:

11. We listen to the weather __ __ __ __ __ __ __ __ every morning.
12. __ __ __ __ looks like balls of ice.
13. We ski during the __ __ __ __ __ __.
14. The three months of summer are June, __ __ __ __ and August.
15. During the day we see the sun; at night we see the __ __ __ __.
16. A __ __ __ __ __ __ __ makes a semicircle of beautiful colours in the sky.
17. The three months of winter are December, January and __ __ __ __ __ __ __ __.
18. In the U.S.A. they use Fahrenheit; in Canada we use __ __ __ __ __ __ __.
19. The schools close when there is a very big snowstorm or __ __ __ __ __ __ __ __.
20. There are twelve __ __ __ __ __ __ in a year.
21. The three months of __ __ __ __ __ __ are March, April and May.
22. We swim during the __ __ __ __ __ __.

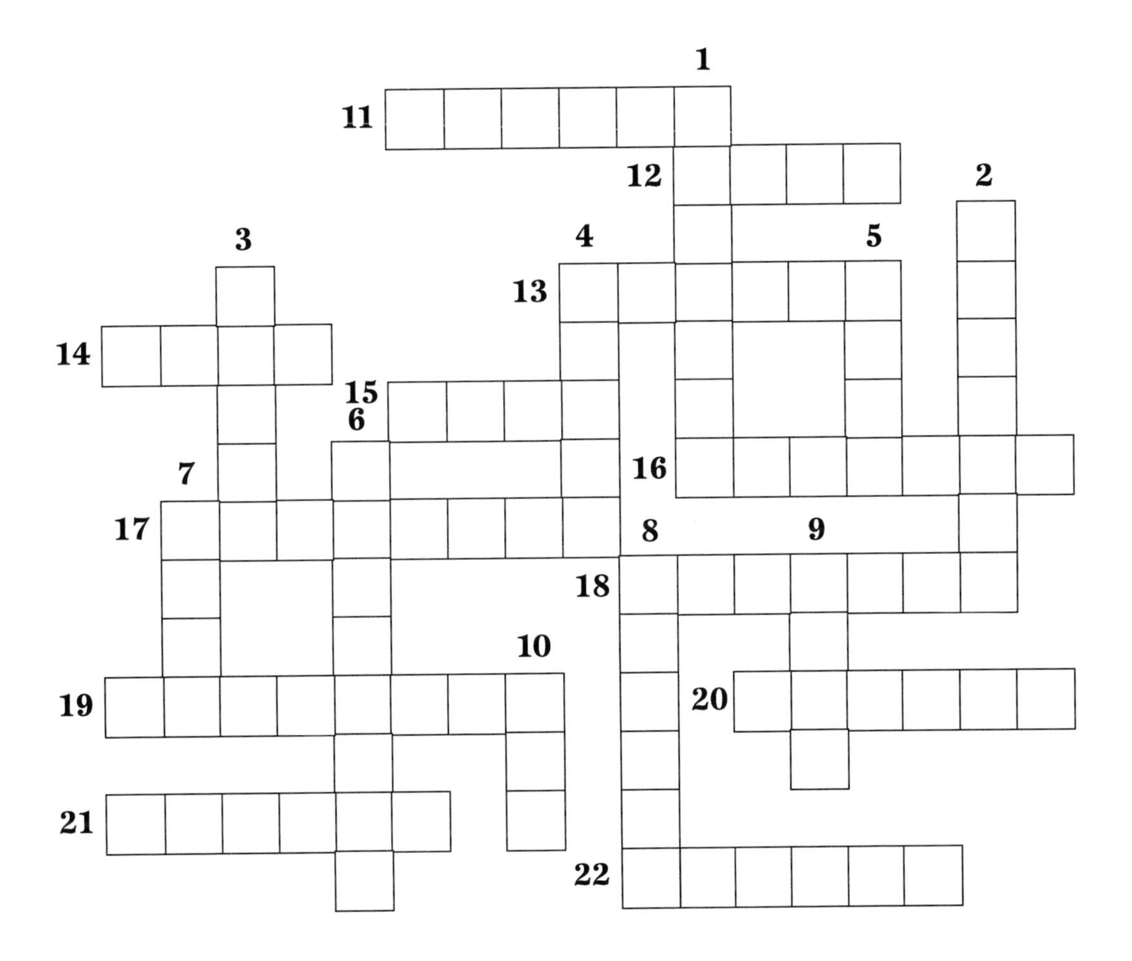

Activity 1, Part 4
Write the definition of the words and expressions that are new to you.

Vocabulary List

I. Nouns

1. air: ________________
2. astronaut: ________________
3. beauty: ________________
4. bed: ________________
5. blanket: ________________
6. blossom: ________________
7. breath: ________________
8. bubble: ________________
9. car: ________________
10. front: ________________
11. ground: ________________
12. hill: ________________
13. light (n): ________________
14. moment: ________________
15. sidewalk: ________________
16. step: ________________
17. sunshine: ________________

II. Adjectives

1. awake: ________________
2. curious: ________________
3. deep: ________________
4. hard: ________________
5. refreshing: ________________
6. surprised: ________________
7. tight: ________________

III. Clothes

1. boots: ______
2. gloves: ______
3. hat: ______
4. pocket: ______
5. scarf: ______
6. snowsuit: ______

IV. Body

1. eye: ______
2. face: ______
3. foot ➜ feet: ______
4. finger: ______
5. hand: ______
6. leg: ______
7. muscle: ______
8. nose: ______

V. Homonyms

a. whole: ______

b. hole: ______

VI. Other Words/Expressions

1. as long as possible: ______
2. I didn't care.: ______
3. in bloom: ______

VII. Verbs

1. to bend: ______
2. to blow: ______
3. to breathe: ______
4. to burn: ______
5. to cover: ______
6. to fly: ______
7. to freeze: ______
8. to hold: ______
9. to land: ______
10. to lift: ______
11. to look around: ______
12. to look back: ______
13. to move: ______
14. to notice: ______
15. to pick up: ______
16. a. to put on: ______
    b. to take off: ______
17. to reflect: ______
18. to share: ______
19. to sink: ______
20. to sleep: ______
21. to surround: ______
22. to wear: ______
23. to throw: ______
24. to tingle: ______
25. to touch: ______
26. to wake up: ______

VIII. Literary Words

1. metaphor: ______
2. simile: ______

IX. Irregular Simple Past Tense

become ➜ became

bend ➜ bent

blow ➜ blew

fly ➜ flew

get out ➜ got out

hold ➜ held

hit ➜ hit

put on ➜ put on

run ➜ ran

take off ➜ took off

throw ➜ threw

wake up ➜ woke up

is/am/ are [com]ing ➜ was [com]ing

Activity 1, Part 5
Toni uses many similes and metaphors in her descriptive essay about her first winter morning in Doveside. Read the essay again and complete the following sentences.

1. The snow on the ground is compared to a ______________________ of snow.
2. The snowsuit and winter clothes make Toni feel like she is a/an ______________________.
3. The snow covered cars look like white ______________________.
4. The snow covered trees look like ______________________.
5. Touching snow is like touching ______________________.
6. The snow that is falling from the trees is compared to a ______________________ of snow.

Activity 1, Part 6
Rewrite the verbs of the following text in the present tense.

"My First Winter Morning in Doveside" by Toni Garboni

When I woke (1) _____________ up, I looked (2) _____________ at the clock near my bed. It was (3) _____________ only 7:00 in the morning. It is usually dark at 7:00 in the morning, but not today. My room is bright and the light is coming through the window. I got (4) _____________ out of bed and look out of the window. The whole world is white! The whole world is covered with a white blanket of snow. When I went to bed last night, it was autumn, and when I woke (5) _____________ up this morning, it is winter!

I ran (6) _____________ to the closet and put (7) _____________ on my snowsuit, boots, scarf, thick gloves and hat. I felt (8) _____________ like an astronaut. I couldn't (9) _____________ walk! I go to the front door and opened (10) _____________ it quietly to look at my first winter. The cold refreshing air hit (11) _____________ my face. I took (12) _____________ several deep breaths. The cold air burned (13) _____________ my nose and eyes as I breathe. Now I am completely awake.

I look around me. Everywhere I look, I see mountains and blankets of snow. I am surrounded by beauty. I noticed (14) _____________ the bright, cloudless sky. The snow began (15) _____________ to reflect the sunshine, and it started (16) _____________ to look even whiter.

The blanket of snow is so bright that it looks blue. I stayed (17) ______________ there for a few minutes and did (18) ______________ not move a muscle. I wanted (19) ______________ to enjoy this moment for as long as possible. Soon, I became (20) ______________ very curious and impatient. I have never walked in snow. I had (21) ______________ never touched snow. I lifted (22) ______________ my leg and take my first step. I am very surprised. The snow is not hard. It is soft. I saw (23) ______________ my boot sink into the snow. My first step made (24) ______________ a deep hole in the white blanket. It also makes a soft sound. I walk slowly to the sidewalk and look back. There were (25) ______________ deep holes where I walked. And now I am near the street, but it is impossible to see where the sidewalk ended (26) ______________ and the street begins. Everything is white. Even the cars look like white hills. The trees look like they are covered with new white blossoms. Every tree looks like an apple tree in bloom.

I take off my gloves and put them in my pocket. I can now feel the tingling cold in my fingers, but I don't care. I bent (27) ______________ down and gently touched (28) ______________ snow for the first time in my life. It is so soft, so light! It is like touching bubbles of soap. I picked (29) ______________ up some snow and held (30) ______________ it close to my face. I blew (31) ______________ on the snow and watched (32) ______________ the small flakes fly up in the air. They flew (33) ______________ around for a few seconds and landed (34) ______________ gently at my feet. I put some more snow in my hands and hold it tightly this time. The snow in my hands becomes smaller and smaller until it becomes a ball. I threw (35) ______________ the ball at a tree and a shower of snow flakes fell (36) ______________ gently to the white ground. My hands are freezing now. I put my gloves on and walk back to the house. This moment is very special! I have to wake up the rest of the family and share my first winter morning with them!

Activity 2, Part 1
Write the definition of the words and expressions that are new to you.

Vocabulary List

I. Clothes

1. bathing suit/swimsuit: ____________
2. bathrobe: ____________
3. belt: ____________
4. blouse: ____________
5. boots: ____________
6. bracelet: ____________
7. a. brooch: ____________
   b. pin: ____________
8. buckle: ____________
9. button: ____________
10. cap: ____________
11. coat: ____________
12. collar: ____________
13. contact lenses: ____________
14. dress: ____________
15. earrings: ____________
16. a. gloves: ____________
    b. mittens: ____________
17. a. gold: ____________
    b. silver: ____________
18. handkerchief: ____________
19. hat: ____________
20. jacket: ____________
21. a. jogging suit: ____________
    b. sweat suit: ____________
    c. sweatshirt: ____________
22. key chain: ____________
23. necklace: ____________
24. a. nightgown: ____________
    b. pyjamas (pajamas): ____________
25. a. purse: ____________
    b. bag: ____________
    c. handbag: ____________
    d. shoulder bag: ____________
26. ring: ____________
27. scarf: ____________
28. shirt: ____________
29. shoes: ____________
    a. high heels: ____________
    b. sandals: ____________
    c. sneakers: ____________
    d. running shoes: ____________
30. shorts: ____________
31. skirt: ____________
32. sleeve: ____________
33. slippers: ____________
34. socks: ____________
35. suit: ____________
36. a. sunglasses: ____________
    b. eyeglasses: ____________
37. sweater: ____________
38. T-shirt: ____________
39. tie: ____________
40. raincoat: ____________
41. a. trousers: ____________
    b. pants: ____________

42. turtleneck (sweater): ____________

43. umbrella: ____________

44. underwear: ____________

45. vest: ____________

46. watch: ____________

....

1. a. fashion: ____________

   b. fashionable: ____________

2. a. peacock: ____________

   b. peahen: ____________

   c. peachick: ____________

3. teenager: ____________

II. Body

1. chest: ____________
2. stomach: ____________
3. waist: ____________
4. hip: ____________
5. head: ____________
6. body: ____________
7. arm: ____________
8. leg: ____________

III. Head

1. hair: ____________

2. face: ____________

   a. forehead: ____________

   b. eye: ____________

   - eyebrow: ____________
   - eyelash: ____________
   - eyelid: ____________

   c. cheek: ____________

   d. nose: ____________

   e. mouth: ____________

   - lip: ____________
   - tooth/teeth: ____________
   - tongue: ____________

   f. ear: ____________

   g. chin: ____________

IV. Arm

1. shoulder: ____________
2. elbow: ____________
3. wrist: ____________
4. hand: ____________
5. palm: ____________
6. thumb: ____________
7. finger: ____________
8. nail: ____________

V. Leg

1. knee: ____________
2. ankle: ____________
3. foot/feet: ____________
4. heel: ____________
5. sole: ____________
6. toe: ____________

Activity 2, Part 2

a. **Write the word that matches each definition.**

b. **Find the mystery words in the puzzle. Circle each letter in each word.**

c. **Put the letters that are not circled in order to complete the mystery sentence.**

It is jewellery for your neck. ___ ___ ___ ___ ___ ___ ___ ___

It is jewellery for your wrist. ___ ___ ___ ___ ___ ___ ___ ___

It is jewellery for your ears. ___ ___ ___ ___ ___ ___ ___ ___

It is another name for running shoes. ___ ___ ___ ___ ___ ___ ___ ___

It is jewellery for one of your fingers. ___ ___ ___ ___

Men usually wear these to go to sleep. ___ ___ ___ ___ ___ ___ ___

Women usually wear it to go to sleep. ___ ___ ___ ___ ___ ___ ___ ___ ___

You wear them on your feet (without socks) during the summer. ___ ___ ___ ___ ___ ___ ___

Men put on their ties around the collar of these. ___ ___ ___ ___ ___ ___

People wear it around their waists. ___ ___ ___ ___

People wear them on their heads when it is cold. ___ ___ ___ ___

It is another name for men's pants. ___ ___ ___ ___ ___ ___ ___ ___

You need one on each foot to play outside in the summer. ___ ___ ___ ___

You wear them on your hands. They have one place for the thumbs and one place for all of your other fingers. ___ ___ ___ ___ ___ ___ ___

You wear them on your hands. They have one place for the thumb and a place for each of your fingers. ___ ___ ___ ___ ___ ___

You wear it on your body after your shower. ___ ___ ___ ___ ___ ___ ___ ___

You wear it to protect your eyes on a bright day. ___ ___ ___ ___ ___ ___ ___ ___ ___ ___

They are thick blue pants that students often wear to school. ___ ___ ___ ___ ___

It is like a shirt for women. Women wear it with pants or skirts. ___ ___ ___ ___ ___ ___

It's a long rectangle you wrap around your neck in winter. ___ ___ ___ ___ ___

They are high shoes you wear during the winter when there is a lot of snow. ___ ___ ___ ___ ___

You wear them before you wear your running shoes. ___ ___ ___ ___ ___

It is a hat for baseball. ___ ___ ___

You wear it to tell the time. ___ ___ ___ ___ ___

You wear it on top of all your clothes when it is winter. ___ ___ ___ ___

It is another name for a brooch. ___ ___ ___

They are the shoes you wear with your pyjamas or nightgown. ___ ___ ___ ___ ___ ___ ___ ___

It is the top part of a businessman's suit. ___ ___ ___ ___ ___ ___

It is another word for purses. ___ ___ ___ ___

S	D	P	A	C	P	I	N	S	H	I	R	T	S	B	P	A	J
N	S	Y	R	I	N	G	W	A	T	C	H	E	R	A	E	T	A
E	R	J	E	A	N	S	O	B	A	G	S	L	M	T	C	R	C
A	E	A	E	S	U	N	G	L	A	S	S	E	S	H	A	O	K
K	P	M	T	C	O	A	T	O	B	H	C	C	K	R	L	U	E
E	P	A	N	S	T	A	H	U	O	O	A	A	C	O	K	S	T
R	I	S	E	V	O	L	G	S	O	E	R	R	O	B	C	E	L
S	L	A	D	N	A	S	I	E	T	E	F	B	S	E	E	R	E
T	S	E	A	R	R	I	N	G	S	M	I	T	T	E	N	S	B

Many people enjoy shopping at ___ ___ ___ ___ ___ ___ ___ ___ ___ ___ stores.

Activity 2, Part 3
Write the correct article of clothing or accessory in each column. Use each word only one time. What do you wear...

bathrobe blouse boots bracelet cap coat contact lenses dress eyeglasses	gloves hat high heel shoes jacket jeans mitten necklace nightgown pants	pyjamas ring running shoes sandals scarf shirt shoes shorts skirt	sneakers socks sunglasses sweater sweatshirt T-shirt trousers watch

...on your head?	...on your hand?	...on your wrist?
______ ______	______ ______ ______	______ ______
...around your neck?	**...in the bedroom?**	**...on your eyes?**
______ ______	______ ______ ______	______ ______ ______
...on your feet?	**...from your neck to your hips?**	**...from your neck to your knees?**
______ ______ ______ ______ ______ ______ ______	______ ______ ______ ______ ______ ______	______ ______
...from your waist to your ankles?	**...from your waist to your knees?**	
______ ______ ______	______ ______	

Unit III - Text 17

Josef's Letter

Activity 1, Part 1
Classify the words listed on the left by writing them in the correct column.

	Things You Can Count	Things You Cannot Count
food	______	______
salt	______	______
glass of milk	______	______
cup of tea	______	______
music	______	______
help	______	______
cup of coffee	______	______
sugar cube	______	______
meat	______	
homework	______	
brothers	______	
cheese		
slice of bread		
dollars		
glass of water		
sandwiches		
bowl of soup		
traffic		
information		

*Never use "a" or "one" when you use nouns that you cannot count!

Activity 1, Part 2
Fill in the blanks using the words "much", "some", "a lot", or "a little" for things that you cannot count. Use "many" with things that you can count.

1. I drink ______________________ glasses of water every day.
2. I drink ______________________ of water every day.
3. I spend ______________________ dollars on books every week.
4. Children don't eat ______________________ food when they are sick.
5. Children eat ______________________ snacks and sandwiches when they are hungry.
6. Some people drink ______________________ of coffee every day.
7. She drinks ______________________ cups of coffee every day.

Activity 1, Part 3

Fill in the blanks using the words "too" or "very".

Example: This desk is too heavy. I cannot move it!
This desk is very heavy, but I can move it if you want.

1. This exercise is ________________ difficult. It took me half an hour to finish it.
2. This exercise is ________________ difficult. We tried, but we couldn't do it.
3. This soup is ________________ hot. It is perfect for a winter day like today!
4. This soup is ________________ hot to eat. I will wait a few minutes before I eat it.
5. This dish is ________________ spicy. I love it!
6. This dish is ________________ spicy. I have to order another dish from the menu.
7. This dress is ________________ long. I cannot walk if I wear it because I will fall.
8. This dress is ________________ long. It is the kind of dress a princess wears to a party!
9. This music is ________________ loud. I cannot stay here for the rest of the concert.
10. The music is ________________ loud. I think that that is why the students like it so much.

Activity 1, Part 4

Write the definition of the words and expressions that are new to you.

Vocabulary List

I. Nouns	**II. Adjective**
1. advice: ________________	thoughtful: ________________
2. article: ________________	**III. Verbs**
3. luck: ________________	1. to coach: ________________
4. neighbourhood: ________________	2. to grow: ________________
5. a. primary school: ________________	3. to pick up: ________________
b. elementary school: ________________	4. to tutor: ________________
6. salt: ________________	5. to waste: ________________
7. writer: ________________	

Activity 1, Part 5
Text 17: Josef's Letter

(today's date)

Dear Tina, Chantal, Omar and Hamid,

Thank you so much for your thoughtful birthday gift. I enjoyed reading your *Guide to Doveside.* Mr. Perreault had a great idea. I think it is very useful, especially for the new students and their families. I hope new students take Omar's advice and ask a real estate agent to help them find a place to live. I remember we tried to look for an apartment or a house in the real estate section of the newspaper. It took us a long time to understand how to read the ads and ask the right questions.

I also like the maps you included in your guide. When I looked at them, I remembered when we all went to Swanville. Do you remember Giovanni's Restaurant? Omar ordered spaghetti and a whole pizza! Omar, do you still eat more than any other person at school? Are you still growing two centimetres taller each month?

When I look at the map of Swanville, I also remember the many times we brought sandwiches and ate a picnic lunch in Lily Pool Park after going to the Swanville Library.

Chantal and Ricardo are very lucky! They tried the famous spaghetti dinner at Keiko's house. She sounds like a very nice and friendly student. So does Toni. I love her description of winter mornings in Doveside! She described her first winter morning so well. I felt I was there with her. It reminded me of my first winter morning in Doveside. I think she will become a writer when she finishes university.

The parts of the guide that did not surprise me were the articles by Hamid and Tina. I am not surprised that Hamid wrote the article about supermarket shopping. He has always hated to waste time. When I first went shopping in a supermarket, I wasted a lot of time looking for the things I wanted to buy. But Hamid explained that you can save time if you remember that the supermarket is divided into sections and that the aisles have signs listing the things you can find on the shelves. Of course, Tina was the right person to write an article about clothes shopping. She always said she shopped to relax. I think she knew every store in Doveside and every new fashion, because she enjoyed looking at the photographs in magazines. Tina, do you still walk around the school with your camera and your fashion magazines?

I want to tell you about my school project. It is very interesting because we have to do volunteer work in our community for the whole year. All the teachers and students have to volunteer four to six hours a week in our neighbourhood. I am a volunteer in the after-school activities for the primary school down the street. Six other students and I work at the school from 3:30 to 5:00 or until the parents pick up their children. We tutor the children or help them with their homework. Sometimes we play games with them and coach them in sports. All the volunteers are becoming good friends.

Please write and tell me about your other school projects. Take care!

Your friend,
Josef

Activity 1, Part 6
Replace the underlined direct objects with the pronoun "him", "her", "it", or "them".

Example: What did Josef do with the letter he wrote? Josef sent the letter to his friends.
Josef sent **it** to his friends.

1. What did Josef do with the *Guide to Doveside*? Josef read *the Guide to Doveside*.

   ______________________________________.

2. Which articles did Josef like? Josef liked all of the articles.

   ______________________________________.

3. Does Josef think about Giovanni's Restaurant sometimes? Yes, he thinks about Giovanni's Restaurant all the time.

   ______________________________________.

4. How long did it take Josef to learn how to read ads in the newspaper?

   Josef remembers that it took him a long time to learn to read ads in the newspaper.

   ______________________________________.

5. Who cooked the spaghetti dinner? Keiko's father cooked the spaghetti dinner.

   ______________________________________.

6. Did Josef like Toni's article about a winter morning in Doveside very much?

   Josef liked Toni's article about a winter morning in Doveside very much.

   ______________________________________.

7. Did Hamid describe the supermarkets well? Hamid described the supermarkets very well.

   ______________________________________.

8. What did the teachers ask Josef to do after school? The teachers asked Josef to tutor Bobby after school.

   ______________________________________.

9. What did the teachers ask Josef to do after school? The teachers asked Josef to tutor Susie after school.

   ______________________________________.

10. Is Josef spending time with his new friends? Josef is spending time with his new friends.

    ______________________________________.

Activity 1, Part 7
Combine the following sentences.

Example: place: Josef walks to the primary school. He works at the primary school.
Josef walks to the primary school,where he works.

person: Josef likes Tina. Tina is a good photographer.
Josef likes Tina, who is a good photographer.

1. Josef writes letters to Chantal. Chantal is going to visit Italy this summer.

   ____.

2. Students go to the library. In the library, they can work quietly.

   ____.

3. Josef likes Mr. Perreault. Mr. Perreault is the new APD teacher at ESDP.

   ____.

4. Josef likes to go to his room. In his room, he can read quietly.

   ____.

5. Josef goes to the gym. Josef plays soccer in the gym after school.

   ____.

6. Josef and his new friends go to the primary school. They do volunteer work at the primary school.

   ____.

7. Josef likes his little sister. His little sister always makes delicious after-school snacks.

   ____.

8. Hamid goes to the supermarket. At the supermarket, he buys groceries.

   ____.

9. Mr. Perreault looks at the articles before they are published. Mr. Perreault is the APD teacher.

   ____.

10. The basketball team likes Omar. Omar wants to play in the NBA in a few years.

    ____.

Activity 1, Part 8

Change the following nouns to adjectives that mean "with..." or "with the quality or qualities of..." by adding the letter "y", and use them in the sentences below.
(Drop the "e" if the word ends with the letter "e".)

Example: wind

There is a lot of wind today. ➔ Today is very windy. [wind + y]

1. The students are making a lot of noise. They are very ______________.
2. It is like a day in the middle of winter. It is a ______________ day.
3. I love Indian food because it has a lot of spices. It is very ______________.
4. The popcorn has a lot of butter. It is very ______________.
5. This soap smells like a bowl of fruit. It has a ______________ smell.
6. This paragraph has many unnecessary words. It is ______________.
7. There is a lot of rain today. It is very ______________.
8. Did you cook fish today? The house has a ______________ smell.
9. You put too much water in this soup. The soup is very ______________.
10. The moon looks like it is made of silver. We have a ______________ moon tonight.
11. You put a lot of salt on the salad. It is very ______________.
12. This orange has a lot of juice in it. It is very ______________.
13. I put soap in the water because I like to wash dishes in ______________ water.
14. Chantal and Ricardo have a lot of good luck. They are very ______________.

Unit III - Text 18

The School Paper

Activity 1, Part 1

Use object pronouns (me, you, him, her, it, us and them) to replace the indirect objects as you rewrite the sentences below.

FIRST: Put the direct object (D.O.) first and indirect object (I.O.) second.

SECOND: Put the indirect object (I.O.) first and the direct object (D.O.) second.

Example: Please give the books to Tina.
Please give the books (D.O.) to her. (I.O.)
Please give her (I.O.) the books. (D.O.) [Do not use "to".]

1. Please give the books to my classmates and me.
   D.O./I.O. ____.
   I.O./D.O. ____.
2. Chantal wrote a long letter to her uncle.
   D.O./I.O. ____.
   I.O./D.O. ____.
3. Please give the newspaper to (your name).
   D.O./I.O. ____.
   I.O./D.O. ____.
4. Please give this letter to your mother.
   D.O./I.O. ____.
   I.O./D.O. ____.
5. I will throw the ball to (the person to whom you are speaking).
   D.O./I.O. ____.
   I.O./D.O. ____.
6. Omar showed the project to Tina and Chantal.
   D.O./I.O. ____.
   I.O./D.O. ____.
7. Please give this letter to your mother and father.
   D.O./I.O. ____.
   I.O./D.O. ____.
8. I will pass the ball to (the person to whom you are speaking) and Tina.
   D.O./I.O. ____.
   I.O./D.O. ____.
9. Omar tells the ending of the movie to Tina and Chantal.
   D.O./I.O. ____.
   I.O./D.O. ____.
10. I will show the sports magazine to (the person to whom you are speaking).
    D.O./I.O. ____.
    I.O./D.O. ____.

Activity 1, Part 2
Write the definition of the words and expressions that are new to you.

Vocabulary List

I. Nouns	III. Demonstrative Pronouns and Adjectives
1. career: ____________	1. singular:
2. event: ____________	a. this: ____________
3. issue: ____________	b. that: ____________
4. personality: ____________	2. plural:
5. trip: ____________	a. these: ____________
	b. those: ____________
II. Verbs	**IV. Expressions**
1. to announce: ____________	1. to change one's mind: ____________
2. to believe: ____________	2. to give someone a chance: ____________
3. to get (better): ____________	
4. to publish: ____________	
5. to suggest: ____________	

Activity 1, Part 3
Use the correct object pronoun (me, you, him, her, us, or them) to rewrite the following sentences.

1. If you want to write an article, give it to Mr. Perreault first.

   ____.

2. Next, take the articles to the members of the Student Council.

   ____.

3. Mr. Perreault returned the first article to Keiko.

   ____.

4. The students gave a copy of last month's newspaper to (the speaker).

   ____.

5. Mr. Perreault returned the articles to (the speaker and the speaker's classmates).

   ____.

6. Josef, we will send a copy to (Josef) next month.

   ____.

Activity 1, Part 4
Fill in the blanks with the demonstrative adjectives and pronouns "this" or "that," and "these" or "those".

Once a week, the teacher returns all the pens and pencils on her desk to her students. She asks them, "Whose pens and pencils are (1) ________________?"

Jean goes to the desk and takes a green pencil. "(2) ________________ green pencil belongs to me," he says. He then returns to his desk and sits down.

The teacher holds up a yellow pencil. "Whose pencil is (3) ________________?"

David raises his hand. "I think (4) ________________ yellow pencil belongs to Tina."

"Does (5) ________________ pencil belong to you, Tina?"

Tina smiles and walks to the teacher's desk. "Yes, it does. And (6) ________________ purple pencil belongs to Chantal. I'll give it to her." Tina takes the yellow and purple pencils from the teacher, gives the purple one to Chantal, and then returns to her desk with her yellow pencil.

"Whose red pens are (7) ________________?"

Eric walks to the teacher's desk and looks at the pens carefully. (8) "________________ red pencils belong to Dani and me."

The teacher holds two green pens. "And (9) ________________?"

Omar raises his hand. "Oh, I know! (10) ________________ two green pens belong to Hamid. He's not here, but I can give them to him tomorrow."

"Good. I don't have any other pens or pencils on my desk! Thank you, class!"

Activity 1, Part 5
Text 18: The School Paper

(today's date)

Dear Josef,

Your school project sounds like a great idea. Wow! All the teachers and students are working a few hours every week as volunteers in the community. That's great! It gives you a chance to help your community, and it also gives you a chance to try different careers. We know that you are going to be the most popular volunteer at the primary school. You are so good with young children. We remember how patient you were with your younger sister, Angelica. Do you think it's possible that after doing this work you will write us a long letter and tell us you have changed your mind about becoming a computer programmer? Maybe you will tell us that you want a career in which you work with young kids. Who knows? In a few years you might become a teacher, principal, school counsellor, or sports coach!

We are also excited about your school project and volunteer work, because they give you an opportunity to spend time with some of the other students at your school. We are very happy that you are beginning to make new friends. We know that one can feel very lonely when one moves to a new country. Please tell us about your new friends in your next letter.

We want to tell you about ESDP's new and exciting school project. You will not believe it! ESDP has a student newspaper this year for the APD classes. It was suggested by the members of the Student

Council at our last general assembly, and we all thought it was a great project. It is a monthly newspaper called *News from the Bridges*. We voted for this name because, as you know, it translates part of our school name. Any student can write an article for the paper. Articles can be about sports, the arts, special projects, trips, or any other kind of news about ESDP. They can be fun articles too. In the last issue, for example, there were tests called "Choose Your Colour, Choose Your Career" and "Your Favourite Ice Cream and Your Personality". The newspaper also announces contests and provides a monthly calendar of events.

News from the Bridges is a lot of fun to read. Guess what? We decided to write some articles for the next issue. Mr. Perreault told us not to worry about our English. He said our English is getting better and better every day. He also told us that he will be happy to read all of our articles before we take them to the Student Council Office. We will send you a copy of the next issue. Maybe they will publish our articles and we will become famous reporters before we finish school.

Take care and write soon!

Your friends,
Chantal, Tina, Omar and Hamid

Activity 1, Part 6
Change the verbs listed on the left to the simple past tense and use them to fill in the blanks. Use each word only once.

<table>
<tr>
<td>can
come
eat
feel
go
have
hold
is
run
say
sit
speak
tell
think
wake
write</td>
<td>The following day Josef (1) _______________ up very early in the morning. He showered, changed into his school clothes and went down for breakfast. After he (2) _______________ breakfast, he hurried to school because he (3) _______________ a great idea. He (4) _______________ the letter from Tina, Chantal, Hamid and Omar in his hand because he wanted to read it to the principal.

When he arrived at his school, he (5) _______________ to the school office right away. He wanted to see the secretary. He walked to her desk and waited patiently. Then he (6) _______________ calmly and slowly to her. He (7) _______________ her that he wanted to speak to the principal about starting a school newspaper. The secretary telephoned the principal and they talked for a few seconds. Then she looked at Josef and (8) _______________ that the principal (9) _______________ see him for only five minutes because he (10) _______________ very busy. Josef thanked the secretary and walked into the principal's office. He (11) _______________ down in a big comfortable chair and waited for the principal to sit down too.</td>
</tr>
</table>

Josef explained that he wanted to start a newspaper at his school. The principal listened quietly and asked him some questions. Josef showed him the letter in his hands. The principal looked at it quietly as he (12) ________________ about Josef's suggestion. He looked like he was interested in the idea of a school newspaper. He promised to suggest the idea for the project to the students and the teachers at the next general assembly.

Josef smiled and thanked the principal before he returned to the school office. He (13) ________________ wonderful!

That day when Josef (14) ________________ home, he (15) ________________ up the stairs and (16) ________________ a letter to his friends, telling them about his day.

Activity 2

Combine the following sentences using a list or the conjunction "and" or "but". Remember to punctuate your sentences correctly.

Example:

I have a brother. I have a sister, too. ➜ I have a brother and a sister.
I like baseball. My brother likes soccer. ➜ I like baseball but my brother likes soccer.
The book was big. The book was green. The book was on the table.
The big, green book was on the table. (list)

1. All the teachers will volunteer. All the students will volunteer.

   ____.

2. I go to a French school. My best friend goes to an English school.

   ____.

3. I have a long project. It is a science project. It is difficult. I don't have to finish it on the weekend.

   ____.

4. I have one sister. She has one brother.

   ____.

5. It gives you a chance to help the community. It gives you a chance to try different careers.

   ____.

III - Text 19

News from the Bridges

Activity 1, Part 1

Use the following possessive pronouns in the sentences below: "mine", "yours", "his", "hers", "ours" and "theirs".

Example: This is Julie's book. ➔ This is hers. (used without nouns)

1. This is [(speaker's) book]. ______________________.
2. This is [Ricardo's book]. ______________________.
3. This is [(person you are speaking to and his/her partner's) dictionary]. ______________________.
4. This is [(speaker's and his/her partner's) dictionary]. ______________________.
5. This is [(Keiko's) book]. ______________________.
6. This is [Toni and Henri's dictionary]. ______________________.

Activity 1, Part 2

Use an appositive to combine the following sentences. Check your punctuation.

Example: Mr. Perreault is the APD teacher. Mr. Perreault is a new teacher at ESDP.
Mr. Perreault, the APD teacher, is a new teacher at ESDP. (appositive)

1. I met Emile Daigle at the party last night. Emile Daigle is a famous writer.

   ____

2. David is a new student. He is making many new friends at ESDP.

   ____

3. Miss Morel is very friendly and helpful. Miss Morel is the school librarian.

   ____

4. Mr. Horishmo is an excellent cook. Mr. Horishmo is Keiko's father.

   ____

5. Angelica likes to make special snacks for Josef. Angelica is Josef's sister.

   ____

6. Mr. Lauzon is the basketball coach. Mr. Lauzon is the physical education teacher.

   ____

7. Mr. Perreault is the advisor for the APD newspaper. Mr. Perreault is one of the teachers at ESDP.

   ____

8. Tina explained many things to the new students. Tina is a member of the Welcoming Committee.

____

9. Mrs. McDonald and Mrs. Dubois are very friendly and helpful. They are the school secretaries.

____

10. Mr. Bleau is very easy to talk to. He is the student counsellor.

____

Activity 1, Part 3
Write the definition of the words and expressions that are new to you.

Vocabulary List

I. Nouns	II. Adjectives
1. announcement: ________	1. final: ________
2. caption: ________	2. funny: ________
3. caricature: ________	3. personal: ________
4. cartoon: ________	4. playful: ________
5. direction: ________	5. real: ________
6. editorial: ________	6. serious: ________
7. entertainment: ________	
8. horoscope: ________	**III. Verbs**
9. index: ________	1. to exchange: ________
10. page: ________	2. to impress: ________
11. penguin: ________	3. to place: ________
12. print: ________	4. to try on: ________
13. quiz: ________	**IV. Where**
14. result: ________	1. against: ________
15. score: ________	2. beneath: ________
16. size: ________	3. a. bottom: ________
17. story: ________	b. top: ________
18. trivia: ________	4. front: ________
19. trophy: ________	5. following: ________
20. uniform: ________	6. right/left hand...: ________
21. variety: ________	

Activity 1, Part 4
Text 19: *News from the Bridges*

When Josef received *News from the Bridges*, he was very surprised. It looked like a real newspaper, only shorter and smaller in size. It had six pages, and each page had one or two photographs or cartoons. Josef started to read the newspaper. He began with the first page. He liked it very much. The name of the newspaper was printed at the top of the page in very large and interesting print: *News from the Bridges*. Beneath the name of the newspaper was the date. The front page had one article and two small photographs. The photographs were about the article, and under each photograph was a short caption that explained the picture. In the bottom right-hand corner there was a small box called the index. In the index was a list of sections and articles, with their page numbers.

The second page had a cartoon and an editorial. The cartoon was very funny. It was a caricature of students. Some of the students were wearing very traditional school uniforms while the other students were dressed in regular clothes. The groups were exchanging ties, vests, shoes, caps and jackets. They looked like they were having a lot of fun trying on each other's clothes. Under the cartoon was a serious editorial. Josef knew that the editorial was an opinion about the cartoon.

The third page was called "Arts and Entertainment". There was a photograph of five students running in different directions and a play review. Next to the play review there was a cartoon of a small penguin sitting on a trophy with the caption "Winner!" above it. Below the cartoon was a short story.

Page 4 was the "The Sports Page". There were two photographs of students playing against other school teams and an article about each picture. In the corner, there was a box that had a list of results and final scores of the games that the ESDP students played in the last month.

The fifth page was the section called "Variety". This section included contest announcements and a list of the following month's activities and events. It also included games, trivia tests, personal quizzes and other fun activities. All of the activities looked interesting. Josef couldn't wait to do them.

The last page was called "People". It had a playful monthly horoscope. It also had the latest announcements about the school, students and staff. At the end of this section were classified ads placed by students who were looking for work. Some ads also announced the things some students wanted to buy or sell.

Josef was very impressed. He could not wait to begin reading *News from the Bridges*!

Activity 1, Part 5
Read the following description of *News from the Bridges* and draw the layout of the first page of *News from the Bridges*.

The name of the newspaper was printed at the top of the page in very large and interesting print: *News from the Bridges*. Beneath the name of the newspaper was the date. The front page had one article and two small photographs. The photographs were about the article, and under each photograph was a short caption that explained the picture. In the bottom right-hand corner there was a small box. In the box was a list of sections and articles with their page numbers.

Activity 1, Part 6
Associate each word on the right with its synonym on the left.

Synonyms	
1. ___L___ woman	A. begin
2. ________ big	B. call
3. ________ right	C. cool
4. ________ sad	D. correct
5. ________ a lot of	E. every
6. ________ beside	F. fall
7. ________ bright	G. finish
8. ________ telephone	H. friendly
9. ________ complete	I. happy
10. ________ difficult	J. hard
11. ________ each	K. jacket
12. ________ autumn	**L. lady**
13. ________ chilly	M. large
14. ________ wife	N. look at
15. ________ job	O. many/much
16. ________ store	P. next to
17. ________ trousers	Q. occupation
18. ________ pleased	R. pants
19. ________ put on	S. purse
20. ________ bag	T. shiny
21. ________ speak	U. shop
22. ________ nice	V. spouse
23. ________ start	W. street
24. ________ road	X. talk
25. ________ coat	Y. toilet
26. ________ seller	Z. unhappy
27. ________ washroom	AA. vendor
28. ________ watch	BB. wear

Activity 1, Part 7

Associate each word on the right with its antonym on the left.

Antonyms	
1. __G__ top	A. adult
2. ______ right	B. answer
3. ______ above	C. before
4. ______ up	D. behind
5. ______ after	E. below
6. ______ aunt	F. big
7. ______ buy	**G. bottom**
8. ______ child	H. careless
9. ______ cold	I. different
10. ______ wrong	J. down
11. ______ everything	K. early
12. ______ day	L. easy
13. ______ ask	M. hard
14. ______ small	N. hot
15. ______ careful	O. last
16. ______ far	P. left
17. ______ dark	Q. light
18. ______ same	R. love
19. ______ difficult	S. near
20. ______ east	T. night
21. ______ first	U. nothing
22. ______ happy	V. old
23. ______ soft	W. out
24. ______ hate	X. right
25. ______ husband	Y. sad
26. ______ in front of	Z. sell
27. ______ in	AA. short
28. ______ late	BB. uncle
29. ______ long	CC. west
30. ______ new	DD. wife

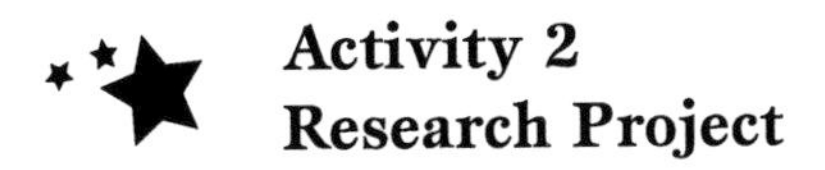

Activity 2
Research Project

a. Go to a library or visit newspaper websites, and list six of each of the following types of publications.

Daily Newspapers	Weekly Magazines	Monthly Magazines

b. Note the following information in point form.

1. How many of the newspapers have a "Sports" section?

2. How many of the newspapers have a weather forecast?

3. How many of the newspapers have a "Classified" section?

4. Copy the index (on the first page) of one of the newspapers.

5. List two magazines that are about world news.

6. List two magazines that are about business.

7. List two magazines that are about fashion.

8. List two magazines that are about sports.

III - Text 20

The Front Page

Activity 1, Part 1
Punctuate the following conversation between Tina and her family. Use commas(,), periods (.), question marks (?), exclamation marks (!), quotation marks (“ ”), colons (:), hyphens (-) and apostrophes (’) where necessary.
(When you are finished, your teacher will read this conversation again while you examine the punctuation marks you used before.)

Mrs Wong cooked Tinas favourite dinner The family missed her and they wanted to hear all about her trip

How many boys and girls were there on your trip Doreen Tinas younger 12 year old sister asked She was very interested in the subject of boys

We were twelve boys and ten girls answered Tina

Joy Tinas older sister was very curious about the tours Which was your favourite part of the historic tour Tina

I really loved walking with my friends on the Plains of Abraham and looking at the St Lawrence River from the fort Ive never seen such a beautiful river

Thomas Tinas brother wanted to know about the food and restaurants Are the restaurants as good as they say they are he asked

Theyre unbelievable All the restaurants we tried were small quiet and charming and the food was delicious especially the desserts

Did Mr Perron and Mrs Beauchemin enjoy the trip too asked Mr Wong

Oh yes They were very happy with the inn the tours the weather and the students They said they would do it again next year

Mrs Wong smiled at Tina and said You said you wanted to do a little shopping in Quebec City but I see a lot of big packages What did you buy there Mrs Wong looked at the packages near the front door

Tina smiled I went to a very nice clothes store with some of my friends I remembered to take the list of things I wanted to buy I bought five things a hat a scarf gloves a pair of jeans and a sweater My friends helped me choose the hat and scarf

Are you and your friends going to buy a small thank you present for Mr Perron and Mrs Beauchemin

Absolutely Were thinking of getting them a nice small album filled with the best photographs of our trip Well give them the albums at our next general assembly

Thats a great idea Whose idea was it

Tina smiled Mine of course

Activity 1, Part 2
There are many words that Omar forgot to capitalize in his letter to Josef. Circle all the letters that should be capitalized.

(today’s date)

dear josef,

i want to write you a very short letter to tell you about our trip to quebec city. all the students in mr. perron’s class went on a four-day trip from monday to friday last week because we wanted to be there for part of the long weekend. we stayed at a lovely inn called the soft dreams inn on dumas road. we read about it in a book called city of memories. our teachers were great and they treated us like adults. we spent a lot of time doing the things we wanted to do and we ate at different restaurants each day. one of the best restaurants was fantasmeals where i ate a belgian breakfast for the first time in my life. it was also a lot of fun walking around in a city where everyone speaks french. we loved our trip. when you visit canada next time be sure to visit quebec city too. our next trip is at the end of may. we are going to visit ottawa. i’ll write about it when we come back.

sincerely,

omar

How many capitalization mistakes did you find in Omar’s letter? I found _____ capitalization mistakes.

Activity 1, Part 3
Imagine you are a reporter. Use the past continuous tense in each of your answers.

At the train station...	What did the reporter see at the train station?
1. Mrs. St. Louis is waiting for the students.	1. Mrs. St. Louis **was waiting** for the students.
2. Keiko is taking notes for her newspaper article.	2. ______________________
3. The students are leaving the train slowly.	3. ______________________
4. They are looking exhausted but happy.	4. ______________________
5. Some of the students are singing songs.	5. ______________________
6. They are carrying bags and packages.	6. ______________________
7. The students are walking to the school bus.	7. ______________________
8. Keiko is interviewing the students on the bus.	8. ______________________

Activity 2, Part 1
Write the definition of the words and expressions that are new to you.

Vocabulary List

I. Nouns

1. inn: ______________________
2. midnight: ______________________
3. photographer: ______________________
4. ride: ______________________
5. river: ______________________
6. tours: ______________________

II. Adjectives

1. amazing: ______________________
2. cooperative: ______________________
3. exhausted: ______________________
4. narrow: ______________________
5. responsible: ______________________
6. superb: ______________________

III. Verbs

1. to behave: ______________________
2. to develop: ______________________
3. to discover: ______________________
4. to find out: ______________________
5. to laugh: ______________________
6. to leave: ______________________
7. to melt: ______________________
8. to recognize: ______________________
9. to treat: ______________________

Irregular Simple Past Tense

1. leave ➔ left
2. sing ➔ sang

Activity 2, Part 2

Why did everyone enjoy the trip to Quebec City? Use "because" to combine the following sentences.

Example: The students enjoyed Quebec City. The students had a lot of fun.
The students enjoyed Quebec City because they had a lot of fun.

1. Jeannine liked the trip. She made new friends on the train.

   ____.

2. Toni liked the trip. She likes well guided historic tours.

   ____.

3. Tina liked the trip. She likes to discover new cities.

   ____.

4. Tina liked the trip. She loves to take photographs.

   ____.

5. Omar liked the trip. He likes to discover new dishes and new restaurants.

   ____.

6. Julia liked the trip. She likes to be treated like a responsible adult.

   ____.

7. Ricardo liked the trip. He liked sharing a room with other students.

   ____.

8. Mr. Perron liked the trip. He enjoys it when history comes alive for his students.

   ____.

9. Mrs. Beauchemin liked the trip. She felt very proud of her school and her students.

   ____.

Activity 2, Part 3
Text 20: The Front Page

Josef looked at the front page of *News from the Bridges* carefully. It had an article and two photographs. The first photograph was a picture of three students walking together in an old, narrow street near a river. Josef did not recognize any of the students. The caption under the photograph said, "Jeannine, Ricardo and Julia enjoying their walk near the St. Lawrence River in Quebec City." The second photograph was a picture of three students in front of a restaurant called La Crêperie. The caption under the photograph said, "Omar, Toni and Jeannine discover another great French restaurant in Quebec City." Josef smiled. He recognized Omar right away. He was pleased to see that

Omar was still busy discovering new restaurants. He was also pleased to see pictures of Ricardo and Toni. Now he knew what they looked like.

In the corner under the pictures, Josef saw the words "Photograph by Tina". He was pleased. Tina was a great photographer. She was probably one of the school photographers this year.

Josef started to read the article on the front page.

"A Fantastic Class Trip" by Keiko Horishimo

The students in Mr. Perron's Canadian History class returned from their four-day trip to Quebec City last Saturday at 4:00 in the afternoon. Mrs. St. Louis, the principal, and I were waiting for the ESDP students at the train station. The students stepped off the train looking exhausted but happy. Then we all took the school bus to ESDP where the parents were waiting for the students. During the bus ride, I had a chance to interview some of the students. Here are some things the students said when I asked them to describe their favourite part of the trip.

Jeannine: The best part of the trip was the train ride. We sang songs, played games, and just sat together and talked. The train trip gave us an opportunity to get to know all the students in the class. I spoke to people I did not know before. Another great thing was spending time with the teachers who came on the trip with us. We spent time with them and learned a lot about them, too. We even saw pictures of Mrs. Beauchemin's three-year-old son playing with their dog, Michou. Of course, Mr. Perron was great. He was more excited about visiting Quebec City than we were, and he made us laugh a lot.

Toni: My favourite part of the trip was the historic tour of Old Quebec. There was one guide for each group of six students. Our guides were superb and they encouraged us to ask questions. They were all history students studying at Laval University. They knew a lot about the city and its history.

Tina: I loved the city! Everything about it! I loved the historic areas. I loved the shops. I loved the narrow streets. I loved the sidewalk restaurants. I loved the St. Lawrence River. I loved every moment I was in Quebec City. I think I took about a hundred pictures. I plan to develop the pictures and mount a small display in the school office so that everyone can see how beautiful Quebec City is.

Omar: My favourite part of the trip was trying different restaurants. Mr. Perron and Mrs. Beauchemin said we could decide where we wanted to eat. I ate with a different group of students each time we had a meal. I tried as many French restaurants as I could! The restaurant I enjoyed the most was the Fondue Restaurant. Many of us ate fondue for the first time in our lives. It was fun sharing the different cheese fondues we ordered. And of course, we couldn't leave the restaurant without trying the Chocolate Fondue Dessert. It was amazing! The melted chocolate tasted great, especially with pieces of pineapple and strawberries. It was as good as the ice cream and fresh fruit crepe I had for lunch at La Crêperie.

Julia: I loved being in a new city with my friends. No parents! No brothers! No sisters to watch everything you do! Our teachers said they wanted to treat us like responsible adults, and we did not disappoint them. We behaved like responsible adults. It was nice to feel like adults and be treated like adults.

Ricardo: For me, the best part of the trip was the wonderful new friends I made. We all stayed at an old inn and, as you know, I am an only child. It was a fun experience sharing a room with students I did not know. We became friends very quickly. Sometimes we stayed awake until midnight and just talked and listened to music. I made some wonderful new friends on the trip!

Mr. Perron: I enjoyed seeing the excitement of the students when they were asking questions during the tours. They were seeing history. History came alive for them. It wasn't just words on a page anymore.

Mrs. Beauchemin: I have to say the best part of the trip was the ESDP students. I was very pleased to see that the students were responsible, cooperative and well behaved the entire time. People stopped me in the street because they wanted to know the name of our school. They said that they were very impressed by the students and that they wanted to send their own children to our school. They were disappointed to find out that ESDP is in Ontario.

After reading the front page, Josef put *News from the Bridges* on his desk. He wanted to enjoy the newspaper for as long as possible. He decided he would read only one article a day. Tomorrow he would read page two, the editorial page.

Activity 2, Part 4

Use this business letter template to write a letter template to a tourist office requesting information for a school trip. Check your spelling, punctuation and capitalization.

____
______________________] Your Mailing Address
____
______________________] Your E-Mail Address

______________________] Date

____
______________________] Name and Address of Tourist Office
____
____

Dear Sir or Madam:

____
______________________________________] Explain why you are writing and why you need the information.
____
____

____
______________________________________] Give details of the planned trip. (When? How many people? School's name?)
____
____

____
______________________________________] Repeat request and say thank you.
____

Yours sincerely,]

[ ] Signature

[ ] Printed Name

Unit III - Text 21

The Editorial Page

Activity 1, Part 1
Write the definition of the words and expressions that are new to you.

Vocabulary List

I. Nouns

1. argument: ____________________
2. label: ____________________
3. loafers: ____________________
4. pressure: ____________________
5. price: ____________________
6. schoolwork: ____________________
7. separation: ____________________
8. tags: ____________________
9. tool: ____________________
10. wood: ____________________

II. Adjectives

1. expensive: ____________________
2. part-time: ____________________
3. strong: ____________________

III. Verbs

1. to apply: ____________________
2. to create: ____________________
3. to debate: ____________________
4. to employ: ____________________
5. to express: ____________________
6. to focus: ____________________
7. to get dressed: ____________________

IV. Work

1. applicant: ____________________
2. employer: ____________________
3. employment: ____________________
4. surname: ____________________
5. skills: ____________________

V. Root Words

apply ➜ applicant ➜ application

employ ➜ employer ➜ employment

Activity 1, Part 2
Text 21: The Editorial Page

The following day, Josef turned to the second page of *News from the Bridges*. It had an article called "The Editorial of the Month." He was not surprised that the editorial was by Hamid. Hamid liked to think about everything carefully before he spoke. He had strong opinions about many things.

Above the article was a cartoon. Josef examined the cartoon again. The cartoonist was a very good artist. And the cartoon was very funny. It was a caricature of students trying on each other's clothes. All the clothes had labels and price tags. Some of the labels said "No Name" but many of the other labels had fashionable brand names. Josef knew that the editorial would probably present an opinion about the situation in the cartoon. He studied the cartoon carefully. He tried to guess the subject of the editorial. Can you guess the subject of the editorial? Josef could not wait to read the editorial. He wanted to know if he had guessed the subject of the editorial correctly!

"This Month's Editorial" by Hamid Moussa

At the Parents and Teachers Committee (PTC) next week, the question will be "Should ESDP students wear school uniforms?" The parents and teachers will discuss this question. We know that the debate is going to be long and serious.

Many parents and teachers insist that school uniforms are a good idea. They have the usual arguments for this. They say that students spend too much time buying clothes at malls or looking at fashion magazines. They also say that some of ESDP students take more than an hour to choose their clothes and get dressed in the morning. They want their children to wake up in the morning and know what they will wear: a light blue shirt, a red and green vest, a green jacket and a pair of green trousers or a green skirt. They would also wear black loafers, green socks and no jewellery.

The parents who are against school uniforms for the students of ESDP also feel very strongly. They have the usual arguments too. They insist that students should choose what they want to wear each morning. They say choosing clothes is part of adult life. When people leave the house and go to their jobs or go out for the afternoon or evening, they choose what they wear. The parents also say that choosing clothes gives their children an opportunity to express their personalities. They insist that this is one of the things that students have to learn before they enter the adult world.

Parents also realize that clothes are beginning to create a serious problem in our school. For the ESDP students, clothes are becoming a dangerous tool of separation. Clothes are separating the students into two groups: the "in group" and the "others". The "in group" are the fashionable teenagers who spend a lot of money on clothes. They wear the latest fashions, colours and accessories. Some of the ESDP students spend hundreds of dollars on a pair of shoes! Fashions change very quickly. Many of the clothes are used for only a few months. Many of these students even find part-time jobs in the evenings and on the weekends so that they can buy their fashionable and expensive clothes.

This puts a lot of pressure on the other students. They want to spend more money on clothes and accessories too. They want to be fashionable too. They ask their parents for more money to spend on clothes and, if their parents refuse, the ESDP students begin to look for after-school or weekend jobs. This is the real problem that clothes create. It is time for students to stop focussing on clothes and to start focussing on schoolwork!

Activity 1, Part 3
Answer the following questions on Text 21.

1. a) Read the editorial again and list the two reasons why parents or teachers believe that students should not wear school uniforms.

   1. ____________________

   2. ____________________

   b) Give another reason why you think students should not wear school uniforms.

   ____

   ____

2. a) Read the editorial again and list the three reasons why parents and teachers believe that students should wear school uniforms.

1. ______

2. ______

3. ______

b) Give another reason why you think students should wear school uniforms.

______

______

Activity 1, Part 4

People also express their opinions when they participate in debates. Before debating, people list their reasons and arguments. List three reasons for each of the following.

1. a) Parents should pay for their children's vandalism or graffiti.

1. ______

2. ______

3. ______

b) Children/students should pay for their own vandalism or graffiti.

1. ______

2. ______

3. ______

2. a) Students with less than a 70% average should participate in after-school activities.

1. ______

2. ______

3. ______

b) Students with less than a 70% average should not participate in after-school activities.

1. ______

2. ______

3. ______

3. a) The age for "dropping out" of school should stay at 16.

1. ______

2. ______

3. ______

b) The age for "dropping out" of school should be 18.

1. ______________________________

2. ______________________________

3. ______________________________

Activity 1, Part 5
Arguments FOR and AGAINST

1. List three reasons why some people believe that students should not pay for their schoolbooks.

   a) ______________________________

   b) ______________________________

   c) ______________________________

2. List three reasons why some people believe that students should pay for their schoolbooks.

   a) ______________________________

   b) ______________________________

   c) ______________________________

3. Many people agree that books are expensive, but they believe that students can do several things that can help them spend less money on books. List two things that students can do to spend less money on their schoolbooks.

   a) ______________________________

   b) ______________________________

Activity 1, Part 6
Write an opinion text.

Using the arguments you listed in the last activity, write an opinion text that explains the reasons why you think students should or should not pay for the books they use at school.

- Don't forget to begin your opinion text with a topic sentence that introduces the subject to your readers and that states your position.
- Don't forget to end your text with a concluding sentence that tells your readers that you have finished giving your opinion.

First Draft:

Final Copy:

Activity 2, Part 1
The Successful Job Interview.

Many students look for part-time work. To get a job, they must complete a job application and attach letters of reference, or list persons (and their telephone numbers) as references. If the employer is happy with the information on the job application and is satisfied with the personal references, he or she asks the job applicant to come for an interview. Answer the following questions, and you will know if you are ready for your interview.

Write a number after every question.

3 = very important **2 = important** **1 = not important**

1. I try to arrive 5 to 10 minutes before my interview.	
2. My clothes are clean and well ironed.	
3. I wear clothes that are nicer than my "everyday" school clothes.	
4. My shoes are shined and clean.	
5. I do not wear a cap or a coat during an interview.	
6. I am clean and look neat (shampooed and combed hair, deodorant).	
7. I wear very little make-up/I am clean-shaven.	
8. If I am wearing a religious headdress, it is clean and neat. If I have a beard, it is clean and neat.	
9. My body language is relaxed: no foot/finger tapping or other nervous behaviour.	
10. At the interview, I sit straight and keep a good posture.	
11. When answering questions, I look at and speak to the interviewer.	
12. My voice is loud and my pronunciation is as clear as possible.	
13. I take time to answer all the questions, and I answer them honestly.	
14. I use standard English. I don't use slang or impolite language.	
15. My words and body language show that I would appreciate the job opportunity.	
16. I ask short and clear questions about the job after the interview is finished.	
17. I thank the interviewer for his or her time before I leave.	
TOTAL:	

42-51: You will probably get the job.
34-41: Your interview will be okay, but there will be competition for the job.
17-33: Your interviewer will probably give the job to another person.

Job Application

(Please print clearly in ink.)

Good Times Travel Agency

Surname: ______________________ Given Name: ______________________

Date of Birth: ______________________ Telephone Number: ______________________

Address: ____
(street) (apartment no)

____
(city/town) (province) (postal code)

E-Mail Address: ____

Education:

Institution	Year(s) Attended	Degree/Diploma/Certificate

Work Experience: (List most recent job first.)

Dates of Employment	Employer	Employer's Telephone Number	Duties

Personal Skills and Interest:

____

____

____

References:

____

____

____

______________________ ______________________
Applicant's Signature Date

Activity 2, Part 3

Write the correct occupations on the lines below, and then find the occupations in the puzzle. Circle each of the letters separately. Use a dictionary when necessary.

1. I help or assist a doctor. I am a _ _ _ _ _.
2. I am the boss of a school. I am a _ _ _ _ _ _ _ _ _.
3. I make bread. I am a _ _ _ _ _.
4. I cut men's hair. I am a _ _ _ _ _ _.
5. I help you to buy things at a store. I am a _ _ _ _ _ _ _ _ _ _ _.
6. I give you help on the telephone. I am an _ _ _ _ _ _ _ _.
7. I am the boss of an office or store. I am a _ _ _ _ _ _ _.
8. I am the boss of Canada. I am the _ _ _ _ _   _ _ _ _ _ _ _ _.
9. I take money from you at the supermarket. I am a _ _ _ _ _ _ _.
10. I am the doctor for your teeth. I am a _ _ _ _ _ _ _.
11. Call me if your water pipes break. I will fix them. I am a _ _ _ _ _ _ _.
12. I speak for you in court when you have legal problems. I am a _ _ _ _ _ _.
13. I am the boss of a city. I am the _ _ _ _ _.
14. I stay at home and take care of my spouse and children. I am a _ _ _ _ _ _ _ _ _.
15. People take my pictures so that I can advertise clothes, cars, etc. I am a _ _ _ _ _.
16. I take care of the flowers, grass and trees on your property. I am a _ _ _ _ _ _ _ _.
17. I sell diamond rings. I am a _ _ _ _ _ _ _ _.
18. I build tables, chairs, etc. with wood. I am a _ _ _ _ _ _ _ _ _.
19. I teach at a university, not at a school. I am a _ _ _ _ _ _ _ _ _.
20. I give you books for two weeks ONLY. I am a _ _ _ _ _ _ _ _ _.
21. Call me if your lights stop working. I will fix them. I am an _ _ _ _ _ _ _ _ _ _ _.
22. I serve food on an airplane. I am a _ _ _ _ _ _   _ _ _ _ _ _ _ _ _.
23. I clean buildings and schools, etc. I am a _ _ _ _ _ _ _.

B	O	P	E	R	A	T	O	R	E	L	L	E	W	E	J	W	O
A	R	L	D	N	O	S	R	E	P	S	E	L	A	S	O	F	P
K	T	N	A	D	N	E	T	T	A	T	H	G	I	L	F	P	L
E	L	I	B	R	A	R	I	A	N	T	S	I	T	N	E	D	U
R	P	R	I	M	E	M	I	N	I	S	T	E	R	O	Y	A	M
E	S	R	U	N	H	O	M	E	M	A	K	E	R	O	S	S	B
Y	B	A	R	B	E	R	I	P	R	O	F	E	S	S	O	R	E
W	B	I	R	E	T	N	E	P	R	A	C	A	S	H	I	E	R
A	J	A	N	I	T	O	R	L	L	A	P	I	C	N	I	R	P
L	G	A	R	D	E	N	E	R	E	G	A	N	A	M	I	T	I
E	L	E	C	T	R	I	C	I	A	N	E	L	E	D	O	M	S

To find the mystery answer, write the letters you did not circle on the lines below.

_ _ _ _ _ _   _ _   _ _ _ _ _ _ _ _ _ _ _ _ _ _ _!

Unit III - Text 22

The Arts and Entertainment Section

Activity 1, Part 1
Write the definition of the words and expressions that are new to you.

Vocabulary List

I. Nouns

1. actor: ________________
2. advisor: ________________
3. author: ________________
4. background: ________________
5. cell phone: ________________
6. change: ________________
7. character: ________________
8. coffee table: ________________
9. comedy: ________________
10. costume: ________________
11. director: ________________
12. dishes: ________________
13. drama club: ________________
14. exam: ________________
15. floor lamp: ________________
16. girlfriend: ________________
17. glass: ________________
18. impression: ________________
19. interruption: ________________
20. laughter: ________________
21. panic: ________________
22. pan: ________________
23. permission: ________________
24. pots: ________________
25. review: ________________
26. roommate: ________________
27. set: ________________
28. setting: ________________
29. sofa: ________________
30. success: ________________

II. Adjectives

1. angry: ________________
2. anxious: ________________
3. delightful: ________________
4. dirty: ________________
5. empty: ________________
6. frustrated: ________________
7. messy: ________________
8. neat: ________________
9. obvious: ________________
10. organized: ________________
11. terrible: ________________
12. total: ________________

III. Verbs	
1. to confuse: ______________	7. to set: ______________
2. to dress: ______________	8. to take (a bath): ______________
3. to drive: ______________	**Irregular Simple Past Tense**
4. to hang: ______________	1. build ➜ built
5. to perform: ______________	2. drink ➜ drank
6. to put away: ______________	

Activity 1, Part 2
Text 22: The Arts and Entertainment Section

When Josef came home the next day, the house was empty. No one was home. He was very pleased, because he knew he could read the Arts and Entertainment section of *News from the Bridges* without any interruptions from his kid sister. He took off his jacket, drank a glass of juice and sat in the most comfortable chair in the living room. Then he opened the newspaper to the Arts and Entertainment section. In this section, there was a photograph with a review by Chantal. There was also a cartoon next to a short story. He decided to read Chantal's review first.

Josef smiled as he examined the photograph of five young men running in different directions, totally confused! Four of them were wearing dirty T-shirts and jeans. Their hair was messy and they looked like they needed to sleep or take a long shower. But one of them was neatly dressed. He looked like he was ready to go to a party. It was obvious that he was feeling angry and frustrated as he examined the messy living room around him. The floor was covered with books, notebooks and papers. There were two empty pizza cartons on the coffee table. There were empty soft drink cans everywhere. There were CDs and cell phones on the sofa. There was even a dirty T-shirt hanging from a floor lamp. In the background there was a kitchen that was also very messy. There were dirty pots, pans and dishes on the counters, in the sink and on the kitchen table. The place looked terrible! The caption read: David, Bruno, Henri, Jules and Ricardo in this year's school play, "Unprepared!"

Josef started to read the review of the school play. He was very curious. He wanted to know more about it.

"This Year's School Play" by Chantal Leclerc

This year, the Drama Club surprised the students, parents, staff and other guests who came to see the play "Unprepared!"

Every year, we see a serious play by a famous writer. And this year we were ready to see another serious play by another famous writer. But we were surprised! Instead of a serious play, we saw a wonderful comedy that the Writing Club wrote a few months ago. Catherine, Maya, Christophe, Christian and Toni are the authors of this excellent comedy. They wrote the play together. When their advisor, Mrs. Roy, read it, she insisted that they show it to the members of the Drama Club. When the members of the Drama Club read the play, they were very excited. They said it was delightful and asked for permission to perform it as this year's school play. We are very pleased they did.

The play is set in an old house in Kingston, Ontario, during final exams. The characters are five university students who live together. Four of them are very exhausted and anxious about their exams. But not the fifth one. The fifth young man is the perfect student who is neat, organized and always prepared. He doesn't even need to study for his exams because he is an excellent student. One night, instead of studying, he plans to go out for dinner with his girlfriend and her parents. He is going to meet her parents for the first time, and he wants to make a good impression. He then receives a telephone call! It is his girlfriend. She tells him that there is a change in plans. It is not necessary for him to drive to her apartment. She and her parents will be happy to drive to his place and pick him up. She also tells him that her parents want to visit for a few minutes because they want to meet his roommates! The rest of the play is about the panic and all the funny things that happen as the students try to clean the living room and impress the girlfriend's parents.

Bravo ESDP students! The writers, actors, director and students who built the set and chose the costumes did an excellent job! Thanks to them, we had a wonderful evening full of laughter and fun.

* * *

When Josef finished reading the review of the play, he smiled. The play sounded like it was very funny. He was very happy that ESDP's school play was a big success this year. He looked at the photograph again before he put the newspaper away. He would read the rest of the Arts and Entertainment section the following day.

Josef started to think about the special show his school was planning. He wanted to write a letter to Tina, Chantal, Omar and Hamid about it. He wanted to tell them that he and his new schoolmates were doing a show called "Talent Night". It was going to be a night full of singing, dancing, music, acrobatics and even magic. And he was the person responsible for the lights and the audio equipment. He really wanted to share this with his friends, but he decided not to. He was determined to keep "Talent Night" a secret because he planned to send them a video of the show as a surprise.

Activity 1, Part 3
Fill in the blanks with the prepositions "at", "on", "in", "for", "from" and "to".

	at	on	in	for	from-to/until
TIME	Specific times: at 9:15 at night Meals: at lunch	Days of the week/ dates: on Sunday on June 3, 2006 on the weekend	Month/year/season: in July in 1989 in the winter in the morning in the evening in the afternoon	Period of time: for six days	Start to finish: from June until August
PLACE	Specific address: at 31 Erin Blvd. General locations: at that table Buildings: at the mall Names of places: at Harvey's	Names of streets: on Main Street On a surface: on the wall/poster On TV, radio On the phone On a bike/bus/ train/plane	Cities, towns, etc. in Ottawa Inside: in the book in bed in a picture or photograph		Movement: trip to.... From....to...: They moved from Sudbury to Plantagenet

When Mr. Perreault's students came to class on Monday morning, they each said a few sentences about their weekend.

Omar: I woke up late (1) _________ Saturday. I always wake up late (2) _________ winter. I read the newspaper (3) _________ breakfast. After breakfast, I worked on my computer project (4) _________ about two hours. Then I took a bus (5) _________ Catherine Boulevard. I finally found Second Chance, the used book store I was looking for. It was (6) _________ Léger Avenue, just (7) _________ the corner of Léger and Harold. I spent the rest of the morning (8) _________ Second Chance. I found two books there that I want to use for my history project. I then came home and watched TV (9) _________ 4:30 (10) _________ 6:30.

Chantal: My family and I went (11) __________ Sudbury (12) __________ the morning. We wanted to see Laurentian University. The university office told me the best time to visit the campus is (13) __________ the weekends. We walked (14) __________ Ramsey Lake Road. Then we had lunch (15) __________ a nice restaurant. We drove back (16) __________ night. We listened to an interesting program (17) __________ the radio. We enjoyed our Saturday (18) __________ Sudbury very much.

Tina: I woke up (19) __________ 9:30 (20) __________ Saturday morning. I wanted to go shopping (21) __________ the morning and do my homework (22) __________ the afternoon. (23) __________ the evening I met my friends (24) __________ McGregor's Restaurant. We sat (25) __________ a table in the corner. We were at the restaurant (26) __________ 6:00 (27) __________ 9:00 p.m. We had a wonderful time looking at my photographs of Quebec City. The city looked wonderful (28) __________ the pictures. I think I will move (29) __________ the province of Quebec and live (30) __________ Quebec City when I become a dentist.

Activity 1, Part 4

In groups of 2 or 3, brainstorm names of TV programs or movies and list them in the following categories or genres.

Horror	Cartoon	Documentary	Game Show
__________	__________	__________	__________
__________	__________	__________	__________
__________	__________	__________	__________
Musical	**News**	**Comedy**	**Soap Opera**
__________	__________	__________	__________
__________	__________	__________	__________
__________	__________	__________	__________
Talk Show	**Sports**	**Drama: Family/Medical**	**Action Drama: Police**
__________	__________	__________	__________
__________	__________	__________	__________
__________	__________	__________	__________

Activity 1, Part 5
Read a review in a newspaper, magazine, or TV guide and answer the following questions.

1. What is the title of the show/movie/program?

   ____

2. What is the genre?

   ____

3. Who are the main characters/actors?

   ____

4. What happens (plot) in the show/movie/program?

   ____

   ____

5. What are the good and bad things about the show, movie or program?

   ____

   ____

   ____

6. Is there a rating system? Does it use points? Stars? Other?

   ____

Activity 1, Part 6
Review a TV program (drama, action, or comedy) you enjoyed this week.

1. Give the name of the program and its genre.

   ____

2. List the main characters and describe them.

   ____

   ____

   ____

3. Summarize the action and events in the program.

   ____

   ____

   ____

4. Explain the things you like most about this program.

____

____

____

5. Give two reasons why you would recommend this show to your peers.

____

____

Unit III - Text 23

Arts and Entertainment: The Winner!

Activity 1, Part 1
Write the definition of the words and expressions that are new to you.

Vocabulary List

I. Nouns

1. ache: ____________________
2. bargain: ____________________
3. beach: ____________________
4. boat: ____________________
5. fable: ____________________
6. fish ➜ fish (plural)
7. fishermen: ____________________
8. harbour: ____________________
9. lesson: ____________________
10. nonsense: ____________________
11. noon: ____________________
12. pond: ____________________
13. quality: ____________________
14. quantity: ____________________

II. Adjectives

1. fat: ____________________
2. thin: ____________________
3. wrong: ____________________

III. Expressions

1. He didn't get it!: ____________________
2. Once upon a time...: ____________________

IV. Verbs

1. to apologize: ____________________
2. to bother: ____________________
3. to cancel: ____________________
4. to jump: ____________________
5. to repeat: ____________________
6. to scold: ____________________

Irregular Verbs

1. catch ➜ caught
2. hear ➜ heard
3. hold ➜ held
4. sell ➜ sold
5. swim ➜ swam
6. teach ➜ taught

V. Elements of the Short Story

1. character
   a. antagonist
   b. protagonist
2. plot
3. setting
4. theme/message

....

VI. Other Words

1. as: ____________________
2. while: ____________________

Activity 1, Part 2
Text 23: Arts and Entertainment: The Winner!

The following evening, Josef completed his homework quickly and sat down to finish the Arts and Entertainment section of *News from the Bridges*. He examined the cartoon of a small penguin sitting on a trophy with the caption "Winner!" above it. Why was the penguin sitting on the trophy? Why did he have a fish in his hand? Josef didn't get it! He decided to read the short announcement above the story. Maybe the announcement would explain the cartoon.

Announcement: Last month *News from the Bridges* held a short story contest. We are pleased to announce that the winner of the short story contest is Toni Gardoni. She wrote a fable called "The Penguins and the Fish". Congratulations, Toni! Your prize is waiting for you in the principal's office. Here is the prize-winning story.

"The Penguins and the Fish" by Toni Gardoni

Once upon a time, in a faraway country called the Parctic, there lived a small group of black and white penguins. The penguins were very nice and very friendly. They swam together in the cold water; they played together on the beaches; they shopped together at their favourite stores; and they went to penguin parties together. It was fun living in this small penguin community.

The best day of the week for the penguins was Wednesday. Why? Because Wednesday was Barbecue and Picnic Day. Every Wednesday morning, the penguins woke up early and walked together to the fish market in the harbour. There, they waited for the fishermen to arrive in their long boats. When the fishermen arrived, they opened their large boxes and showed the penguins all the fresh fish they had caught. All the fish were for sale. The fishermen sold their fresh fish to the penguins. They sold big fish and small fish, long fish and short fish. They sold fat fish and thin fish. They sold blue, red, yellow and purple fish. They sold many different kinds of fish to the penguins. The penguins enjoyed choosing their fish. Every Wednesday, after they bought their fish, the penguins walked together to the town park near the small Parctic Pond. There, they barbecued the fish while the young penguins skated on the ice and played hockey. That's why Wednesday was such a special day. It was Barbecue and Picnic Day for all the residents of Parctic.

One Wednesday morning, the penguins arrived at the harbour at the usual time. They waited and waited for the fishermen to come, but nothing happened. There were no fishermen; there were no boats; there were no boxes of fresh fish. The penguins were very disappointed! Finally, at noon, they decided it was time to go home. They walked back slowly to their ice condos and apartments. That day's Barbecue and Picnic was cancelled. For lunch, many of the penguins ate peanut butter and jam sandwiches instead of their favourite fresh and juicy barbecued fish.

At 8:00 on Thursday morning, the penguins were woken up by loudly ringing bells in the harbour. The harbour bells rang only when there was an emergency. The worried penguins jumped out of their beds and ran to the harbour to see what was wrong. There, at the fish market, they saw the fishermen with their boxes of fish. The penguins were surprised but pleased to see the fishermen. They were even more pleased to hear that the fishermen were selling the fish for half price. That's right! Two fish for the price of one...because the fish were two days old.

The penguins started to choose their fish. Some wanted to buy four fish. Others wanted to buy six fish. Everyone was talking and laughing. There was a lot of excitement and noise.

Suddenly, the penguins heard Little Yona's voice. "Wait, everyone!" the little voice said. "I don't think this is such a good idea!"

The adult penguins looked at each other. What was Little Yona saying? Was he saying that buying old fish at bargain prices was a bad idea? What nonsense! The fish were only two days old! Everyone knows that two fish for the price of one is much better than one fish for the price of one!

"Look, Little Yona," one of the adult penguins scolded. "We know what we are doing. We are getting quantity for our money. Now go away and stop bothering us!"

"I don't think buying old fish is a good idea," repeated Little Yona. "Don't forget, quality is more important than quantity!"

But the penguins did not listen to Little Yona. They bought their fish and went to Parctic Pond where they started the Barbecue and Picnic Day. They ate their fish and had a wonderful time. All the penguins except Little Yona. He ate a peanut butter and jam sandwich and was completely alone because no one wanted to talk, skate, or play hockey with him.

The next day, all the penguins in Parctic were sick. They all had stomach aches. All except Little Yona...

Several days later, when the penguins were feeling better, they decided to apologize to Little Yona and thank him for the important lesson he had taught them. After all, Little Yona was right. Now they agreed with him: Quality is more important than quantity!

Activity 1, Part 3
Answer the following questions about Toni's short story in Activity 1, Part 2.

1. Who is the main character of the short story? ______________________________

2. What two adjectives best describe the main character? Why?

 ____________: ______________________________

 ____________: ______________________________

3. What two adjectives best describe the adult penguins? Why?

 ____________: ______________________________

 ____________: ______________________________

4. What is another possible theme (or message) in this story?

 ____

5. What is the setting of the story? ______________________________

6. Summarize the plot in six sentences using the following words to clarify the sequence: "first", "second", "before", "then", "during", "later", "next", "afterwards" and "finally".

 a. ______________________________

 b. ______________________________

 c. ______________________________

 d. ______________________________

 e. ______________________________

 f. ______________________________

Activity 1, Part 4
Number the following ten events in the order that they happen in the story in Activity 1, Part 2.

________ Little Yona told the penguins that buying old fish was a bad idea.

________ The penguins went home and ate peanut butter and jam sandwiches.

________ They went to Parctic Pond and had a wonderful Barbecue and Picnic Day with two-day-old fish.

________ They ran to the harbour and saw the fishermen opening their boxes of fish.

________ The next day, all the penguins were sick.

____1____ Every Wednesday, the penguins went to the harbour to buy fresh fish from the fishermen.

________ The happy penguins bought four or six fish.

________ When they felt better, they apologized to Little Yona.

________ One Wednesday, the penguins waited and waited for the fishermen to come, but they didn't.

________ None of the penguins listened to Little Yona.

________ Everybody had a wonderful time except Little Yona, because no one wanted to play with him.

________ The following morning, the penguins woke up when the harbour bells were ringing.

Activity 1, Part 5
Circle the letter of the answer that best completes each statement about the events in the story of Activity 1, Part 2.

1. Everyone was ________ Little Yona because he was saying something that they did not want to hear.
   (A) happy with (B) angry at (C) confused by (D) jealous of

2. In the beginning, the penguins insisted that ________.
   (A) quantity is better than quality (B) quality is better than quantity

3. Little Yona ate ________ at the picnic when the penguins cooked the two-day-old fish.
   (A) peanut butter and jam sandwiches (B) barbecued fish (C) chicken sandwiches

4. The harbour bell rang when there was ________.
   (A) a meeting (B) a party (C) a picnic (D) an emergency

5. Little Yona told the penguins his opinion because he was ________.
   (A) shy (B) proud (C) athletic (D) worried

6. The penguins learned the following lesson: ________.
   (A) Adults are right. (B) You should never listen to others. (C) You can learn from anybody.

Activity 1, Part 6

Use the past progressive to answer the following questions about Toni's story in Activity 1, Part 2.

> When do you use the past progressive (also called "past continuous") [was/were (verb) + ing]?
>
> ***Use the past progressive with the words "while", "during" and "as".
>
> **Example:** Yona spoke to the adult penguins while they were buying fish.
> Yona spoke to the adult penguins as they were examining the fish.

1. What were the penguins doing when the bell rang at the harbour?

____.

2. What were the adult penguins doing when Little Yona spoke?

____.

3. What were the fishermen doing as Little Yona spoke?

____.

4. How do you think Little Yona was feeling at the picnic after the fish sale?

____.

5. What did Little Yona eat at the picnic while the other penguins were eating juicy fish?

____.

6. How do you think Little Yona was feeling when the other penguins were playing hockey?

____.

7. How do you think Little Yona was feeling when the adult penguins were apologizing to him?

____.

Activity 1, Part 7

Use the past progressive to answer the following questions about your day, yesterday.

1. What were you doing yesterday at 6:00 a.m.?

____.

2. What were you doing at noon, yesterday?

____.

3. What was your brother/sister doing when the telephone rang last night?

____.

4. What was your mother doing when you came home late last night?

____

Activity 1, Part 8

Fill in the blanks with the correct pair of homonyms from the list on the left.

<table>
<tr>
<td>

List A
add/ad
ate/eight
blew/blue
buy/bye
choose/chews
eye/I
grate/great
guessed/guest
hole/whole
hour/our
in/inn
it's/its

</td>
<td>

Example: We can buy **our** tickets for the concert in one **hour**.

1. ________________ went to the ________________ doctor. I have to wear glasses now.
2. Keiko's mother ________________ that Keiko's father was going to invite only one ________________ for the following Sunday's spaghetti dinner!
3. The mouse who lives in the ________________ ate the ________________ box of nuts.
4. Old paintings were ________________ every room of the old ________________.
5. The wind ________________ the white clouds in the ________________ sky.
6. My friends and I ________________ ________________ doughnuts!
7. "I have to ________________ my bus pass. See you later. ________________!"
8. I ________________ this kind of cookie because I like to watch my kid brother as he ________________ it slowly!
9. After I ________________ this cheese, I will cook a ________________ omelette.
10. ________________ a story about a mouse and ________________ tail.
11. I will ________________ this magazine ________________ to my examples of how the media influence teenagers. It will be a great presentation!

</td>
</tr>
</table>

List B	
knows/nose mail /male meat/meet pear/pair read/red tale/tail waist/waste weak/week who's/whose wood/would you're/your	12. Sometimes I talk to ______________ sister when ______________ studying at the library. 13. I ______________ the little story about the ______________ dragon for my niece. 14. She loved it! It was a ______________ about its long ______________. 15. I will ______________ my mother at the ______________ counter in the supermarket. We want to buy some steaks. 16. I was not feeling well. I had no energy. I felt very ______________ all ______________ long! 17. Everyone ______________ that my ______________ is red because I have allergies. 18. ______________ you please return that piece of ______________ to the carpenter? 19. ______________ is this book? ______________ the person who put it here? 20. I bought a ______________ of ______________(s) to add to the fruit salad. 21. Our ______________ letter carrier brings our ______________ at 9:00 a.m. 22. Don't ______________ your time with exercises that promise to make your ______________ smaller. They just don't work!

Activity 2, Part 1
Write sentences using the past perfect tense and the word "before".

When do you use the past perfect tense (had + past participle)?

If two things happened in the past, use the past participle for the thing that happened first.

Example: [in The Penguins and the Fish]
The fishermen showed the penguins all the fresh fish they had caught.
What happened first? The fishermen caught the fish.
What happened next? The fishermen showed the fish to the penguins.

The adult penguins thanked Little Yona for the important lesson they had learned.
What happened first? The adult penguins learned a lesson from Little Yona.
What happened next? The adult penguins thanked Little Yona.

	May	June
Example: I **had read** the article **before** he showed it to me.	I read the article.	He showed it (the article) to me.
1. ______ ______	I sold my old house.	I bought a new house.
2. ______ ______	I thought for a long time.	I chose my essay topic.
3. ______ ______	I built a small table.	You gave me your old one.
4. ______ ______	I read the book.	The teacher told us to read the book.
5. ______ ______	I heard the news.	I read about it in the newspaper.

Activity 2, Part 2
Complete the following list of irregular verbs by filling in the blanks. Check your spelling.

Present	Simple Past	Past Participle
be	was/were	________
become	became	________
begin	________	begun
________	broke	broken
bring	________	brought
________	bought	bought
choose	________	chosen
come	________	come
do	did	________
draw	drew	________
drink	drank	________
drive	________	driven
eat	ate	________
forget	forgot	________
get	________	got
give	gave	________
go	went	________
know	________	known
pay	paid	________
put	________	put
ring	rang	________
run	________	run
say	said	________
see	saw	________
sit	________	sat
speak	spoke	________
spend	________	spent
swim	swam	________
take	________	taken
teach	taught	________
think	________	________
wear	wore	________
write	wrote	________

Activity 2, Part 3

Fill in the blanks with the simple past or past participle of the verb in parentheses.

Have you ever (be) 1. ____________________ to Ottawa on Canada Day?

I (go) 2. ____________________ last summer and I loved it! There (be) 3. ____________________

so much to do! I (spend) 4. ____________________ most of my day downtown.

First I (eat) 5. ____________________ a big breakfast at a small restaurant at the Byward Market

and then we walked along the Rideau Canal up to Parliament Hill. At 10 o'clock

we (see) 6. ____________________ the Changing of the Guards. Those soldiers (wear) 7.

____________________ big furry hats and red coats even on a warm day. Then we

(buy) 8. ____________________ a ticket for a tour of the Parliament Buildings. We

(see) 9. ____________________ many paintings of past prime ministers, and I learned things

I never (know) 10. ____________________ about the Canadian government.

I (take) 11. ____________________ a picture of the beautiful old library with all its books and

wood carvings. I even (go) 12. ____________________ up the Peace Tower. The clock

(ring) 13. ____________________ while I was standing beneath it. By the time our tour finished,

the festivities on Parliament Hill had already (begin) 14. ____________________. One singer

had already (sing) 15. ____________________ our national anthem. We (sit) 16. ____________________

on a blanket that we had (bring) 17. ____________________ and (eat) 18. ____________________

a few sandwiches and some fruit. We all (drink) 19. ____________________ a lot of water as we

listened to the singers and bands because it (be) 20. ____________________ very warm.

We (speak) 21. ____________________ to people who had (come) 22. ____________________ from

all parts of Canada. The fireworks after the concert (be) 23. ____________________ so colourful!

When we (drive) 24. ____________________ back to Hanmer we were tired but happy. I still have not

(forgot) 25. ____________________ that very special day!

Activity 2, Part 4
Write the definition of the words and expressions that are new to you.

Vocabulary List

I. Nouns

1. forest: ______________________
2. kindness: ______________________
3. kiss: ______________________
4. lion: ______________________
5. monster: ______________________
6. mouse: ______________________
7. net: ______________________
8. trap: ______________________

II. Adjectives

1. afraid: ______________________
2. courageous: ______________________
3. cute: ______________________
4. dangerous: ______________________
5. free: ______________________
6. golden: ______________________
7. huge: ______________________
8. weak: ______________________

III. Homonyms:

1. tail: ______________________
2. tale: ______________________

IV. Verbs

1. to beg: ______________________
2. to carry: ______________________
3. to chew: ______________________
4. to explore: ______________________
5. to let: ______________________
6. to pull: ______________________
7. to repay: ______________________
8. to roar: ______________________

Irregular Verbs

1. shake ➜ shook ➜ shaken
2. sleep ➜ slept ➜ slept

V. Expressions

1. Oh dear.: ______________________
2. Leave me alone!: ______________________
3. Yes/No, sir.: ______________________
4. even though...: ______________________

Activity 2, Part 5
Complete the short story by writing the correct verb in each of the sentences below.

ate	closed	lived	remember	standing
began	decided	looked	returned	thought
begged	examined	made	said	tried
breathe	found	picked up	shaking	understand
came	gave	promise	should	wake
chew	heard	ran	sounded	went

"The Lion and the Mouse"
(adapted from the fable by La Fontaine)

Once upon a time, in a country far away, there (1) _____lived_____ a small brown mouse who had a very long tail. He was an old mouse who lived a very quiet life. He didn't speak to anyone; he didn't play with anybody. During the day, he went into the forest and (2) __________ for food to eat. When he (3) __________ some nuts or seeds or fruit, he carried them to his little home. His home was a little hole under a tall tree. That is where he rested, (4) __________ his small dinner of fruit and nuts, and (5) __________ to sleep.

One day, after looking for food all day, the little mouse (6) __________ to his little hole feeling very tired, disappointed and hungry. He had no food to eat that night. "Maybe," he thought, "I (7) __________ look for food in the cave." But he was afraid. The little mouse did not like the cave that was near his little home because it was big, empty, dark and cold. But the mouse was very, very hungry. He (8) __________ to be courageous. He walked slowly into the cave and (9) __________ to explore it.

He suddenly stopped exploring, because he felt that he was (10) __________ on a soft carpet. Why was there a soft carpet in a dark, empty cave? The mouse was curious. He (11) __________ to pull some of the carpet up to examine it. Nothing happened! He pulled harder, and this time he (12) __________ a very loud noise.

"ROAAARRRR!"

The mouse (13) ________________________ his eyes, afraid to look. Had a dangerous monster (14) ________________________ that sound? He did not want to know!

"ROAAARRRR!" He heard the sound again. Then he felt something very big and strong take hold of him tightly. He could not move; he could not (15) ________________________!

"ROAAARRRR!" He heard for the third time. The mouse knew he had to open his eyes even though he was (16) ________________________ with fear. He waited for a few seconds. He heard no noise. He opened his eyes slowly. In front of him were two huge, furious circles. They were the eyes of an angry lion!

"Oh dear," (17) ________________________ the little mouse in his little voice. "I'm sorry. I did not mean to bother you, Mr. Lion."

"What are you doing in my cave?" roared the lion loudly.

"I was looking for something to eat."

"Eat? Now that's a good idea! I think I will eat you!" roared the lion.

"Oh, please, please don't eat me!" (18) ________________________ the mouse. "I (19) ________________________ you that if you don't eat me, I will repay your kindness one day."

The lion began to laugh. He could not stop laughing. He thought the little mouse was so cute! How could a little old mouse repay a big, strong lion?

"Okay," said the lion, who wasn't very hungry. "I'll let you go, but don't ever come into my cave again! Do you (20) ________________________?"

"Yes, Sir," said the little mouse as he (21) ________________________ away quickly.

Several months later, as the mouse was looking for food in the forest, he heard a strange noise. It (22) ________________________ like a soft "roaaarrrr!"

The mouse walked slowly toward the noise. There, in front of him, was a BIG net, and in the net was a BIG lion with huge, golden eyes.

"Hello, Mr. Lion," said the little mouse. "Do you (23) ____________________ me?"

The lion (24) ____________________ for a few seconds. "Oh, yes. I remember you. You (25) ____________________ into my cave one night. Now go away and leave me alone!" He tried to roar but he couldn't. He was too tired and weak.

But the little mouse did not leave the lion alone. He did not go away. He came closer and closer, until he was standing in front of the lion's nose. Then he did something very strange. He jumped on the net and started to (26) ____________________ it. He continued all night long. In the morning, the tired old mouse looked at the lion, who was sleeping quietly in the trap.

"(27) ____________________ up, Mr. Lion," said the mouse. "You are free! You can go back to your cave now!"

"What?" roared the lion as he woke up. Then the lion (28) ____________________ the net. The mouse was right. The mouse had chewed a huge hole in the net and the lion was able to get out of the trap without any difficulty.

The happy lion (29) ____________________ the little mouse and (30) ____________________ his little brown friend with the very long tail a small kiss on the nose. "Thank you, my little friend," he roared. He then put the mouse down and walked away.

Activity 2, Part 6
Answer the following questions about the fable that you have just read.

1. What are the two morals or themes of this fable?

   a) ______________________________

   b) ______________________________

2. Which two adjectives would you use to describe the lion and the mouse? Why?

   Lion: ____________: ______________________________

   ____

   Lion: ____________: ______________________________

   ____

   Mouse: ____________: ______________________________

   ____

   Mouse: ____________: ______________________________

   ____

Activity 2, Part 7
There is an English proverb that says, "Don't judge a book by its cover." In a few sentences, explain why this proverb is one of the themes of *The Lion and the Mouse.*

____

____

____

____

____

Activity 2, Part 8
Number the following events in the order that they occur in *The Lion and the Mouse.*

_______ The mouse heard a soft and weak "roaaarrr!" when he was walking.

_______ The lion woke up, and he was very angry at the mouse.

_______ The lion escaped through the big hole in the net.

___1___ The mouse walked into the lion's cave because the mouse was very hungry.

_______ The lion kissed his little friend on the nose.

_______ The lion could not stop laughing when he heard that.

________ He saw the lion with the golden eyes in the net.

________ He thought he was walking on a carpet, but he was walking on the lion's nose.

________ The lion roared weakly, "Leave me alone."

________ The mouse begged the lion to let him go and promised to help the lion one day.

________ He was chewing all night long, while the tired and weak lion slept.

Activity 2, Part 9
Use the simple past, past progressive or the past participle to answer the following questions about La Fontaine's fable.

1. What was the lion doing when the mouse walked into the cave?

 ____.

2. What was the mouse looking for when he walked on the lion's nose?

 ____.

3. What did the mouse do when the lion wanted to eat him?

 ____.

4. What did the mouse hear as he was walking in the forest?

 ____.

5. What was the lion doing while the mouse was chewing the net?

 ____.

6. What did the mouse do with the trap before the lion woke up?

 ____.

7. What did the lion do when he saw a hole in the net?

 ____.

8. What did the lion do to the mouse after he walked out of the trap?

 ____.

9. How did the mouse feel at the end of the story?

 ____.

10. What did the proud lion learn?

 ____.

III - Text 24

The Sports Page

Activity 1, Part 1
Write the definition of the words and expressions that are new to you.

Vocabulary List

I. Sports Nouns

1. basket: ____________________
2. captain: ____________________
3. championship: ____________________
4. court: ____________________
5. defence: ____________________
6. dunk shot: ____________________
7. field: ____________________
8. goal: ____________________
9. goalie: ____________________
10. foul: ____________________
11. half-time: ____________________
12. hoop: ____________________
13. offense: ____________________
14. penalty kick: ____________________
15. point: ____________________
16. referee: ____________________
17. save: ____________________
18. semifinal: ____________________
19. shot: ____________________
20. soccer: ____________________
21. period: ____________________

II. Verbs

1. to block: ____________________
2. to design: ____________________
3. to dribble: ____________________
4. to form: ____________________
5. to graduate: ____________________
6. to lose: ____________________
7. to score: ____________________
8. to tie: ____________________

Irregular Verbs

1. win ➜ won ➜ won
2. lose ➜ lost ➜ lost

III. Nouns

1. bear: ____________________
2. comet: ____________________
3. dragon: ____________________
4. effort: ____________________
5. knight: ____________________
6. motto: ____________________
7. speed: ____________________
8. whistle: ____________________
9. wolf: ____________________

IV. Adjectives

1. amazing: ____________________
2. exceptional: ____________________
3. fair: ____________________
4. fearless: ____________________
5. proud: ____________________

Comparing Things

difficult ➜ more difficult than ➜ the most difficult

difficult ➜ less difficult than ➜ the least difficult

.... as difficult as....................

Activity 1, Part 2
Text 24: The Sports Page

Josef sat down to read the Sports Page of *News from the Bridges*. He was very interested in the ESDP sports news. He wanted to know everything! How was the basketball team this year? Were Les Étoiles filantes stronger than last year? And what about the swim team? Did they get the team swimsuits they designed? Did the girls form a hockey team this year? Who was their coach? And what about Les Comètes? Les Comètes was one of the best girls' soccer teams in Ontario. Were they going to win the championship again?

Josef turned to the fourth page of *News from the Bridges*. There were two photographs and two articles. The first picture was a photograph of a player jumping up to make a basket. The caption read "Omar's famous slam dunk!" The second picture was a photograph of a soccer field and a goalie catching the ball before it entered the goal. The caption read "Another save by Geneviève Granger." Josef started to read the articles immediately.

"Les Étoiles filantes Lose an Exciting Game" by Ricardo Mendez

Last Thursday, Les Étoiles filantes played against Les Dragons verts, one of the best basketball teams in Ontario. Les Dragons verts have won the basketball championship for the last three years. Their star player, Denis Carrière, hopes to play in the NBA when he graduates from university. But our players were fearless. Their motto is, "If at first you don't succeed, try, try again!" They played an amazing game and made Les Dragons verts work hard for every point they scored. The score was 30-24 at the end of the first half.

During the second half of the game, the score became closer. With just seconds to go, the score was tied, thanks to Omar's dunk shot. Then Denis Carrière, the guard of Les Dragons verts, caught the ball and started dribbling down the court. In seconds, he was under the hoop. As Jérôme Brunet ran to block him, the referee blew the whistle. He called a foul on Jérôme. Denis made two successful foul shots. The game ended with Les Étoiles filantes losing 56-58. Les Étoiles filantes were disappointed but proud. Omar, the captain of Les Étoiles filantes said, "I am very proud of every member of our team. We played an excellent game! We are getting better with every game. Next time, we will win!"

The referee said it was one of the best games of the season. He said, "It's always nice to referee a game where all the players play fairly."

Les Comètes won another soccer game last week when they played the semifinal game against Les Louves alertes in Hamilton, Ontario. Les Louves alertes is an excellent team with a very strong offence. Many students think that Les Louves alertes could win the championship this year. But Les Louves alertes were not prepared for the Comètes' exceptional speed, effort and teamwork! Our defence did an excellent job, making it difficult for Les Louves alertes to score. Geneviève, our goalie, played an excellent game and stopped many of their shots. She made many fine saves!

At half-time, the score was tied at 3-3 and no one knew who was going to win the semifinal. With 14 minutes to go, the goalie of Les Louves alertes fouled Annick Gendron. The referee gave Les Comètes a penalty kick and Les Comètes scored another goal. The score was now 4-3. In the last few exciting minutes of the game, Les Comètes scored another goal! Les Comètes won with a final score of 5-3. Now ESDP's Les Comètes are in the finals. Next week, they will play against Les Ourses polaires for the championship. Way to go, Comètes! ESDP is waiting for another championship trophy!

Josef finished the articles and smiled. A school newspaper was an excellent idea. He was happy that his friends planned to send him *News from the Bridges* once a month. When he looked at the photographs and read the articles, he felt like he was still a student at École secondaire Des Ponts. Maybe he could start a small newspaper in his new school.

Josef examined the next section of the newspaper. It was the Variety section. It had games and quizzes. They looked interesting and fun, especially the quiz called "Which of These Animals Are You Today?" He planned to do the games and quizzes on the weekend when he had more time.

Activity 1, Part 3
How often did the sports teams at ESDP win, lose, or tie?

Here are the results of last year's ESDP's Sports Tournaments.

	Wins	Ties	Losses
Boys' basketball: Les Étoiles filantes	5	1	7
Girls' soccer: Les Comètes	4	0	4
Boys' volleyball: Les Intrépides	5	2	1
Girls' badminton: Les Tigres	4	0	4
Girls' swimming: Les Flamants roses	6	2	0

always	usually	often	sometimes	seldom	rarely	never

Use the adverbs to describe each team's winning record.

1. In last year's tournaments, Les Étoiles filantes ____________________ won.
2. In last year's tournaments, Les Étoiles filantes ____________________ lost.
3. In last year's tournaments, Les Étoiles filantes____________________ tied.
4. In last year's tournaments, Les Comètes ____________________ won.
5. In last year's tournaments, Les Comètes ____________________ lost.
6. In last year's tournaments, Les Comètes____________________ tied.
7. In last year's tournaments, Les Intrépides ____________________ won.
8. In last year's tournaments, Les Intrépides ____________________ lost.
9. In last year's tournaments, Les Intrépides____________________ tied.
10. In last year's tournaments, Les Tigres ____________________ won.
11. In last year's tournaments, Les Tigres ____________________ lost.
12. In last year's tournaments, Les Tigres____________________ tied.
13. In last year's tournaments, Les Flamants roses ____________________ won.
14. In last year's tournaments, Les Flamants roses ____________________ lost.
15. In last year's tournaments, Les Flamants roses____________________ tied.

Activity 1, Part 4

There are many regular and irregular verbs in the text of Activity 1, Part 2. Write the present, past, or past participle of the verbs listed below to solve the crossword puzzle.

DOWN:

1. Past tense of shoot: _ _ _ _
2. Past participle of end: _ _ _ _ _
3. Past participle of know: _ _ _ _ _
4. Present tense of dribbled: _ _ _ _ _ _ _
5. Past tense of hope: _ _ _ _ _
6. Past participle of become: _ _ _ _ _ _
7. Past tense of wait: _ _ _ _ _ _
8. Past participle of win: _ _ _
9. Past tense of play: _ _ _ _ _ _
10. Past participle of tie: _ _ _ _
11. Past tense of can: _ _ _ _ _
12. Past participle of say: _ _ _ _
13. Past tense of speak: _ _ _ _ _
14. Past participle of read: _ _ _ _
15. Past tense of catch: _ _ _ _ _ _ _

ACROSS:

1. Past tense of stop: _ _ _ _ _ _ _
6. Past tense of blow: _ _ _ _
9. Past participle of plan: _ _ _ _ _ _ _
12. Past participle of send: _ _ _ _
13. Past tense of score: _ _ _ _ _ _
16. Past participle of look: _ _ _ _ _ _
17. Past tense of get: _ _ _
18. Past tense of try: _ _ _ _ _
19. Past participle of do: _ _ _ _
20. Past tense of make: _ _ _ _
21. Past tense of go: _ _ _ _
22. Past participle of give: _ _ _ _ _
23. Past participle of have: _ _ _
24. Past tense of call: _ _ _ _ _ _
25. Present tense of blocked: _ _ _ _ _
26. Past participle of be: _ _ _ _

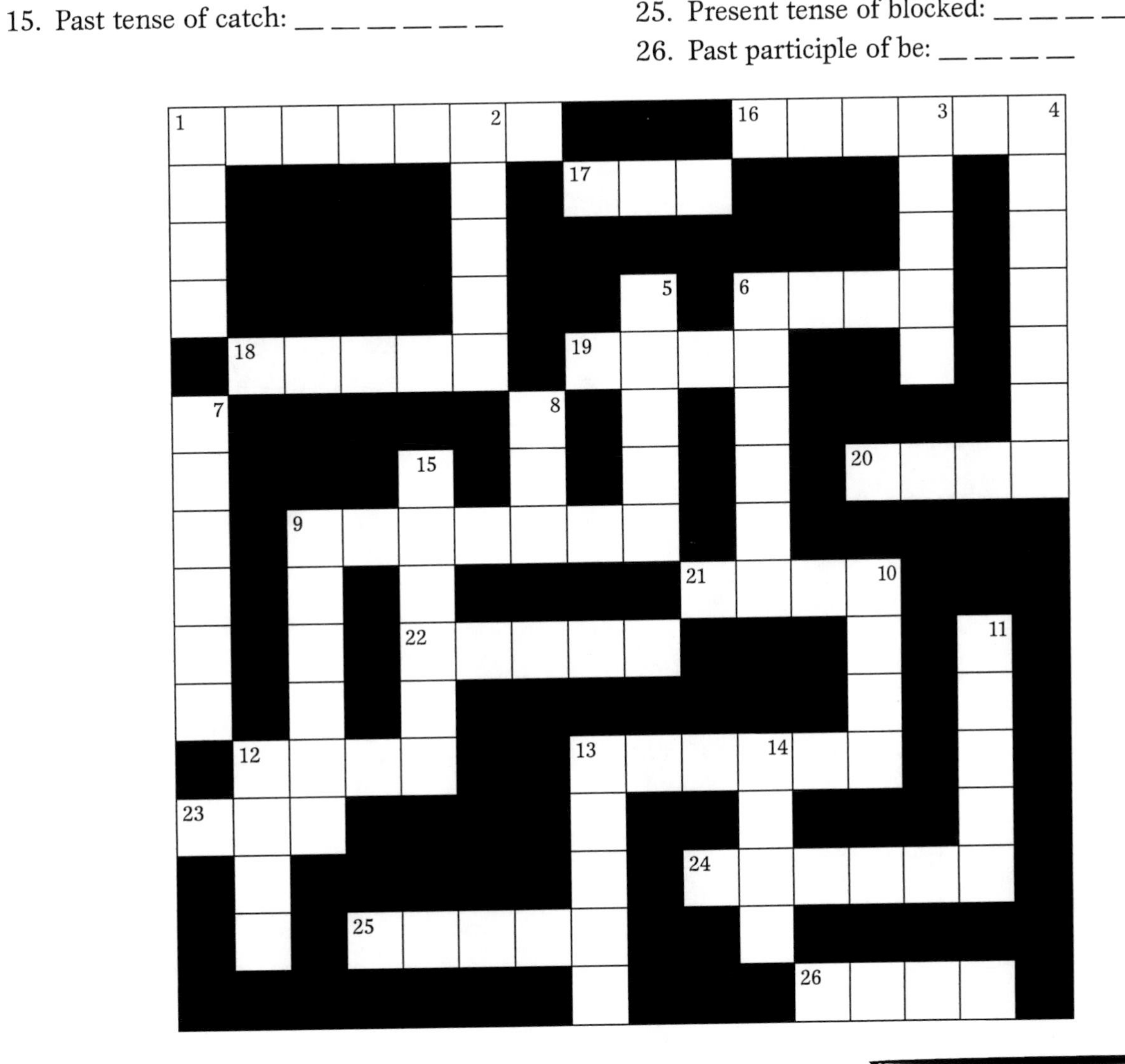

Activity 1, Part 5
Write a two-paragraph journal entry on your favourite sport.

Paragraph 1: Explain the reasons why you like to play or watch this sport.

Paragraph 2: Describe the sport. Include the following information:

- field? rink? court? etc.,
- number of players,
- scoring and rules of the game,
- special equipment needed, etc.

Paragraph 1 ______________________________

Paragraph 2 ______________________________

Activity 2, Part 1

Write complete sentences to compare the following sports and use the words "more than/less than", "the most/the least" and "as ________ as...". Mention every sport in the list.

Example: dangerous: surfing/speed skating/cycling/badminton/rowing

a. In my opinion, surfing is more dangerous than rowing.
b. In my opinion, badminton is less dangerous than speed skating.
c. In my opinion, surfing is the most dangerous of these sports.
d. In my opinion, badminton is the least dangerous of these sports.
e. In my opinion, rowing is as dangerous as cycling.

1. complicated: fencing/golf/football/baseball/snorkelling
   more...than: In my opinion, ____.
   less...than: In my opinion, ____.
   the most...: In my opinion, ____.
   the least...: In my opinion, ____.
   as...as...: In my opinion, ____.
2. exciting: basketball/ice hockey/boxing/water polo/field hockey
   more...than: In my opinion, ____.
   less...than: In my opinion, ____.
   the most...: In my opinion, ____.
   the least...: In my opinion, ____.
   as...as...: In my opinion, ____.
3. technical: judo/shooting/skiing/wrestling/bowling
   more...than: In my opinion, ____.
   less...than: In my opinion, ____.
   the most...: In my opinion, ____.
   the least...: In my opinion, ____.
   as...as...: In my opinion, ____.
4. difficult: archery/volleyball/soccer/weightlifting/swimming
   more...than: In my opinion, ____.
   less...than: In my opinion, ____.
   the most...: In my opinion, ____.
   the least...: In my opinion, ____.
   as...as...: In my opinion, ____.
5. beautiful: gymnastics/diving/figure skating/horseback riding/lacrosse
   more...than: In my opinion, ____.
   less...than: In my opinion, ____.
   the most...: In my opinion, ____.
   the least...: In my opinion, ____.
   as...as...: In my opinion, ____.

Activity 2, Part 2

Associate each sport listed on the right with the matching set of terms on the left. Use each sport only once. Use your dictionary when necessary.

Example: weightlifting: metal, strength

1. ______________________: diamond, mitt, "Home run!"	archery
2. ______________________: rifle, target, "Bull's eye!"	badminton
3. ______________________: oar, water, stroke	baseball
4. ______________________: net, fists, fingers, "Spike!"	basketball
5. ______________________: alley, pins, "Strike!"	bowling
6. ______________________: racket, ball, singles, doubles, "Love!"	boxing
7. ______________________: flippers, mask, coral reef	cycling
8. ______________________: épée, mask, "Touché!"	diving
9. ______________________: board, swimming pool, jackknife	horseback riding
10. ______________________: snow, mountains, slalom	fencing
11. ______________________: ice, triple axel jump	field hockey
12. ______________________: ice, skates, oval	figure skating
13. ______________________: tackle, helmet, "Touchdown!"	football
14. ______________________: mat, hold, submit	golf
15. ______________________: bicycle, gears, yellow jersey	gymnastics
16. ______________________: lengths, pool, backstroke, or butterfly	ice hockey
17. ______________________: hoops, dribble, "Slam Dunk!"	judo
18. ______________________: club, hole, par, "Fore!"	lacrosse
19. ______________________: field, ball, stick, "Bully-off!"	rowing
20. ______________________: board, ocean waves, "Hang Ten!"	shooting
21. ______________________: shuttlecock or birdie, racket, net	skiing
22. ______________________: swimming pool, goalie, net	snorkelling
23. ______________________: ring, gloves, "K.O." (Knockout)	soccer
24. ______________________: parallel bars, balance beam, uneven bars	speed skating
25. ______________________: horse, rider, jump	surfing
26. ______________________: field, kick, throw-in	swimming
27. ______________________: bows, arrows, target	tennis
28. ______________________: stick, puck, "Face off!"	volleyball
29. ______________________: Japan, self-defence, black belt	water polo
30. ______________________: North American Indian sport	wrestling

Activity 2, Part 3

a. Write the possessive form of each of the following nouns.

Example: boy ➜ boy's ➜ boys'

Nouns	Singular Possessive	Plural Possessive
1. teacher		
2. class		
3. woman		
4. team		
5. friend		
6. box		
7. mouse		
8. knight		
9. wolf		
10. parent		

b. Write the possessive form of the underlined word in each sentence. Where do you put the apostrophe?

1. I have three sisters. My __sisters__ eyes are brown. ________________
2. I have one sister. My __sisters__ eyes are brown. ________________
3. I have one friend. My __friends__ name is Eric. ________________
4. I have several friends. My __friends__ names are Eric, Sara, Ahmed and Marie. ________________
5. The __boys__ basketball team is called Les Étoiles filantes. ________________

Unit III - Text 25

The Variety Section

Activity 1, Part 1
Write the definition of the words and expressions that are new to you.

Vocabulary List

I. Animals and Insects	27. eagle: ______
1. alligator: ______	28. elephant: ______
2. ant: ______	29. flamingo: ______
3. bat: ______	30. fly: ______
4. bee: ______	31. fox: ______
5. bear: ______	32. frog: ______
6. beaver: ______	33. giraffe: ______
7. bird: ______	34. goat: ______
8. bug: ______	35. gorilla: ______
9. bull: ______	36. hamster: ______
10. butterfly: ______	37. hen: ______
11. calf: ______	38. hippopotamus: ______
12. camel: ______	39. horse: ______
13. canary: ______	40. hummingbird: ______
14. cat: ______	41. kangaroo: ______
15. chicken: ______	42. kitten: ______
16. cow: ______	43. koala: ______
17. coyote: ______	44. lamb: ______
18. crocodile: ______	45. lion: ______
19. crow: ______	46. llama: ______
20. deer/deer (plural): ______	47. ladybug: ______
21. dinosaur: ______	48. leopard: ______
22. dog: ______	49. lizard: ______
23. dolphin: ______	50. monkey: ______
24. donkey: ______	51. moose: ______
25. dove: ______	
26. duck: ______	

52. mosquito: ____________________

53. mouse/mice: ____________________

54. mule: ____________________

55. ostrich: ____________________

56. owl: ____________________

57. panda: ____________________

58. parrot: ____________________

59. pig: ____________________

60. pigeon: ____________________

61. piglet: ____________________

62. polar bear: ____________________

63. puppy: ____________________

64. rabbit: ____________________

65. raccoon: ____________________

66. rhinoceros: ____________________

67. rooster: ____________________

68. seal: ____________________

69. shark: ____________________

70. sheep/sheep (plural): ____________________

71. skunk: ____________________

72. snake: ____________________

73. sparrow: ____________________

74. spider: ____________________

75. squirrel: ____________________

76. swan: ____________________

77. tiger: ____________________

78. tortoise: ____________________

79. turkey: ____________________

80. turtle: ____________________

81. whale: ____________________

82. wolf: ____________________

83. worm: ____________________

84. zebra: ____________________

II. Adjectives

1. brave: ____________________
2. cute: ____________________
3. furry: ____________________
4. gentle: ____________________
5. hungry: ____________________
6. mature: ____________________
7. low: ____________________
8. lucky: ____________________
9. sly: ____________________
10. smart: ____________________
11. stubborn: ____________________
12. unique: ____________________
13. wide: ____________________
14. wild: ____________________
15. wise: ____________________

III. Nouns

1. back: ____________________
2. boxer: ____________________
3. cave: ____________________
4. cage: ____________________
5. chocolate bar: ____________________
6. cup: ____________________
7. desert: ____________________
8. farm: ____________________
9. field: ____________________
10. forest: ____________________
11. heart: ____________________
12. honey: ____________________
13. hump: ____________________
14. mammal: ____________________
15. mystery: ____________________

16. penny: ______	8. to fly: ______
17. pet: ______	9. to grunt: ______
18. stripe: ______	10. to hiss: ______
19. tablespoon: ______	11. to kick: ______
20. trunk: ______	12. to kill: ______
21. tusk: ______	13. to meow: ______
22. woods: ______	14. to moo: ______
23. world: ______	15. to neigh: ______
IV. Expressions	16. to notice: ______
1. go away: ______	17. to quack: ______
2. take advantage: ______	18. to remain: ______
V. Verbs	19. to roar: ______
1. to bark: ______	20. to smell: ______
2. to bite: ______	21. to squeak: ______
3. to bleat: ______	22. to stink: ______
4. to chatter: ______	23. to swing: ______
5. to chirp: ______	24. to unscramble: ______
6. to cluck: ______	25. to warn: ______
7. to crow: ______	26. to weigh: ______
	27. to wrestle: ______

Activity 1, Part 2

a. Animals and their babies: Associate each baby animal on the right with an adult on the left.

1. __A__ people	A. baby
2. _____ hen	B. calf
3. _____ dog	C. chick
4. _____ cow	D. kitten
5. _____ sheep	E. lamb
6. _____ cat	F. piglet
7. _____ pig	G. puppy

b. Animals make sounds. Write the correct verb from the list on the left next to each animal.

bark bleat **chatter** chirp cluck crow hiss meow moo neigh grunt quack roar squeak	1. Monkeys **chatter**. 2. Dogs ____________________. 3. Cows ____________________. 4. Sheep ____________________. 5. Horses ____________________. 6. Cats ____________________. 7. Ducks ____________________. 8. Mice ____________________. 9. Roosters ____________________. 10. Lions ____________________. 11. Snakes ____________________. 12. Pigs ____________________. 13. Birds ____________________. 14. Hens ____________________.

Activity 1, Part 3

Complete each sentence with the name of an animal. Use your dictionary if necessary.

1. The **eagle** is the national bird of the United States of America.
2. A ____________________ looks like a small alligator.
3. A ____________________ looks like zebra, but doesn't have stripes.
4. A ____________________ looks like a very, very big monkey.
5. A ____________________ and a ____________________ look like big grey dogs.
6. A ____________________ looks like a big deer with flat antlers.
7. A ____________________ looks like a duck with a very long neck.
8. A ____________________ looks like a very small grey bear.
9. A ____________________ looks like a very big black and white bear.
10. A ____________________ looks like a very, very big shark.
11. A ____________________ looks like a llama with a hump.
12. A ____________________ looks like a big alligator.
13. A ____________________ looks like an insect, but has eight legs.
14. A ____________________ and a ____________________ look like very, very big cats.
15. A ____________________ is the mother of a chicken.
16. A ____________________ is the father of a chicken.
17. A ____________________ is the mother of a calf.
18. A ____________________ is the father of a calf.
19. A ____________________ is a red insect. It has black spots.
20. A ____________________ is a very beautiful insect. It has big colourful wings.
21. A ____________________ is a bird with a very beautiful tail that opens like a semi-circle.
22. ____________________ and ____________________ have shells.

Activity 1, Part 4

What is its "usual" colour? Write the colour from the list on the left that best describes each of the following animals. Some colours are used more than once.

Example: A fox is usually red.

black
brown
green
grey
pink
red
white
yellow

1. A chicken is usually ____________________.
2. A crow is usually ____________________.
3. A dove is usually ____________________.
4. A flamingo is usually ____________________.
5. A frog is usually ____________________.
6. A camel is usually ____________________.
7. A seal is usually ____________________.
8. A polar bear is usually ____________________.
9. An elephant is usually ____________________.
10. A pig is usually ____________________.
11. A canary is usually ____________________.
12. A ladybug is usually ____________________ and ____________________.

Activity 1, Part 5
Text 25: Animal Trivia

On the weekend, Josef remembered the Variety section of *News from the Bridges*. He opened the newspaper to page five. At the top it said, "Please complete the following trivia tests and return this page to the Student Council Office. Do not forget to complete the form at the bottom of the page. The winner of the trivia contest will be announced in next month's issue." Josef looked at the bottom of the page. There was a small box where you had to write your first name, family name, grade and age. Josef looked at the page carefully. All the games, quizzes and trivia tests that month were about animals. He sat at his desk. He wanted to try to complete the page. He had a pencil and a dictionary within reach. He knew he needed both.

As Josef started to do the games, he realized that many of the animals listed in the variety section of the newspaper were not found in Canada. Many animals, such as elephant, giraffe, lion and hippopotamus were found only in warm countries. Others, like the penguin, lived only in very cold areas of the world. Josef wondered if he could see some of these animals at the zoo.

Once, when he went to Verner, Ontario, he saw horses and cows in farmers' fields. Some farmers even had sheep. He had not seen any beavers or bears because those animals lived in forests far away from cities. Those animals were wild animals.

During his trip, Josef had noticed road signs warning drivers to watch for deer. Skunks were also found in cities. Joseph had once seen a skunk in the park. It's too bad that such a cute animal smelled so terrible. It stank!

Josef thought of his cat, César. Animals were so much fun! Josef was lucky to have a pet that he could love and care for.

Activity 1, Part 6
Which of these animals are you today?

a. **Fill in each blank with the correct animal from the list below.**

b. **Circle the correct indefinite article (a) or (an).**

bee	dog	mouse	sheep
bird	duck	mule	turtle
bug	fox	mule	wolf
butterfly	kitten	owl	
cat	lamb	ox	
chicken	lion	peacock	

1. If you love parties and fun you are a "social ____________________."
2. If you are always nice and kind and never angry, you are as gentle as a/an ____________________.
3. If you are exhausted because you worked hard all day, then you are ____________________ tired.
4. If you do whatever people tell you to do without asking questions, then you follow others like ____________________.
5. If you are good at boxing, judo, or karate because you lower your head quickly (so that you are not hit), then you ____________________ very well.
6. If you like to bother people and you refuse to leave them alone even when they ask you to go away, then you like to ____________________ people.
7. If you are very hungry you say, "I'm as hungry as a/an ____________________."
8. If you take advantage of others because you are smart, then you are as sly as a/an ____________________.
9. If you are always working and you never rest, people say you are as busy as a/an ____________________.
10. If you are a boxer or a wrestler, then you are as strong as a/an ____________________.
11. If you always take too much time then you are as slow as a/an ____________________.
12. If you think carefully and make intelligent decisions, then you are as wise as a/an ____________________.
13. If you are very quiet and talk very rarely, then you are as quiet as a/an ____________________.
14. If you want to know everything about everything, then you are as curious as a/an ____________________.
15. If you never feel calm or relaxed, then you are as nervous as a/an ____________________.
16. If you can do what you want to do and go where you want to go, then you are as free as a/an ____________________.
17. If you are fearless, courageous and unafraid, then you are as brave as a/an ____________________.
18. If you love your clothes and how you look, then you are as proud as a/an ____________________.
19. If you never change your mind, then you are as stubborn as a/an ____________________.
20. If you change your mind about doing something dangerous and you lose courage, you are wise, but some immature students may call you a/an ____________________.

Today I am a ____________________ because ____________________.

Activity 1, Part 7

a. Did you know that...? Fill in each blank with the correct word from the list on the left. Some words may be used more than once.

bat camel elephant giraffe hippopotamus penguin pig polar bear swan	1. The ____________ has two stomachs. It can fill one stomach with water. 2. The ____________ is the only mammal that flies. 3. Human beings have unique fingerprints and ____________ have unique noseprints. 4. The ____________ is the only animal with four knees. 5. The ____________ is the only bird that can swim but cannot fly. 6. A 4-foot-tall child can stand inside the open mouth of a ____________. 7. The ____________ can kill a lion with one kick. 8. The ____________ has three eyelids. 9. The ____________ always turns left when it leaves its cave. 10. The ____________ is a bird that can live until it is 70 years old. 11. The ____________ is the only animal that can stand on its head.

b. Did you know that...? Select the word in parentheses that best completes each sentence.

1. It takes 12 bees their whole lives to make a (cup – tablespoon – kilogram – litre) ____________ of honey.
2. Mosquitoes prefer to bite you after you eat a (steak – chocolate bar – salad – banana) ____________.
3. A hummingbird weighs a little less than a/an (egg – penny – apple – CD) ____________.
4. Earthworms have (two – three – four – five) ____________ hearts.
5. Some dinosaurs were as small as (horses – goats – elephants – hens) ____________.

Activity 1, Part 8
Fun and Games with Animals!

a. Fill in each blank with the name of the correct mammal.
b. Find the name of each mammal in the puzzle and circle each letter.
c. Write the uncircled letters on the short lines.
Unscramble the letters. They spell a mystery mammal! Good luck!

1. The ___ ___ ___ ___ ___ ___ ___ ___ has a trunk and tusks.
2. The ___ ___ ___ ___ is a gentle, dark-coloured mammal that lives in the water and likes to play with a ball.
3. The ___ ___ ___ ___ ___ is a Chinese bear.
4. ___ ___ ___ ___ ___ ___ ___ have long ears and live in the woods or are domesticated.
5. The ___ ___ ___ ___ ___ ___ ___ is a pet that lives in a cage and looks like a mouse.
6. Some people sit/ride on the back of a ___ ___ ___ ___ ___.
7. The ___ ___ ___ ___ ___ ___ ___ is a gentle, light-coloured mammal that lives in the water and loves to jump.
8. The ___ ___ ___ ___ is a very big, furry, forest animal that sleeps in winter.
9. The ___ ___ ___ gives us milk on the farm and says, “Moo!”
10. The ___ ___ ___ ___ ___ is the biggest mammal in the world.
11. The ___ ___ ___ says “Meow” and loves milk and mice.
12. The ___ ___ ___ ___ ___ is a small Australian bear.
13. The___ ___ ___ ___ ___ ___ looks like a small gorilla. It likes to swing in trees.
14. The ___ ___ ___ ___ ___ has black and white stripes on its back and sends a bad smell when it is afraid.
15. ___ ___ ___ ___ ___ have wool and say, “Baa, baa!”
16. The ___ ___ ___ ___ ___ has a hump and lives in the desert.

P	E	E	H	S	T	A	C
E	Y	E	K	N	O	M	O
R	A	B	B	I	T	S	W
E	R	E	W	H	A	L	E
T	N	A	H	P	E	L	E
S	E	R	D	L	A	E	S
M	A	L	A	O	K	M	R
A	P	A	N	D	A	A	O
H	K	N	U	K	S	C	H

The remaining letters are ___ ___ ___ ___.

The mystery animal is a ___ ___ ___ ___!

III - Text 26

Horoscopes and People

Activity 1, Part 1
Write the definition of the words and expressions that are new to you.

Vocabulary List

I. Nouns

1. aim: ____________
2. ambition: ____________
3. battle: ____________
4. dream: ____________
5. ecology: ____________
6. education: ____________
7. equipment: ____________
8. fact: ____________
9. fate: ____________
10. future: ____________
11. honesty: ____________
12. justice: ____________
13. knowledge: ____________
14. leadership: ____________
15. media: ____________
16. mind: ____________
17. nature: ____________
18. ox/oxen: ____________
19. passion: ____________
20. patience: ____________
21. reporter: ____________
22. ski: ____________
23. strength: ____________
24. talent: ____________
25. tennis racket: ____________
26. thirst: ____________
27. thorn: ____________
28. treasure: ____________
29. truth: ____________
30. view: ____________
31. vision: ____________
32. wealth: ____________

II. Expressions

1. Go for it!: ____________
2. not for long: ____________
3. You've got nothing to lose!: ____________
4. to get to know: ____________

....

1. none: ____________
2. few: ____________
3. among: ____________

III. Adjectives

1. brilliant: ____________
2. critical: ____________
3. delicate: ____________
4. determined: ____________
5. inner: ____________
6. less: ____________
7. magical: ____________
8. modest: ____________
9. optimistic: ____________
10. plenty: ____________
11. sensitive: ____________
12. superstitious: ____________
13. true: ____________

IV. Verbs	
1. to appear: ______________	7. to invent: ______________
2. to dance: ______________	8. to pursue: ______________
3. to defend: ______________	9. to reach: ______________
4. to earn: ______________	10. to reform: ______________
5. to fight: ______________	11. to search: ______________
6. to improve: ______________	12. to sketch: ______________
	13. to spread: ______________

Activity 1, Part 2
Text 26: Horoscopes and People

Josef examined the last page of *News from the Bridges*. It had a monthly horoscope that was playful and fun. Josef was not surprised to see that Tina had written it. He was sure that all the students loved to read their horoscopes every month. The People page also had announcements about the school, students and staff. At the end of this section, there were some classified ads of students looking for part-time work or used equipment, like tennis rackets and skis, or computers and printers.

Josef began to read his horoscope. He enjoyed Tina's creativity and playfulness so much that he decided to read all the horoscopes to see if they were true about his family and friends.

"Tina's Horoscopes" by Tina Wong

The "Birds"
For you who are born on the first, second, or third,
When on a court or a field, you're free as a bird.
To excel in sports is your passion – this we all say.
It's not just your energy; it's the fair way you play.
This is the month when you can reach for success,
So work hard, play hard, and do not aim for less!

The "Cats"
For those of you born on six, five, or four,
You're as curious as cats, and you love to explore.
You love all knowledge; you want all to know.
Your book is your friend and far you will go.
To learn and to grow is your journey's end.
Searching for knowledge is your goal, my friend.

The "Owls"
For those who are born on seven, eight, or nine,
Your ambitions and dreams will help you do fine.
Wise as an owl, you think, plan, prepare;
You take your time and do things with care.
In the world of business, you'll study and learn.
With effort and hard work, much money you'll earn.

The "Peacocks"
For those who are born on twelve, eleven, or ten,
You will be famous among all women and men.
Intelligent and brilliant! None have your mind –
You're as proud as a peacock, immodest but kind.
A career in health care is the future for you.
You want to help others, and that's what you'll do.

The "Lambs"
If on the thirteenth, fourteenth, or fifteenth you were born,
Then you are a delicate rose without a thorn.
Gentle as a lamb, so sensitive, so true,
You touch every person who gets to know you.
Your passion for dance, for music, for colours,
Opens doors of beauty for many others.
Magical worlds with your talents you create;
And sharing these gifts is your pleasure and fate.

The "Bees"
If sixteen, seventeen, or eighteen is your day,
Then you're busy as a bee in the month of May.
Optimistic and cheerful, everywhere...
A smile, a kind word, we all know you care.
Working with people is the career for you –
Like counselling or advising, just to name two.

The "Lions"
Nineteen, twenty, or twenty-one?
Fight and your battles will soon be won.
You're as brave as a lion and as fearless too;
Once you are determined, your goals you pursue.
With courage and strength, for justice you will aim.
To change and improve is the name of your game.

The "Elephants"
Born on twenty-four, twenty-two, or twenty-three,
Stubborn as a mule is what you will always be.
Determined and hardworking with much inner strength,
Your dreams of a great country are part of your wealth.
With leadership, you'll build and create loyal teams
That will work together and make real all your dreams.

The "Mice"
If the twenty-fifth, twenty-sixth, or twenty-seventh is your star,
Goals in architecture, visual arts, or design will take you far.
Drawing a structure or sketching a house,
Alone you work best, as quiet as a mouse.
All your dreams chase! All your goals pursue!
With patience and vision, it's easy to do.

The "Tigers"
If your birthday is twenty-eight, twenty-nine, or thirty,
Then in life and in nature you will find friends plenty.
Nervous as a kitten about your plans you are not!
To save the planet is the idea you have got,
A career in ecology is what you will choose.
Go for it! You'll love it. You've nothing to lose!

The "Oxen"
And if you are born on the thirty-first,
For truth in the media you'll always thirst.
Strong as an ox, you defend all your views,
To write about facts and tell us the news.
Critical and serious you appear to a few,
But not for long...'til they get to know you!

Activity 1, Part 3

a. Fill in the blanks with the correct animal listed on the left. Reread *Tina's Horoscopes* if necessary.

	1. The __________ will be famous for helping people.
	2. The __________ are very creative and artistic.
	3. The __________ will become teachers or professors.
	4. The __________ will be very rich.
Birds	5. The __________ want to go to the Olympics.
Cats	6. The __________ love to create and share beauty.
	7. The __________ have excellent business minds.
Owls	8. The __________ are great athletes.
	9. The __________ know answers to many different kinds of questions.
Peacocks	10. The __________ make people feel better physically.
Lambs	11. The __________ love to play. Losing or winning doesn't matter.
	12. The __________ will become dancers, musicians, or painters.
	13. The __________ will be doctors, surgeons, or medical researchers.
	14. The __________ like to plan everything in life very carefully.
	15. The __________ spend a lot of time in bookstores and libraries.

b. Fill in the blanks with the correct animal listed on the left. Reread *Tina's Horoscopes* if necessary.

Bees Lions Elephants Mice Tigers Oxen	1. The ________________ are members of the Green Party. 2. The ________________ will be a good psychologists. 3. The ________________ will be excellent reporters. 4. The ________________ will be politicians, ministers, mayors, etc. 5. The ________________ will work against pollution. 6. The ________________ are very busy doing things. 7. The ________________ love everything in nature. 8. The ________________ make you feel good when you are feeling sad. 9. The ________________ pursue the truth. 10. The ________________ always take public transport and recycle. 11. The ________________ will become architects or engineers. 12. The ________________ will become judges or a lawyers. 13. The ________________ are great captains. 14. The ________________ fight for human rights. 15. The ________________ don't like to work on teams.

Activity 1, Part 4
Find a word that rhymes with each of the following pairs of words.
Example: fate – great → late

1. aim – claim: ____________________
2. dream – team: ____________________
3. leader – feeder: ____________________
4. mind – find: ____________________
5. ox – clocks: ____________________
6. passion – fashion: ____________________
7. thorn – born: ____________________
8. long – strong: ____________________
9. few – new: ____________________
10. inner – sinner: ____________________
11. less – mess: ____________________
12. dance – lance: ____________________
13. earn – burn: ____________________
14. fight – light: ____________________
15. reach – beach: ____________________
16. search – perch: ____________________
17. spread – Fred: ____________________
18. luck – truck: ____________________
19. wife – knife: ____________________
20. rhyme – time: ____________________

Activity 1, Part 5

Rewrite the following sentences in the plural. Use your dictionary if necessary.

Example: The child has a new friend. (3 changes; –1 [don't use one of the words]).
The children have [a] new friends.

1. The man and the woman went to the city to see the autumn leaf. (4)

 ____.

2. The wife takes care of her child. (4)

 ____.

3. The small child lost his tooth when he was 6 years old. (5)

 ____.

4. The life of a mouse is more difficult than the life of an ox. (5; –2)

 ____.

5. The box on the table is mine. (4)

 ____.

6. The dish with the sandwich is his. (4)

 ____.

Activity 2, Part 1

a. Which adjectives would you use to describe these people? Fill in the blanks with the correct adjective from the list on the left.

ambitious angry brave careful critical curious fashionable fearless friendly happy hungry patient playful sensitive strong thirsty	1. People who always complain that there is something wrong with everything are ______________________. 2. People who feel sad because someone said or did something that upset them are very ______________________. 3. People who talk to everyone are usually very ______________________. 4. People who are never in a hurry are very ______________________. 5. People who lift weights are usually very ______________________. 6. People who want to drink a lot of water or juice say they are feeling very ______________________. 7. People who want to eat a lot of food say they are feeling very ______________________. 8. People who always shout at other people are very ______________________. 9. People who try to make no mistakes are very ______________________. 10. People who spend all their time and money on clothes are usually very ______________________. 11. Small children always want to joke and have a good time. They are very ______________________. 12. People who always have questions about everything are very ______________________. 13. Optimistic people are usually ______________________; they rarely feel sad. 14. Courageous people are called ______________________ and ______________________. 15. People who want to become rich and famous before they are 30 years old are very ______________________.

b. Which adjectives would you use to describe these people? Fill in each blank with the correct adjective from the list on the left.

anxious artistic brilliant busy calm gentle honest interesting lonely messy modest polite popular quiet shy stubborn weak wealthy	1. Active people are usually very ________________ people. 2. Proud people are not very ________________. 3. Nervous people often feel ________________ about everything. 4. A very intelligent person is ________________. 5. People who never get nervous about anything are very ________________ people. 6. People who love to paint are ________________. 7. People who are very rich are ________________. 8. Adults always tell children who want to play with puppies and kittens to be very ________________. 9. People who don't have friends often feel ________________. 10. People who read different books and take trips to different parts of the world are usually very ________________ to talk to. 11. Neat people are rarely ________________. Their clothes, papers and desks are always organized. 12. People who always speak the truth are very ________________. 13. People who feel nervous when they meet new people are usually ________________. 14. People who don't like to talk are called ________________. 15. Old and sick people are not strong. They are ________________. 16. People who have many friends are ________________. 17. People who say "Please" and "Thank you" are very ________________. 18. If you don't listen to people and you never change your mind, then you are very ________________.

Activity 2, Part 2

Form the antonym of each of the words listed below by adding a prefix or changing the suffix. Make any necessary spelling changes as well.

Example: happy ➜ unhappy; resourceful ➜ resourceless

1. ambitious: ____________________
2. careful: ____________________
3. critical: ____________________
4. fashionable: ____________________
5. fearless: ____________________
6. friendly: ____________________
7. patient: ____________________
8. sensitive: ____________________
9. honest: ____________________
10. interesting: ____________________
11. polite: ____________________
12. popular: ____________________
13. determined: ____________________
14. true: ____________________

Activity 2, Part 3

a. People grow and change. Describe the person you were at the end of elementary school. Use at least 3 adjectives and give examples of how you behaved. (Use your dictionary if necessary.)

b. Describe the person you are today. Use at least 3 adjectives and give examples of how you behave today. (Use your dictionary if necessary.)

Read All About It!

Unit III - Text 27

Activity 1, Part 1
Write the definition of the words and expressions that are new to you.

Vocabulary List

I. Adjectives	12. loneliness: ______
1. ambitious: ______	13. perception: ______
2. honest: ______	14. pleasure: ______
3. just: ______	15. publisher: ______
4. natural: ______	16. reality: ______
	17. reassurance: ______
II. Adverb	18. receipt: ______
however: ______	19. stubbornness: ______
III. Verbs	
1. advertise: ______	**V. EI/IE Words**
2. reassure: ______	1. belief: ______
3. succeed: ______	2. brief: ______
	3. cashier: ______
IV. Nouns	4. chief: ______
1. anger: ______	5. deceive: ______
2. anxiety: ______	6. eight: ______
3. bravery: ______	7. friendly: ______
4. curiosity: ______	8. leisure: ______
5. deception: ______	9. neighbour: ______
6. excitement: ______	10. perceive: ______
7. fearlessness: ______	11. receive: ______
8. friendliness: ______	12. relief: ______
9. gentleness: ______	13. weigh: ______
10. hunger: ______	14. weird: ______
11. ink: ______	

Activity 1, Part 2

Change the following verbs to nouns by adding a suffix.
Make any necessary spelling changes. Use a dictionary if necessary.

Example: suggest ➔ suggestion; enter ➔ entry

Verb	Noun
1. excite	
2. reassure	
3. publish	
4. meet	
5. announce	
6. succeed	
7. receive	
8. believe	
9. deceive	
10. please	
11. advertise	
12. relieve	

Activity 1, Part 3

Review adjectives in Unit III – Text 27. Change the following adjectives to nouns by adding a suffix and making any necessary spelling changes. Use a dictionary if necessary.

Example: happy ➜ happiness; artistic ➜ artist

Adjective	Noun
1. honest	
2. natural	
3. strong	
4. patient	
5. just	
6. modest	
7. true	
8. real	
9. ambitious	
10. angry	
11. brave	
12. curious	
13. fearless	
14. friendly	
15. hungry	
16. anxious	
17. busy	
18. gentle	
19. lonely	
20. stubborn	

Activity 1, Part 4

Spell the following words correctly by writing EI or IE.

Example: rec __ __ ve → receive

1. bel __ __ ve: ____________________
2. perc __ __ ve: ____________________
3. rel __ __ f: ____________________
4. l __ __ sure: ____________________
5. n __ __ gh: ____________________
6. dec __ __ ve: ____________________
7. rec __ __ pt: ____________________
8. ch __ __ f: ____________________
9. n __ __ ghbourhood: ____________________
10. w __ __ rd: ____________________
11. br __ __ f: ____________________
12. __ __ ght: ____________________
13. fr __ __ nd: ____________________
14. w __ __ ght: ____________________

Activity 1, Part 5

Fill in each blank with the correct word from the list on the left.

believe brief cashier deceived eight leisure neighbourhood receipt receive relief	1. At the store, the salesclerk forgot to give me a ____________________. 2. I spoke to the manager of the store, but she didn't ____________________ me. 3. According to the ____________________, she charged me the correct price. 4. I disagreed. I told her that I did not ____________________ the correct change. 5. Our conversation was ____________________, but very tense. 6. I think she forgot to give me back ____________________ dollars. 7. What a ____________________ when I finally stepped outside for some fresh air! 8. Next time, I will shop at a small store in my own ____________________. 9. My favourite ____________________ activity is certainly not shopping. 10. I hate being tricked or ____________________ by someone.

Activity 1, Part 6

Punctuate the following sentences correctly. Make sure that the end punctuation is also correct. Check apostrophes carefully.

1. Where did Jean leave Maries car keys

   ____

2. Next Monday Ill bring an apple a salad and some cheese for lunch

   ____

3. Today I think Ill have a bagel with some cream cheese

   ____

4. Dont eat junk food because its bad for your health

   ____

5. Do you like cauliflower and broccoli

   ____

6. I followed my mothers grocery list but I couldnt read her writing

   ____

7. I really hate waiting in line at the cash

   ____

8. Youll find the shopping carts in the parking lot

   ____

9. The store manager is Mr Boileau

   ____

10. These three students work as cashiers Jean Marie and Paul

    ____

Activity 2, Part 1
Text 27: Read All About It!

Mr. Perreault has some announcements to make to the class. First, he says, "I am very proud of you. Our school newspaper is a real success! *News from the Bridges* is almost sold out once again. However, I have been receiving phone calls from parents."

When the students hear the last part of the announcement, they begin to worry. They do not understand the reason why so many parents are calling. Is something wrong?

Mr. Perreault reassures the students by saying, "Believe me, there is nothing wrong. *News from the Bridges* is so popular that parents want to read it too. What can we do? Do you have any suggestions?"

The students are pleased. They begin to chatter with excitement.

"Maybe we could post our newspaper on the school's website," suggests Omar.

"I've got an idea!" says Tina. "We could sell *News from the Bridges* for twenty-five cents at the next parent-teacher meeting."

"I like both ideas, especially the idea of selling the newspaper," says Mr. Perreault. "Publishing a newspaper is expensive. Paper and ink cost a lot of money."

Tina then suggests, "We will need an ad so that parents know that *News from the Bridges* is for sale. Let's create an ad!"

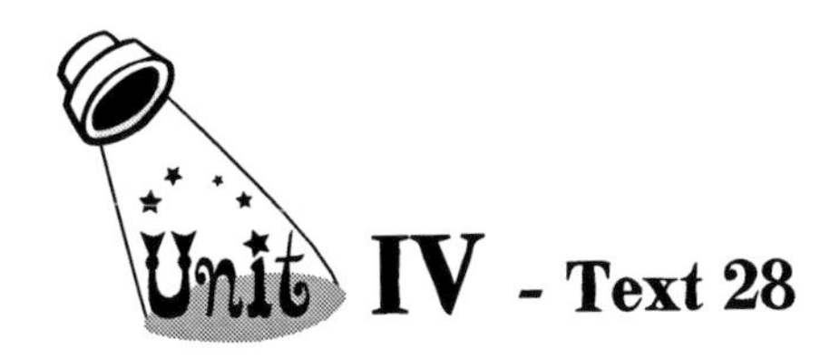

IV - Text 28

Chemical Secret
Chapter 1

Activity 1
Answer the following questions in complete sentences. Use correct punctuation and capitalization.

1. (a) The second paragraph of the introduction says that there are different kinds of "legal crimes". Give an example of each of the following:

   – crimes of greed: ____________________

   – crimes of violence: ____________________

   – crimes of anger: ____________________

   – crimes of hate: ____________________

   (b) What are the consequences of some of these legal but immoral crimes?

   ____

   ____

   ____

   ____

2. The less obvious crimes are crimes we commit against the sky, sea and land. Give three examples of each of the following:

   (a) crimes against the sky:

   ____

   ____

   ____

   (b) crimes against the sea:

   ____

   ____

   ____

   (c) crimes against the land:

   ____

   ____

   ____

3. (a) According to the author, what are the consequences of the “less obvious crimes” we commit against the sky, the sea and the land?

___

___

(b) Do you agree or disagree? Why?

___

___

___

4. The third paragraph of the introduction discusses John Duncan, the main character in the novel. What three things do you learn about him?

(a) ___

(b) ___

(c) ___

Activity 2, Part 1
Answer the following questions in complete sentences. Refer to Chapter 1 of the novel.

1. The first sentence of the chapter is: “Mr. Duncan? Come in, please. Mr. Wilson will see you now.”

(a) In your opinion, where is Mr. Duncan?

___

(b) In your opinion, who is speaking?

___

2. Describe Mr. Duncan.

___

___

3. Is Mr. Duncan rich or poor? Support your answer.

___

___

___

4. What do we learn about Mr. Wilson?

___

___

___

5. Who is Mary Carter? Describe her.

____

____

____

6. (a) Why does John Duncan think he will **not** get the job when he is being interviewed?

____

____

(b) What does this say about John Duncan?

____

7. What are the responsibilities (the job description) of the person this chemical company wants to hire?

____

____

____

8. Number the following sentences about John Duncan's life and career in the correct order.

_______: John Duncan met and married a sailor.

_______: John Duncan's business failed, and he lost all his money.

___1___: John Duncan studied biology and became a biologist.

_______: John Duncan changed professions and started a boating business.

_______: John Duncan was hired and returned to his original profession. He worked as a biologist again.

_______: John Duncan worked as a biologist and was a successful and rich man.

_______: John Duncan was unemployed for several years.

_______: John Duncan became a widower.

_______: John Duncan went for an interview at a paint factory.

9. How did John Duncan become a widower?

____

____

____

10. Mr. Wilson can hire younger and more experienced biologists, but when he speaks to John, he says, "You really need this job, don't you, Mr. Duncan?" and "You need it [this job] a lot" (page 4). Read between the lines. Why do you think Mr. Wilson hires John?

____

____

____

Activity 2, Part 2
Journal Entry 1

JOURNAL ENTRY 1

Examine the title of this chapter again and write two paragraphs. In the first paragraph, explain why the author chose that title and who or what he is thinking about when he says "new start". In the second paragraph, write your own chapter title and explain its meaning.

Activity 2, Part 3
As you read the novel, take notes on each chapter by completing the following Reading Log.

READING LOG	
Name: ______________________________	Date: ____________________
Chapter: ________________	

Something Important:	Something New:
Event 1: Event 2: Event 3:	Characters: Setting:
Something Interesting:	**Something Difficult to Understand:**
Comment/Quotation:	Question 1: Question 2: Question 3:

New Words and their Definitions
1. ____
2. ____
3. ____
4. ____
5. ____

Unit IV - Text 29

Chemical Secret
Chapter 2

Activity 1, Part 1
Answer the following questions in complete sentences. Refer to Chapter 2 of the novel.

1. What do you think this chapter will be about, based on the title?

____

____

____

2. Describe John's family.

____

____

____

3. Describe how the family lived **before** John and his wife started a boat-building business.

____

____

____

4. Describe how the family lives now.

____

____

____

5. Why does the author include the letter about the ski trip?

____

____

____

6. Why are factories usually near rivers or lakes?

____

____

Activity 1, Part 2
John Duncan

Write a paragraph about John Duncan. Describe how he looks. Use three adjectives to describe the kind of person and father he is. Refer to situations in the first two chapters to explain why you chose the three adjectives.

Activity 1, Part 3
Text 29

At Home

(Discussion of the school ski trip)

John: Hi, kids. How was school today?

Christine: Fine.

Andrew: Okay, I guess.

John: Did anything new or interesting happen today?

Andrew: No, not really. But Christine's class is planning an exciting school trip.

John: Really, Christine? Tell me about it.

Christine: It's not important, Dad. It's just another trip for the rich kids.

John: What do you mean?

Andrew: She says it's a trip for the rich kids because only rich kids have the money to go on the trip.

John: I want to know more about the trip. How long is the trip? When is it? And where is the class going?

Christine: Well, it's a ten-day trip to Switzerland. The class is going on the 15th of next month. I guess the students will go to museums and concerts to learn about the history and culture of the Swiss.

Andrew: Yes, but the fun part of the trip will be the skiing. Everyone will ski—even beginners. There will be ski teachers and coaches for all the students. When they come back, they will all be excellent skiers!

John: Would you like to go, Christine?

Christine: No, not really.

Andrew: That's not what she said to me. She said she would love to go! She's just saying she doesn't want to go on the trip because she knows it will cost a lot of money.

Activity 1, Part 4
Journal Entry 2

Journal Entry 2

"If you are not part of the solution, you are part of the problem." (Eldridge Cleaver, 1968)

Do you agree with this quotation? Explain your point of view with examples from your personal knowledge and experience.

___

___

___

___

___

___

___

___

___

___

___

___

___

___

___

___

___

___

___

___

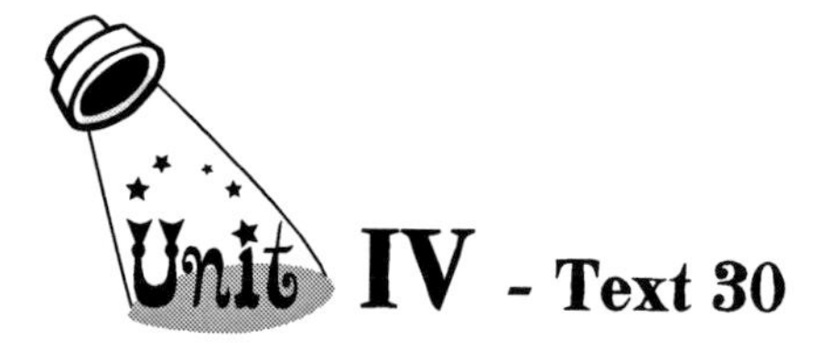

IV - Text 30

Chemical Secret
Chapter 3

Activity 1, Part 1
Answer the following questions in complete sentences. Refer to Chapter 3 of the novel.

1. What do you think this chapter will be about, based on the title?

____

____

____

2. "Neither acid nor salt water could damage it, and cars came back from both the Arctic and the Sahara looking like new" (page 10). What makes the new paint better than all the other paints? What does this quotation tell the reader about the financial future of this factory?

____

____

____

3. The company "had brought four hundred new jobs to the town" (page 10). What will happen to the town and its people if the factory closes?

____

____

____

4. Why does John see the doctor? Why is this incident important?

____

____

____

5. Where do the factory's chemical waste products go?

____

6. Explain the reason why John thinks that the water is safe.

____

____

____

____

7. Where does John buy a new house?

Activity 1, Part 2
Journal Entry 3

Journal Entry 3

People often **rationalize** what they **choose** to do. That means they try to find reasons or excuses for their choices when, deep in their hearts, they know their choices are wrong or selfish. Describe a situation in which a friend (or yourself) justified or rationalized an immoral choice. Do not use real names.

Unit IV - Text 31

Chemical Secret
Chapter 4

Activity 1, Part 1
Answer the following questions in complete sentences. Refer to Chapter 4 of the novel.

1. Why do the seals come to the mouth of the river?

____

2. How often do they come to the mouth of the river?

____

3. Give three examples of other animals that migrate to reproduce.

____

____

____

Activity 1, Part 2
Journal Entry 4

Journal Entry 4

One of the major conflicts in literature is "person versus nature." In most literature, nature is often seen as stronger and more dangerous than people (earthquakes, floods, storms, volcanoes, etc.), because it has the power to destroy people. But this novel is different. In this novel, people are stonger than nature because people have the power to destroy nature.

Authors often use various animals, birds, insects, fish, or things as symbols. In this novel, the author uses the seal as a symbol of the innocence, beauty, vulnerability and weakness of nature. If you were writing a book about pollution, what would you use as your symbol of the innocence, beauty and vulnerability of nature? Why?

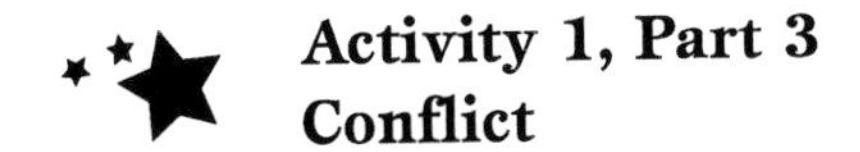

Activity 1, Part 3
Conflict

Find two examples of each of the following conflicts in the novel. Explain each example.

Type of Conflict	Example from the Novel	Explanation of Example
Person versus nature	1. ____________ ____________ 2. ____________ ____________	1. ____________ ____________ 2. ____________ ____________
Person versus person	1. ____________ ____________ 2. ____________ ____________	1. ____________ ____________ 2. ____________ ____________
Person versus self	1. ____________ ____________ 2. ____________ ____________	1. ____________ ____________ 2. ____________ ____________
Person versus society	1. ____________ ____________ 2. ____________ ____________	1. ____________ ____________ 2. ____________ ____________

Unit IV - Text 32

Chemical Secret
Chapter 5

Activity 1, Part 1
Answer the following questions in complete sentences. Refer to Chapter 5 of the novel.

1. "She [Mary] didn't like this kind of experiment, but she knew it was necessary" (page 18).

   (a) What does the author mean by "this kind of experiment"?

   ____

   ____

   (b) Why does the author say that this kind of experiment is "necessary"?

   ____

   ____

   ____

   (c) List three other kinds of testing on animals.

   ____

   ____

   ____

2. The mother rats that drank the contaminated water gave birth to babies with birth defects. "Mary looked away from the rats. She remembered the beautiful afternoon they had spent with John's children, sailing on the clear blue water" (page 19). Why does Mary remember that day after she looks at the baby rats?

   ____

   ____

   ____

3. Mary is upset and frightened. Why does she say the factory has to stop putting waste products in the sea? What is she afraid of?

   ____

   ____

4. Both Mary and John agree that the company must do something about the chemical waste that is being dumped into the sea, but their reactions are different. How is Mary's reaction to the situation different from John's?

   ____

   ____

   ____

Activity 1, Part 2
Journal Entry 5

Journal Entry 5

Write an entry explaining your views on animal testing. Include at least three reasons in your entry. Justify your opinions with examples based on your personal knowledge and experience.

Activity 1, Part 3
Write the definition of the words and expressions that are new to you.

Vocabulary List

I. Nouns	**III. Verbs**
1. cause: ____________	1. to appreciate: ____________
2. coal: ____________	2. to depend: ____________
3. fire: ____________	3. to face: ____________
4. gasoline: ____________	4. to lead: ____________
5. power plant: ____________	5. to nod: ____________
6. smog: ____________	6. to realize: ____________
7. smoke: ____________	7. to solve: ____________
II. Adjective	
depressing: ____________	

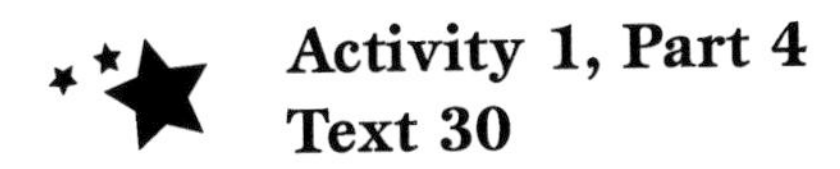

Activity 1, Part 4
Text 30

Let's Find a Solution

Narrator: *The students are in class. While they are discussing the novel, they begin talking about the environment and pollution. They all look serious.*

Mr. Perreault: What do you think, Toni? Do you agree that pollution is the biggest problem we face today?

Toni: Oh yes, Mr. Perreault, and sometimes I feel it is too late to do anything about it.

Keiko: Me too. There is too much pollution, and we won't be able to find all the solutions in the next few years.

Omar: I agree. I think it is impossible to find solutions to so many serious problems.

Mr. Perreault: Do the rest of you agree with Toni, Keiko and Omar?

Chantal: No, I disagree. I think we can solve the pollution problem if we work together, but first we have to make the problem smaller!

Mr. Perreault: How can we make the pollution problem smaller, Chantal?

Chantal: First, we have to divide the pollution problem into different parts.

Mr. Perreault: I think I understand what you mean. That's a good way to understand the causes of pollution and look for some solutions. What are the different types of pollution?

Chantal: There are three kinds of pollution: air, water and land pollution. I think we should discuss the causes and solutions for each kind of pollution separately.

Mr. Perreault: Class, would you like to discuss air pollution first?

Narrator: *The students nod.*

Mr. Perreault: Chantal, why don't you lead the discussion?

Chantal: Okay.

Narrator: *Chantal stands up and walks to the chalkboard. Mr. Perreault sits at Chantal's desk. Chantal writes "air pollution" on the chalkboard. She writes students' remarks as they speak.*

Chantal: Let's begin by discussing the different things that make our air dirty.

Toni: There are things in nature that make our air dirty.

Chantal: That's true! What are some examples of things in nature that dirty our air?

Toni: One example is smoke from volcanoes.

Omar: Another example is smoke from forest fires.

Ricardo: That's true, but it's people who are responsible for serious air pollution. It began 150 years ago with the first factories. The factories burned coal for energy.

Keiko: Many of our modern factories still use coal for energy. Factories pollute the air as much now as they did 150 years ago. Just look at the smoke coming out of some of our factories today!

Hamid: But there are many factories that don't use coal.

Tina: That's true, but they use electricity, and electricity makes our air dirty too.

Toni: How?

Tina: Power plants generate electricity, and to generate electricity, power plants often burn coal. Burning coal to produce electricity is one of the major causes of acid rain.

Keiko: That means that every time we use electricity, we are polluting our air.

Chantal: That's true. What else are we doing that is making our air dirty?

Ricardo: We are driving cars!

Omar: That's right! We can see and smell the air pollution when we drive.

Toni: Every year there are more and more cars on the road.

Ricardo: It's difficult to believe that cars were invented 100 years ago, and we still don't have a car that doesn't pollute the air.

Tina: This is terrible! Every time we use coal or gasoline or electricity, we are polluting the air. No wonder our air is so polluted and dirty!

Narrator: *Students agree that air pollution is everywhere and that it is a part of their everyday lives. On some mornings, they can even see the air pollution, in the form of smog. Sometimes, smog covers entire cities or towns.*

Tina: This is depressing. Now we know why there is air pollution, but that doesn't solve the problem. The problem is still the same. Too much pollution and too little time to find a solution!

Narrator: *The students sit quietly. They feel depressed and worried. They wait for someone to speak.*

Chantal: I think that air pollution is a serious problem, but that doesn't mean we can't find solutions. It really depends on our attitude and our choices. There are many people who are members of the Pollution Solution Team. They are called the PST. They remind us that the big environmental problems we face are the result of little things we do. They say we can all do many little things to solve our big pollution problems.

Narrator: *The students think about what Chantal said. They have heard about the Pollution Solution Team, but they don't know very much about it.*

Hamid: Can we spend some time discussing pollution and the Pollution Solution Team? I think I like their attitude.

Narrator: *The bell rings. The students and Mr. Perreault look at the clock. They are disappointed that the class is finished. Mr. Perreault realizes that the students are interested in learning more about pollution. He was planning to finish studying the novel with his students, but he decides that this is very important too. He decides that they can do the novel and their research on pollution at the same time.*

Mr. Perreault: We will continue our discussion next time. Don't forget to read the next chapter of the novel!

Students: Yes, Mr. Perreault. Bye!

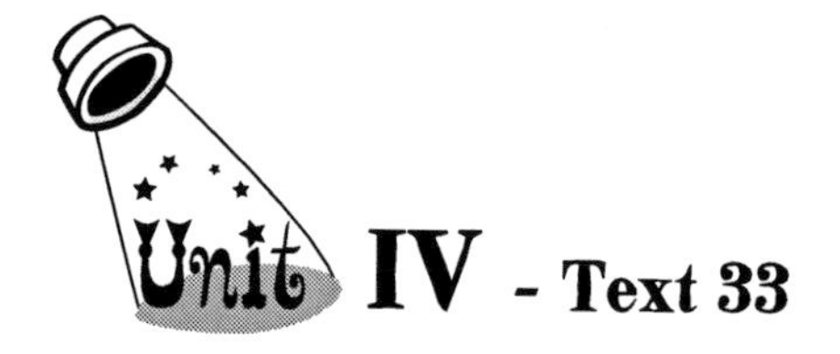

IV - Text 33

Chemical Secret
Chapter 6

Activity 1, Part 1
Answer the following questions in complete sentences. Refer to Chapter 6 of the novel.

1. What do you think this chapter will be about, based on the title?

___

___

___

2. (a) The author writes, "Mr. Wilson wasn't a scientist. He was a businessman. He knew how to run a business, how to make money" (page 21). How do you predict Mr. Wilson, a businessman, will react to the report about the dangerous consequences of waste products in the sea?

___

___

___

(b) How do you think Mr. Wilson would react to the report about the consequences of waste products in the sea if he were a scientist?

___

___

___

3. The author repeats the description of Mr. Wilson's office. He says it was "large, with a thick carpet and beautiful pictures on the walls." It also had large comfortable armchairs and a beautiful view of the river. Why is it important for the author to describe an expensive office at this point in the novel?

___

___

___

4. After Mr. Wilson finishes reading John's report, he says, "I don't like the ideas at the end of the report." What ideas do you think John had put at the end of the report?

___

___

___

5. Why doesn't Mr. Wilson like John's ideas and suggestions?

6. How does the author create irony in this part of the novel?

7. John argues that the machines that clean the waste are very expensive, but not too expensive. Imagine you are John Duncan. What three arguments would you use to convince Mr. Wilson that the machines should be built right away?

8. What three arguments does Mr. Wilson use to explain why the factory does not need to build the machines?

9. (a) When John Duncan says he will report the dangers of the chemical waste to the newspapers, the author describes Mr. Wilson's eyes. "His eyes were cold and grey, like stones from the beach" (page 25). What literary device is the author using to describe Mr. Wilson's eyes?

   (b) What ideas and thoughts come to your mind when you read this description?

10. Mr. Wilson first threatens John. He then offers John a bribe.

    (a) How does Mr. Wilson threaten John?

    (b) How does he bribe John?

Journal Entry 6

Mr. Wilson is upset by John's report. What is written in John's report? Pretend you are John and write a business report according to the following template.

____
Title

____
Date

____
Prepared by

Introduction: ____________________
Topic and Summary of Report
____
____

I. Findings:
  A. ____________________
  ____
  B. ____________________
  ____
  C. ____________________
  ____

II. Recommendations:
  A. ____________________
  ____
  B. ____________________
  ____
  C. ____________________
  ____

Conclusion: ____________________
Main Point of Report
____
____

Activity 2, Part 1
Write the definition of the words and expressions that are new to you.

Vocabulary List

I. Nouns

1. article: ____________
2. carbon dioxide: ____________
3. current: ____________
4. drought: ____________
5. effect: ____________
6. fertilizer: ____________
7. flood: ____________
8. fossil fuel: ____________
9. a. garbage dump: ____________
   b. landfill site: ____________
10. glass: ____________
11. greenhouse: ____________
12. heat wave: ____________
13. light rays: ____________
14. roof: ____________
15. soil: ____________
16. tray: ____________

II. Verbs

1. to bribe: ____________
2. to increase: ____________
3. to mix: ____________
4. to predict: ____________
5. to produce: ____________
6. to raise: ____________
7. to rot: ____________

III. Other Words and Expressions

1. a little bit: ____________
2. high: ____________
3. through: ____________

Activity 2, Part 2
Text 33

Air Pollution

Narrator: *The students are in class. They are discussing the environment and air pollution again. They all look serious.*

Omar: I am very confused about something I hear all the time. Everyone talks about the "greenhouse effect". All the newspapers write articles about it. But I still don't know what it is or where it comes from. What is the greenhouse effect?

Mr. Perreault: That's an excellent question. Can anyone answer Omar's question?

Narrator: *The students sit quietly. They are like Omar. All of them have heard people talk about the greenhouse effect; all of them have seen articles about the greenhouse effect, but none of them really know what it is or where it comes from. No one speaks.*

Mr. Perreault: Maybe we should examine the word "greenhouse". What is a greenhouse?

Chantal: It is a room made of glass where plants grow even when the weather is cold outside.

Mr. Perreault: Excellent! I will write some sentences about greenhouses, and I want you to put them in the correct order.

Narrator: *Mr. Perreault writes the following sentences on the chalkboard. Student read them carefully and number them in the correct order.*

_______: *The trapped heat waves make the greenhouse warmer and warmer.*

_______: *The light rays of the sun turn into heat rays.*

_______: *Many heat rays are trapped in the greenhouse because they cannot easily pass through the glass walls and roof.*

_______: *The sun's light rays pass through the glass walls and roof of the greenhouse.*

The students discuss their answers as Mr. Perreault writes the sentences in the correct order on the chalkboard.

First, the sun's light rays pass through the glass walls and roof of the greenhouse.

Next, the sun's light rays turn into heat rays.

Not all the heat rays can pass through the glass walls and roof.

The trapped heat waves make the greenhouse warmer and warmer.

Mr. Perreault: Do you all understand how a greenhouse works?

Narrator: *The students nod.*

Mr. Perreault: Good. Now I want you to imagine that the planet earth is the "greenhouse" and the glass walls and roof are the atmosphere. Can anyone guess the reason why scientists use the words "greenhouse effect" when they discuss the weather?

Toni: It means that the weather on the planet is getting warmer and warmer every year.

Mr. Perreault: That's true, but this is something new. Why is the weather on the planet getting warmer and warmer every year? And how does dirty air make the temperature warmer?

Narrator: *The students sit and think quietly. Ricardo raises his hand.*

Ricardo: I think I know the answer to that. Every time we use oil or gasoline or wood or electricity for energy, we are putting carbon dioxide into the air.

Omar: Why is that bad? Carbon dioxide is a natural gas. It is found in nature. If it is produced in nature, then why is it bad or dangerous?

Chantal: That's a very good point. The problem is that the things we find naturally in nature can become dangerous if they become too abundant or if they are found where they are not supposed to be. For example, carbon dioxide becomes dangerous when there is too much of it in our air.

Tina: That's right. And when there is too much carbon dioxide in our air, it begins to prevent the heat from leaving the earth. That means our planet becomes warmer and warmer as we put more and more carbon dioxide in the air...just like a greenhouse!

Omar: Now I understand why many people call what's happening the "greenhouse effect" or "global warming."

Toni: Are there other gases besides carbon dioxide that cause the greenhouse effect?

Mr. Perreault: Yes, there are three other gases that cause the greenhouse effect: methane, nitrous acid and CFCs.

Narrator: *Mr. Perreault walks to the chalkboard and writes methane, nitrous acid and CFCs on the board.*

Omar: What's methane? Where does it come from?

Mr. Perreault: It's the gas found in garbage dumps. When plants, animals and garbage rot, they produce methane.

Tina: What about nitrous acid?

Mr. Perreault: When we burn coal or other fossil fuels, carbon dioxide and nitrous acid are released into the air. We also get nitrous acid when fertilizers mix with water.

Chantal: What's fertilizer?

Mr. Perreault: It's what farmers put in the soil to make plants grow bigger faster.

Ricardo: What's CFC? It sounds like a long, complicated word.

Mr. Perreault: "CFC" is the short way of saying chlorofluorocarbon. Nature does not make CFCs. People make CFCs. They are found in refrigerators, air conditioners and plastic foam products like plastic cups, plates and egg containers.

Tina: I think I know what you are talking about. In the supermarket, they sometimes put meat or chicken in plastic foam trays and then wrap them with plastic.

Toni: And they put drinks at fast food restaurants in plastic foam cups too!

Mr. Perreault: That's right.

Keiko: I have one question to ask about global warming. What's so bad about global warming? Imagine Canada getting a little warmer every winter!

Toni: All of us agree warmer winters in Canada sound great, but that is not the way global warming works. It causes major climate changes like storms and floods in one part of the world and droughts in other parts of the world.

Mr. Perreault: Can you predict other things that could happen to our planet if global warming continues?

Hamid: If some of the ice melts at the north and south poles, many cities near oceans and rivers will be flooded.

Keiko: And the temperature of the oceans and rivers will go up. The higher temperatures will affect ocean currents and the animals and plants that live in the water.

Tina: I am beginning to understand how the Pollution Solution Team thinks. Air pollution is a serious problem, that's true. But part of the problem is caused by the carbon dioxide, methane, nitrous acid and CFCs we put into the air. So the solution is simple. If everyone uses less fossil fuel, throws away less garbage and puts less CFC in the environment, we can make the situation better. That means each one of us can do many small things each day to make our planet cleaner. I think I am going to ask my parents to take the bus to work every day.

Narrator: *Mr. Perreault and the rest of the students smile. Tina is right. With just a little bit of effort, we can use less fossil fuel energy. That means we will pollute less, and the less we pollute, the faster we can clean up our planet.*

Activity 2, Part 3

Add the indicated suffix to the following words, doubling the consonant when necessary.

Example: warm + er ➔ **warmer**
spell + ing ➔ **spelling**

1. trap + ed: ____________________
2. happen + ing: ____________________
3. get + ing: ____________________
4. begin + ing: ____________________
5. put + ing: ____________________
6. natural + ly: ____________________
7. can + not: ____________________
8. careful + ly: ____________________
9. turn + ed: ____________________
10. danger + ous: ____________________
11. mean + ing: ____________________
12. dump + ed: ____________________
13. air condition + er: ____________________
14. clean + er: ____________________
15. big + er: ____________________

IV - Text 34

Chemical Secret
Chapter 7

Activity 1, Part 1
Answer the following questions in complete sentences. Refer to Chapter 7 of the novel.

1. What three conflicts are found in this chapter?

   (a) ______________________________

   (b) ______________________________

   (c) ______________________________

2. John and Mary agree that the factory needs cleaning machines for the chemical waste products, but they make different choices.

   (a) What does Mary choose to do and why?

   ____

   ____

   (b) What does John choose to do and why?

   ____

   ____

   (c) Who is right according to you—Mary or John? Why?

   ____

   ____

3. Why is it important for the reader to know that 18 months have passed since Mr. Wilson saw John's report?

   ____

   ____

   ____

4. According to John, the paint factory has helped the town grow and become a better place in which to live. Explain his reasons.

   ____

   ____

   ____

5. Who is Simon?

____

6. (a) In your opinion, what does Greenworld do?

____

____

____

(b) What is the name of the organization that we have that is similar to Greenworld?

____

7. (a) When they are celebrating their engagement, Simon announces that he has received a pay increase because he is going to write a weekly column about the environment. What is the headline of his first article?

____

____

(b) What do you think happened to the seals?

____

____

8. What do you predict will happen in the next few chapters of the novel? How do you think the novel will end?

____

____

____

____

____

____

____

____

Activity 1, Part 2
Write the present participle ("-ing" form) of the following verbs, making any necessary spelling changes.
Example: make ➔ making

1. ring: ____________________
2. walk: ____________________
3. argue: ____________________
4. disagree: ____________________
5. do: ____________________
6. ski: ____________________
7. need: ____________________
8. be: ____________________
9. damage: ____________________
10. cover: ____________________
11. say: ____________________
12. wear: ____________________
13. know: ____________________
14. stop: ____________________
15. put: ____________________
16. cause: ____________________
17. pass: ____________________
18. promise: ____________________
19. write: ____________________
20. discuss: ____________________

Activity 1, Part 3
Journal Entry 7

Journal Entry 7

Simon will be writing a weekly column about the environment. Imagine that you are Simon, and write his first article, focussing on the factory and the issue of chemical waste products. Remember to include the 5W's + H.

Activity 2, Part 1
Write the definition of the words that are new to you.

Vocabulary List

I. Nouns

1. crop: ____________________
2. disease: ____________________
3. filter: ____________________
4. gas: ____________________
5. skin: ____________________
6. smell: ____________________

II. Verbs

1. to agree: ____________________
2. to argue: ____________________
3. to disagree: ____________________
4. to dump: ____________________
5. to rise: ____________________
6. to raise: ____________________

III. IrregularVerbs

raise ➜ raised ➜ raised
rise ➜ rose ➜ risen

Activity 2, Part 2
Text 34

The Ozone Layer

Narrator: *The bell rings and Mr. Perreault walks into his classroom. His students are arguing. When they see Mr. Perreault, several students raise their hand at the same time. Mr. Perreault nods at Ricardo.*

Ricardo: Mr. Perreault, each one of us is saying something different about the ozone layer. Can we talk about it for just a few minutes today?

Mr. Perreault: Sure, but only for a few minutes. Let's list what we know about the ozone layer on the chalkboard.

Narrator: *Mr. Perreault writes the students' remarks as they speak.*

Mr. Perreault: Does anyone know what ozone is?

Hamid: Yes. Ozone is a gas. It doesn't have a colour, but it has a strong smell.

Chantal: The ozone layer is like a blanket that covers our globe's atmosphere the way a blanket covers a bed.

Mr. Perreault: What does this ozone layer do for us?

Keiko: It protects us from the sun's rays.

Omar: But we need the sun's rays. They are very good for the planet.

Keiko: That's true. Many of the sun's rays are very useful and good for us, but there are some that are not good. They are called "ultraviolet" rays.

Omar: Why are the sun's ultraviolet rays bad?

Keiko: They can be very dangerous. Ultraviolet rays can damage crops and plants. They can even damage ocean plants.

Toni: They can be dangerous for people too. That is why we put sunscreen on our skin to protect us from the sun's ultraviolet rays. Without this protection, we could get skin cancer.

Tina: That's also why we should wear good sunglasses on bright days. Ultraviolet rays can cause eye disease too.

Omar: So how does the ozone protect us?

Hamid: It works like a filter. It filters out about 99% of the ultraviolet rays.

Omar: Wow! Ninety-nine percent! Then why do people keep talking about the dangerous ozone layer?

Chantal: Well the ozone layer has holes now. It is like having holes in a blanket.

Toni: Where are the holes?

Ricardo: At the North and South Poles.

Keiko: Many scientists say the holes at the North and South Poles are not new and that their size changes all the time.

Toni: Yes, but many other scientists say that the holes were made by CFCs in the air.

Omar: Are the holes in the ozone layer at the North and South Poles a serious problem?

Hamid: Yes. Without the ozone filter, ultraviolet rays pass right through to the earth.

Keiko: And that's not all! The ozone layer is getting thinner everywhere!

Omar: Now I understand why everyone talks about the holes in the ozone layer. Are there things we can do to stop the ozone layer from getting thinner or getting more holes?

Chantal: Oh yes, the PST has a lot of easy and good ideas!

Narrator: *Mr. Perreault looks at the clock. The students know what he is thinking.*

Tina: Can we discuss some of the things we can do to protect our ozone layer next week?

Mr. Perreault: Yes, I promise we'll discuss pollution and how we can help solve the problem each time we come to class.

Activity 2, Part 3
Use the apostrophe to write the possessive form of the following nouns.

Example: The classroom of Mr. Perreault
Mr. Perreault's classroom

1. The answers of the students: ______________________
2. The rays of the sun: ______________________
3. The ozone layer of our planet: ______________________
4. The causes of air pollution: ______________________
5. The atmosphere of our planet: ______________________
6. The warnings of scientists: ______________________
7. The clock of the classroom: ______________________
8. The holes of the North and South poles: ______________________
9. The protection of the skin: ______________________
10. The blanket of the earth: ______________________
11. The covers of a bed: ______________________
12. The danger of ultraviolet rays: ______________________

Activity 2, Part 4
Review contractions. Use the apostrophe to write the contracted form of the following verbs.
Example: I am ➔ I'm

1. I am ______________________
2. You are: ______________________
3. She is: ______________________
4. We are: ______________________
5. They are: ______________________
6. I have: ______________________
7. He has: ______________________
8. He is not: ______________________
9. He does not: ______________________
10. They do not: ______________________
11. They cannot: ______________________
12. They will: ______________________
13. You will not: ______________________
14. Let us: ______________________
15. I could not: ______________________
16. She would: ______________________
17. He will: ______________________

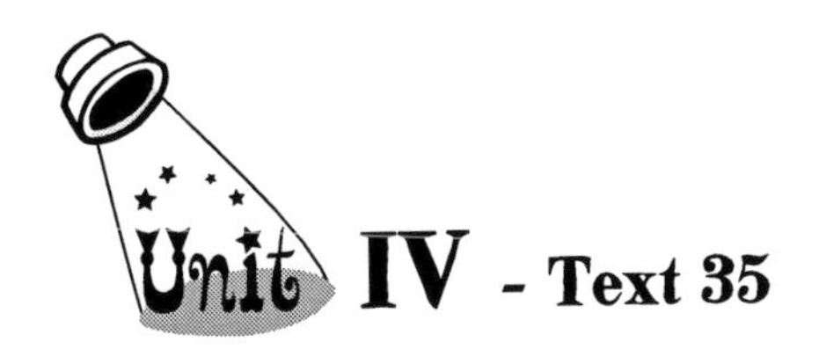

Unit IV - Text 35

Chemical Secret
Chapter 8

Activity 1, Part 1
Complete the plot diagram of the novel by writing the main events in chronological order. Add to the plot diagram as you continue reading the novel.

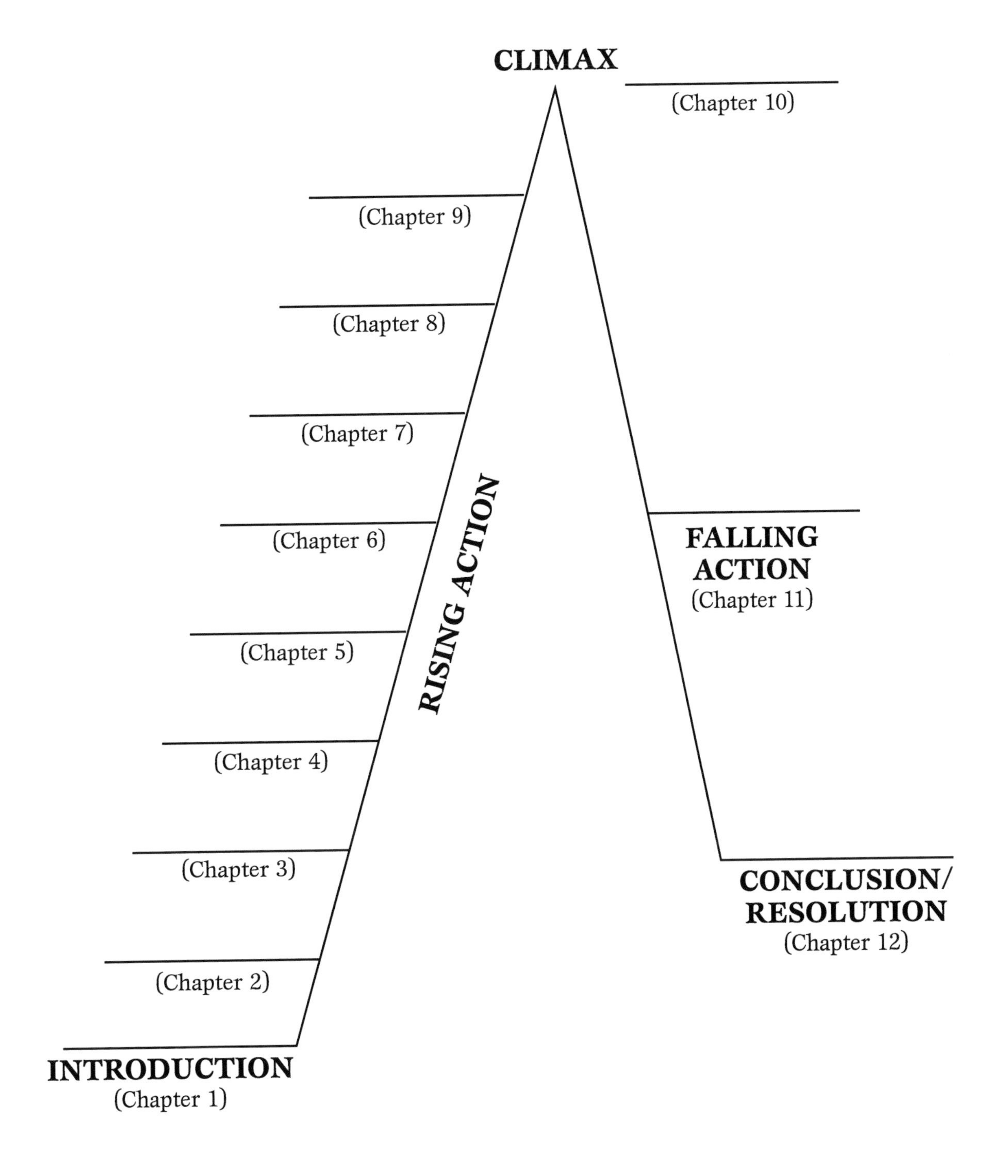

Activity 1, Part 2

Answer the following questions in complete sentences. Refer to Chapter 8 of the novel.

1. What are three moments of suspense in this chapter?

____

____

____

2. Do you think this novel is realistic? Could this novel be based on true events? Why?

____

____

____

____

3. Mr. Wilson asked two young scientists to test the water near the sewage plant upstream. Why?

____

____

4. John remembers his past situation and examines his present situation during his daughter's wedding "garden party." What does he realize?

____

____

____

5. Simon's mother tells John that he should be very pleased that Simon is working hard to find the reason for the seals' disease and is trying to clean the river. Why is this ironic?

____

____

6. Which of the characters in the novel (John Duncan, Mary, Mr. Wilson, Simon, or Christine) do you identify/sympathize with the most? Why?

____

____

____

____

____

Activity 1, Part 3
Journal Entry 8

Journal Entry 8

Who is your favourite character – John, Mary, Mr. Wilson, Simon, or Christine?

Select one of the characters and write a paragraph on a typical day in the life of that character. Use your imagination, but include details from the novel.

Write from the point of view of your selected character by using the pronoun "I".

Activity 2, Part 1
Write the definition of the words and expressions that are new to you.

Vocabulary List

I. Nouns

1. algae (singular, *alga*): ____________
2. bacteria (singular, *bacterium*): ____________
3. balance: ____________
4. bowl: ____________
5. coal: ____________
6. crop: ____________
7. ecosystem: ____________
8. explosion: ____________
9. hull: ____________
10. poison: ____________
11. product: ____________
12. ship: ____________
13. stream: ____________
14. tanker: ____________
15. weed: ____________

II. Expressions

1. cheer them up: ____________
2. supposed to: ____________

III. Verbs

1. to connect: ____________
2. to discourage: ____________
3. to dump: ____________
4. to feed: ____________
5. to leak: ____________
6. to rotate: ____________
7. to spill: ____________
8. to treat: ____________

IV. Adjectives

1. accidental: ____________
2. alive: ____________
3. realistic: ____________
4. toxic: ____________

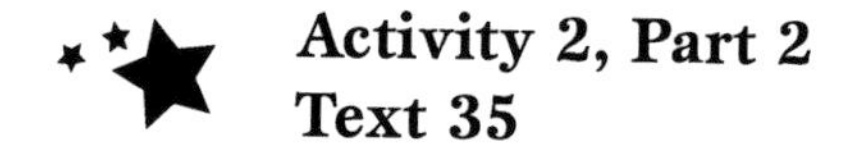
Activity 2, Part 2
Text 35

Water Pollution

Narrator: *The students are in class. They continue their discussion about pollution and the environment. They are going to discuss water pollution.*

Mr. Perreault: Students, we said we would discuss water pollution today. Are you ready?

Narrator: *The students nod.*

Mr. Perreault: Omar, why don't you lead the discussion?

Omar: Okay.

Narrator: *Omar stands up and walks to the chalkboard. Mr. Perreault sits at Omar's desk. Omar writes "Water Pollution" on the board. He writes students' remarks as they speak.*

Omar: Let's begin by discussing what we mean when we say the water is "clean" or "unpolluted."

Keiko: "Clean water" doesn't mean water that looks and smells clean. It means water that does not have toxic chemicals in it. We all know that some toxic chemicals have no smell and others have no colour.

Omar: Good. What else does "clean water" mean?

Chantal: "Clean water" means that the water has the right balance of bacteria. Polluted water often has too many bacteria in it.

Tina: "Clean water" also means water that has the right amount of oxygen. Polluted water often has too little oxygen in it.

Toni: Usually, the temperature of the water has to be cool. Unpolluted water has the right temperature.

Omar: Excellent! Clean water means the water does not have toxic chemicals. It also means that it has the right temperature and the right balance of bacteria and oxygen.

Narrator: *Omar walks to the chalkboard, draws four columns and writes "toxic chemicals", "bacteria", "oxygen" and "temperature".*

Omar: Now we can discuss the things we are doing that are polluting our water. Let's begin with toxic chemicals. When are we putting toxic chemicals in our water?

Hamid: Toxic pollution in the air pollutes our water.

Omar: How?

Hamid: Every time we burn coal to make electricity, we help create acid rain. This rain goes into our oceans and lakes, and rivers too.

Omar: Good. Give me another example of toxic chemicals in our water.

Keiko: Many factories are near water. They dump waste into the water after they are finished making products.

Tina: That's true. Sometimes water pollution is also accidental. For example, there are big ships called tankers. They carry oil in large "hulls." A hull is like a giant bowl. Sometimes the hulls leak or break open when they hit underwater land formations. That's when millions of litres of oil spill into the ocean.

Toni: And the water that they use to clean oil tankers is dumped into harbours, too!

Hamid: What about farming? Farming is a very big cause of water pollution.

Tina: Why?

Hamid: The population explosion. Every year there are more and more people on the planet and more and more people to feed. We don't have regular farms anymore. We have "factory farming."

Toni: How are factory farms different from regular farms?

Hamid: Regular farms rotate crops.

Ricardo: What does that mean?

Hamid: That means farmers plant a different crop each year to make sure that the soil stays healthy. In factory farming, they plant the same crops year after year after year, and each year, the soil becomes weaker and weaker.

Tina: How can soil become weaker?

Hamid: It becomes weaker when it loses its vitamins and minerals. And when the soil is weak, the plants are weak. This means that farmers have to use more and more fertilizers, and they often use chemical fertilizers.

Tina: Are there fertilizers that are not chemical?

Hamid: Oh, yes. Some farmers use only animal products and animal waste for fertilizers.

Toni: What about pesticides? They are poisons, aren't they?

Chantal: They are poisons that are supposed to kill insects and diseases and weeds.

Hamid: That's right. That's another problem with factory farming. Weaker plants need more fertilizer but they also need more pesticides to protect them. Pesticides kill helpful pests and insects, not just the ones that cause crop diseases.

Omar: Can you explain how farming on land can create pollution in the water?

Hamid: That's simple. Many of the pesticides and chemicals that are not used by the plants go into streams, lakes and rivers, especially when it rains.

Narrator: *Omar writes "acid rain", "factory waste", "oil spills", "chemical fertilizers" and "pesticides" in the column marked "toxic chemicals" on the chalkboard.*

Omar: And how are we destroying the water with bacteria?

Ricardo: Human and animal waste. It is very important to treat human waste before it is put into the water. Many people and towns don't treat human waste. They just dump it directly into the water.

Narrator: *Omar writes "human and animal waste" in the column marked "bacteria" on the chalkboard.*

Omar: How are we affecting the balance of oxygen in the water?

Hamid: It's the nitrates. They are affecting the balance of oxygen in our water. We find nitrates in animal and human wastes and fertilizers. Nitrates make algae grow very quickly.

Tina: What are algae?

Ricardo: Algae are very small plants that live in the water.

Hamid: Nitrates create a population explosion of algae. When algae die, they sink to the bottom of the lakes and oceans, and rot.

Tina: Doesn't rotting algae mean that there is more food for the fish?

Hamid: Yes, but not if too many algae die at the same time. If too many algae die at the same time, something terrible happens. When too many algae die and rot at the same time, then too much of the oxygen in the water is used. That means there is less oxygen for the plants and fish that live in the water.

Narrator: *Omar writes "animal and human waste" and "fertilizers" in the column marked "oxygen" on the chalkboard.*

Tina: Why does water have to be at the right temperature?

Ricardo: Because water temperature is an important part of the ecosystem.

Mr. Perreault: Can you tell us what an "ecosystem" is?

Ricardo: Sure. Ecosystems are very complicated. All life is connected in many small and delicate balances. This connection of everything which is alive is called the "ecosystem".

Mr. Perreault: Can you give us an example?

Ricardo: Of course. We can look at the ecosystem of a small lake. At the bottom of the lake, there are very small plants. Small fish eat the small plants. Big fish eat the bigger plants and small fish. Bigger fish eat the big plants and big fish, and so on. A healthy ecosystem means it is a good environment for everything that lives there—all the living things that live in the water. And all the living things can continue to live there in this ecosystem if nothing spoils the balance.

Tina: So why is the right temperature so important?

Ricardo: Without the right temperature, many of these living things in the water can die or grow too quickly. This damages the delicate balance of the ecosystem.

Tina: Wow! I didn't know that the ecosystem was so delicate!

Omar: How are we changing the temperature of the water in our rivers and lakes and oceans?

Tina: With our nuclear power plants and some of our industries. Many of our power plants and factories use water from lakes to cool their machines and equipment. That means they dump hot water into lakes. This raises the temperature of the water. The high temperatures make the algae grow faster and kill many of the fish that need oxygen and cool water to live.

Narrator: *The students look discouraged. The more they discuss the causes of pollution, the more hopeless they feel. The bell rings and they all leave their desks quietly and slowly. As they leave, Mr. Perreault tries to cheer them up. He reminds them that they cannot find solutions to a problem until they understand the causes.*

Activity 2, Part 3
Demonstrate your understanding of the text on water pollution. Fill in each blank with the correct word from the list on the left.

algae bacteria coal cool crops ecosystem electricity hulls nitrates oxygen pesticides tankers	1. Clean water has the right balance of ____________ and ____________. 2. The temperature of the water should be ____________, not warm. 3. Big ships that carry oil are called ____________. 4. Oil spills happen when the ____________ of ships leak or break. 5. When we burn ____________ to make ____________, we help create acid rain. 6. All farmers should rotate their ____________ every year. 7. Weak plants need more fertilizer and more ____________ to protect them. 8. ____________ are found in animal and human waste and fertilizers. 9. Nitrates cause a population explosion of small plants called ____________. 10. The delicate balance of nature is called the ____________.

Unit IV - Text 36

Chemical Secret
Chapter 9

Activity 1, Part 1
Subject-verb agreement: Collective nouns and pronouns can be difficult. Pronouns such as “everyone” and “everybody” are singular. Most collective nouns are also singular unless the focus is on the individual people or things.
Underline the correct verb in the following sentences so that the subject and verb agree.

1. Everyone (agrees, agree) that pollution is a serious problem.
2. No one (wants, want) to see the destruction of the earth’s animal and plant life.
3. The government (has, have) decided to help companies that try to reduce pollution.
4. A company polluting the environment often (pays, pay) fines.
5. Every person in Canada (cares, care) about the future.
6. Human and animal waste (is, are) polluting our soil and water.
7. The class (is, are) doing a project on pollution.
8. One of the students (knows, know) the financial cost of land pollution because she lives on a farm.
9. There (is, are) many things you can do to prevent pollution.
10. Why (does, do) people still use pesticides on their lawns?
11. Both Omar and Tina (draws, draw) very well.
12. The posters on pollution (gives, give) a clear message.

Activity 1, Part 2
Write the definition of the words and expressions that are new to you.

Vocabulary List

I. Nouns	II. Verbs
1. cattle: ____________	1. to absorb: ____________
2. dam: ____________	2. to cut down: ____________
3. grass: ____________	3. to destroy: ____________
4. jungle: ____________	4. to gather: ____________
5. mate: ____________	5. to hunt: ____________
6. rainforest: ____________	6. to prevent: ____________
7. root: ____________	**III. Adjectives**
8. a. ton (imperial): ____________	1. direct: ____________
b. tonne (SI)/metric tonne: ____________	2. extinct: ____________

Activity 1, Part 3
Text 36A

Land Pollution

Narrator: *The students are in class. They continue their discussion about the environment and pollution. They are going to discuss land pollution.*

Mr. Perreault: Class, we said we would discuss land pollution today. Are you ready?

Narrator: *The students nod.*

Mr. Perreault: Ricardo, why don't you lead the discussion?

Ricardo: Okay.

Narrator: *Ricardo stands up and walks to the chalkboard. Mr. Perreault sits at Ricardo's desk. Ricardo writes "land pollution" on the board. He writes the students' remarks as they speak.*

Ricardo: How are we destroying and polluting our land?

Omar: Every year we destroy millions and millions of trees.

Toni: Why? Do we need all that wood?

Chantal: We cut down the trees to make paper and paper products.

Toni: That's very true. Did you know that we have to cut down 20,000 trees just to print the Saturday newspaper of a large city?

Narrator: *The students cannot believe their ears. They knew that people cut down trees to make paper, but they didn't realize that millions of trees were being destroyed each day.*

Hamid: If the trees are cut and not replaced with new trees, good topsoil can blow away on windy days or wash away on rainy days.

Tina: Trees prevent floods because their roots absorb water. If the trees are cut, there are no roots that can absorb water. That means big storms can turn into floods.

Omar: Many trees are destroyed in forest fires too. Of course some forest fires begin naturally, but there are also many forest fires that are started accidentally by careless people.

Narrator: *Ricardo writes "destroy trees" under "land pollution" on the chalkboard.*

Ricardo: What else are we doing that is destroying and polluting our land?

Keiko: We waste the land we have. We don't use our land well. We use too much land to grow food for people who eat meat.

Chantal: That's right. For example, people are burning the jungles and rainforests in Brazil, Asia, Africa, or Australia to create areas where cattle can live.

Hamid: And more jungles and trees are burned each year to make more land for the cattle because the land of the jungle is not good for growing grass or crops. Grass can grow on it for only two or three years.

Toni: And do you know where most of the meat from this cattle goes? It goes to fast food restaurants or it is used to make hot dogs, TV dinners and pet food.

Tina: I think my grandmother is right. Maybe we should all become vegetarians. She says it takes 20 times more land to grow food for a meat eater than for a vegetarian.

Ricardo: Is land for cattle the only reason the rainforests are being destroyed every year?

Omar: No. Many people like to buy furniture made of wood like teak or mahogany. Teak and mahogany trees grow only in jungles and rainforests.

Keiko: A lot of forest land is destroyed by dams too. Some dams are used to help farmers, but many dams are built to produce electricity. Forests are flooded by these dams.

Chantal: These things we are doing don't only destroy trees and other plants. They destroy animals too. Animals need to hunt, gather food, find mates and raise families. When we destroy the forests and jungles where they live, their population grows smaller and smaller each year. Some animals even become extinct.

Hamid: Of course, the growing population of the planet adds to the problem. As more people need food, they resort to farming to feed their families. When there isn't enough farmland, they destroy the forests and jungles outside their towns and villages. Then after a year or two, they have to destroy more land because the jungle land is no longer good for farming! It is all very sad!

Omar: Cities and towns destroy land too. Every time we build a new road or a new mall or a new house or even a new farm, we are covering or destroying our land.

Narrator: *Ricardo writes "farmland", "cattle land", "wood", "dams" and "construction" under "destroy trees" on the chalkboard.*

Ricardo: Are there other things we are doing that destroy or pollute our land?

Chantal: We discussed the ways we are destroying land directly, but we are also destroying a lot of our land indirectly. We throw away tons of garbage every year. Where do we put these tons of garbage? We put them in dumps! Did you know that Ontario loses about one football field of "good" land every day for garbage dumps? Can you imagine how much good farmland we lose each year as we build more and more garbage dumps around the world?

Omar: Not only that! We sometimes put dangerous chemicals in our garbage and when garbage dumps leak, all the poisons and chemicals go into our soil and water.

Toni: When we talked about the greenhouse effect, we said garbage dumps create methane, which increases air pollution. Of course, the more garbage dumps we have, the more methane gas we produce.

Hamid: I am beginning to understand that our whole planet is an ecosystem of delicate balances between the air, water and land.

Keiko: This is very depressing. I can't wait until we begin to discuss solutions for all these problems we have created.

Text 36B

Land Pollution

Narrator: *The students are ready to continue their discussion. They feel more optimistic now because they realize there are many small things everyone can do to help clean the environment. The students are going to discuss the ways people destroy and pollute the land, as Mr. Perreault lists them on the chalkboard. Mr. Perrault draws four columns.*

In the first column, he writes "Trees", and under "Trees", he writes "paper and wood products", "fires" and "floods".

In the second column, he writes "Population explosion", and under "Population explosion", he writes "garbage", "human waste" and "creating new farmland".

In the third column, he writes "Wasting the land", and under "Wasting the land", he writes "cattle farming" and "factory farming".

In the fourth column, he writes "Destroying the land and animal habitats", and under "Destroying the land and animal habitats", he writes "burning rainforests", "new construction" and "dams".

Mr. Perreault: Which of these columns would you like to discuss first?

Hamid: I think it is impossible to discuss the causes and solutions of our pollution problems separately.

Mr. Perreault: What do you mean?

Hamid: Our whole planet is an ecosystem of delicate balances. Many things we do that destroy and pollute the air also destroy and pollute our land and water. Therefore, solutions we find for one problem may help solve other problems.

Mr. Perreault: Can you give us an example?

Hamid: Sure. Look at the first column. It is called "Trees." I have two solutions for this problem. First, if we recycle paper and paper products, we will cut down fewer trees. Second, it makes sense for us to plant a tree for every tree we destroy or cut down.

Mr. Perreault: I agree. You have two very logical and intelligent solutions, but you said solving one problem can solve other problems. Can you explain how?

Hamid: Yes. These two solutions will protect our trees. By protecting our trees and planting more trees, we also clean up our air because trees put oxygen into the air.

Omar: By protecting and planting trees, we reduce water pollution because the tree roots help reduce floods during storms. Reducing floods means that our soil will not be washed away.

Hamid: That's right. So planting trees to help the land can also help our air and water.

Narrator: *The students look at each other. This is great news! Solutions for one kind of pollution can also be solutions for other kinds of pollution.*

Keiko: If the world decides that trees must be protected, then countries will stop burning or cutting down rainforests.

Toni: And if we stop destroying rainforests, we protect the land. Fewer fires means less carbon dioxide in the air. Less carbon dioxide means less global warming; less global warming means fewer floods; fewer floods means less of our soil is destroyed.

Tina: So protecting our land by protecting our rainforests means the air will be cleaner because the rainforests put oxygen into the air.

Mr. Perreault: Your answers are excellent. I am very pleased that you see how all the different kinds of pollution are related and how the solutions for the different kinds of pollution are also related. What about the second column? What suggestions do you have for the "Population explosion"?

Ricardo: Well, I have two solutions for this problem. The first solution is better farming. Better farming means using the land so that it can feed more people. If people know that eating vegetarian meals once or twice a week can help protect our rainforests and can also feed the hungry people of the world, I think many people will be happy to make this change in their diets. With more vegetarian farms we could feed more people. If we feed more people, we do not need to destroy land to make more farmland.

Tina: What's your second suggestion?

Ricardo: I think there should be family clinics all over the world to help people plan the size of their families if they want to. My mother says that there are many people in the world who want family clinics, but there aren't enough of them. With fewer people on the planet, we would use less fossil fuel and less electricity.

Hamid: And with fewer people there would be less human waste and less garbage!

Chantal: I agree with your solutions. If you look at the chalkboard, you will see that your solutions for one problem are also solutions for the other problems. You have good solutions for the way we are wasting and destroying our land and animal habitats. If we protect our land from "bad" farming and focus on growing vegetarian crops, then we would have less factory farming and cattle farming. That would mean fewer chemical fertilizers and toxic pesticides.

Toni: And if we protect the land we have and focus on healthy and intelligent farming, we will not have to destroy rainforests to create new farmland. That means we will not be destroying the natural habitat of many of the beautiful animals on this planet.

Omar: What about the dams we build for our power plants? They destroy a lot of land.

Tina: Most of the dams produce electricity. We already said that we can use 25% less electricity if we use it intelligently.

Omar: What about new construction like houses, roads and malls? They cover a lot of land too.

Hamid: I agree, but I think we can pass laws to protect the land outside our towns and cities. For example, we can make it difficult and expensive for people to move to the suburbs. People who live in the suburbs usually have to travel by car. Often their homes are part of new developments. I think we should pass laws that say new homes or malls can be built only in towns or cities and that people who want to live in newer places can renovate their old homes.

Toni: I agree. We must remember that it's more important for people to live on a healthy planet than in large homes with huge lawns. This is why more and more people in the large cities are beginning to live in condos in the downtown areas.

Narrator: *Mr. Perreault checks the clock. The bell will ring soon. He looks at his students. They look much happier than they did a few days ago.*

Mr. Perreault: I think the world is going to be a better place if it has politicians, engineers and intelligent people and consumers like you!

Narrator: *The bell rings. The students leave the classroom together. They are still talking about the many big and small things they can do to make the planet healthier.*

Activity 2, Part 1
Answer the following questions in complete sentences. Refer to Chapter 9 of the novel.

1. Refer to the title of this chapter. In your opinion, who will say this? To whom? About what?

____

____

____

2. How much time has gone by since Christine and Simon's wedding?

____

____

____

3. What wonderful news does Christine share with her father?

4. How does this happy news make the reader feel? Why?

5. What did Simon write in his recent article about the environment?

6. Why is there going to be a town inquiry (also spelled "enquiry") the following week?

7. Christine and her father argue. When John says, "Can they [the people of the town] give their children photographs of baby seals to eat?" (page 40), what is he saying about the relationship between the factory and the people who live in the town?

Activity 2, Part 2
Journal Entry 9

Journal Entry 9

Write a Letter to the Editor supporting or condemning the paint factory. Justify your position with at least three reasons and with factual research from the skits read in class.

IV - Text 37

Chemical Secret
Chapter 10

Activity 1, Part 1
Answer the following questions in complete sentences. Refer to Chapter 10 of the novel.

1. Which two events earlier in the novel have prepared us for the crisis in this chapter?

2. Why do Christine, Simon, Peter and Susan need the boat today?

3. Why is it important that there be photographers taking pictures?

4. What did the strong wind do to the boat and the people in it?

5. "[Christine] fell into the water like a bag of potatoes." What does this simile tell the reader about Christine?

6. How does this chapter end?

Journal Entry 10

Imagine that you are John Duncan and you saw your pregnant daughter fall into the river. What would you write in your diary?

Activity 1, Part 3

Solve the crossword puzzle with words from the texts on pollution.

DOWN:

1. A cause of land pollution: _ _ _ _ _ _ _ _ _ _ _ _ _ _ _ _ _ .
2. Carbon _ _ _ _ _ _ _ _ _ .
3. A way to reduce land pollution is to _ _ _ _ _ _ _ _ _ _ .
4. The science that tries to protect nature and the ecosystem: _ _ _ _ _ _ _ _ _ _ .
5. _ _ _ _ _ _ _ _ warming.
6. Ultra _ _ _ _ _ _ _ _ rays.
7. The world around us is our _ _ _ _ _ _ _ _ _ _ _ _ _ _ .
8. A synonym for trash: _ _ _ _ _ _ _ _ _ _ .
9. _ _ _ _ _ _ pollution is killing our fish.
10. The _ _ _ can cause skin cancer.

ACROSS:

9. We need to reduce _ _ _ _ _ _ products.
11. To harm or dirty: _ _ _ _ _ _ _ _ _ _ .
12. A synonym of poisonous: _ _ _ _ _ _ _ .
13. The _ _ _ _ _ _ layer is getting thinner.
14. A cloud of pollution: _ _ _ _ _ .
15. What we breathe: _ _ _ .
16. Some factories dump _ _ _ _ _ _ _ _ _ _ _ _ _ _ _ products into rivers.
17. Acid _ _ _ _ _ .
18. Pesticides are one of the sources of _ _ _ _ _ _ _ _ _ _ _ in soil.

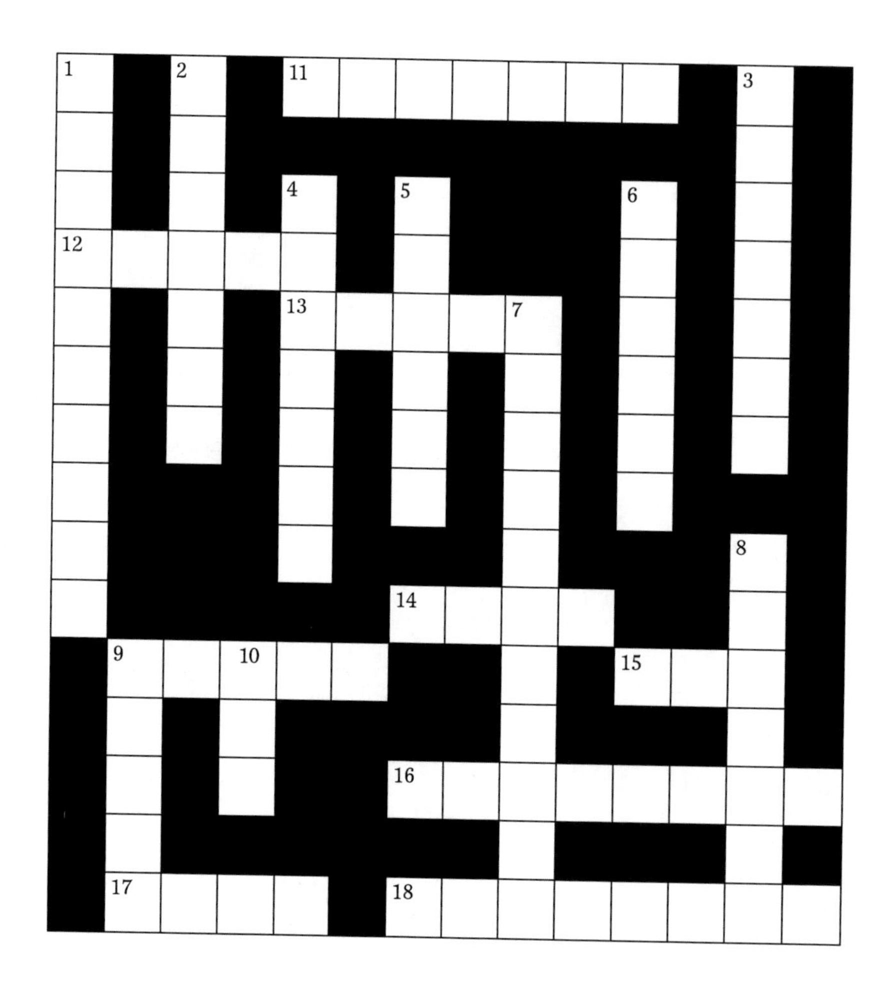

Activity 2, Part 1
Write the definition of the words and expressions that are new to you.

Vocabulary List

I. Nouns	**II. Verbs**
1. aerosol can: ______	1. to cost: ______
2. company: ______	2. to invest: ______
3. current: ______	3. to pass (laws): ______
4. fine: ______	4. to pump: ______
5. law: ______	5. to reduce: ______
6. lead: ______	6. to switch: ______
7. progress: ______	
8. scientist: ______	**III. Adjectives**
9. tide: ______	1. double: ______
10. wave: ______	2. strict: ______
11. windmill: ______	

Activity 2, Part 2
Text 37A

Solutions Big and Small: Our Air

Narrator: *The students are ready to discuss some of the solutions to many of the pollution problems they have discussed in class.*

Mr. Perreault: Today we are going to discuss the different solutions to our pollution problems. The first kind of pollution we discussed was air pollution. When we discussed air pollution, we talked about the greenhouse effect. What are your suggestions for reducing the greenhouse effect?

Keiko: We said the greenhouse effect was caused by the carbon dioxide we release into the air. This is because of the kinds of energy we use. We use a lot of fossil fuels, like oil or coal or natural gas or gasoline. We burn these fossil fuels in our factories and cars and homes, which releases carbon dioxide into the air.

Omar: Maybe we should switch to fuels that pollute less. For example, what is the fuel that people should use to heat their homes?

Chantal: Natural gas pollutes less than gasoline or oil or coal. People should switch to natural gas.

Hamid: Many people are switching to natural gas. And more and more people are beginning to understand that cars are responsible for a lot of our air pollution too. People are walking, cycling, or taking public transportation instead of driving their cars. Isn't that great?

Toni: The government is passing important laws too, to help us find solutions. For example, on January 1, 1990, the Canadian government passed a law that said gasoline had to be "lead free." As you know, lead is a toxic metal. Before that law was passed, all that lead in gasoline used to go into our air.

Tina: Yes, and more car companies are building cars that use less energy. They are called "hybrid" cars.

Toni: What are those?

Tina: They are cars that run on both electricity and gas. They switch to the motor that uses less energy, depending on how fast you are driving.

Hamid: All this is great, but we also use a lot of electricity, and electricity pollutes our environment.

Chantal: I agree, but we can use a lot less electricity if we learn not to waste it.

Keiko: How?

Toni: We can turn off what we are not using, like the TV or the light in a room.

Tina: That's right. And we can also buy things that use less electricity. Some refrigerators and washing machines and other electrical things have labels that say they use less energy.

Omar: How much electricity can we save if we are more careful with the way we use it?

Mr. Perreault: We can use about 25% less electricity if we use our electricity intelligently.

Toni: Wow! I knew we wasted electricity, but I did not think that we wasted 25%!

Ricardo: Maybe if electricity cost a lot more we would be more careful how we use it!

Chantal: Electricity or fossil fuels! It doesn't matter. Both of them pollute our environment because they are not "clean" energy.

Omar: What's "clean" energy?

Tina: Clean energy is energy which does not produce pollution.

Toni: Is there clean energy in the world?

Hamid: Oh yes. There are three kinds of "clean" energy that many countries use today. The first one is solar energy, the second one is wind energy, and the third one is water energy. Water can be very strong and we can use the currents, tides and waves as an energy source.

Omar: "Solar" means from the sun.

Hamid: That's right. Solar energy is the sun's energy. If you think about it, you will agree that the sun has a lot of energy. Look at the way the sun heats our planet every day!

Ricardo: There are many people in the world who use solar energy. They use solar energy to heat their houses and water.

Keiko: I think there are some people who drive cars that use only solar energy.

Toni: Can we buy things at the store that use solar energy?

Chantal: Yes, calculators. We can buy calculators that use solar energy.

Ricardo: Many countries, like Holland, use the wind as an energy source. Windmills are used to pump water. If you visit Holland, you can see hundreds of windmills turning in the wind.

Chantal: That's the real solution. We have to invest money in research to find ways of replacing electricity and fossil fuels with clean energy.

Mr. Perreault: Those are excellent suggestions for reducing the greenhouse effect, but we also discussed the serious changes that are happening to our ozone layer. Let's discuss what we can do to protect our ozone layer now.

Hamid: The ozone layer is damaged by many things in the air, especially CFCs. I did some research about CFCs and am happy to say that, in 1978, Canada banned CFCs in aerosol cans. Then, in 1987, 30 countries decided to stop producing CFCs in 1999. Now that's progress!

Narrator: *The bell rings. The students are feeling better already. They are beginning to understand that although pollution is a serious problem, there are many small things all of us can do until we replace our fossil fuels and electricity with clean energy sources.*

Text 37B

Solutions Big and Small: Our Water

Narrator: *The students are ready to continue their discussion on pollution solutions. Mr. Perreault lists the causes of water pollution on the chalkboard. First he draws a column and writes "Toxic chemicals". In that column he lists "acid rain", "factory wastes", "oil spills", "chemical fertilizers" and "pesticides". Then he draws a second, third and fourth column, and he writes "Bacteria", "Oxygen" and "Temperature".*

Mr. Perreault: We will first discuss some solutions for the toxic chemicals in our water. Let's begin with acid rain. What can we do to reduce acid rain?

Ricardo: We already know that burning coal to produce electricity is one of the major causes of acid rain. So the solution is simple. If we use 25% less electricity, we will reduce acid rain.

Chantal: Another thing we can do is use other fuels like natural gas to produce electricity. Natural gas pollutes less than other fossil fuels.

Mr. Perreault: Good! What about solutions for factory waste? What can we do to reduce that?

Tina: I think we should have very strict laws that fine people who put more factory waste into the water than they are supposed to, and they should close those factories that continue to pollute even after they are fined.

Omar: I think we have such laws already. Maybe we have to make them stricter.

Keiko: We must also learn to buy only what we need. We have to remember that energy is used to make everything we buy.

Hamid: Another thing we should do is encourage research. All factories that pollute the water should have research departments that look for solutions. That would help our water a lot!

Mr. Perreault: But what about oil spills? Remember when we discussed how hulls can leak or break. What suggestions do you have for reducing oil spills?

Toni: I think tankers should be allowed to carry oil only if they have double hulls. That's like having two bowls instead of one. This would make the leaks and breaks happen less often because the hull would be twice as strong.

Mr. Perreault: I agree with you, Toni. That's a very good suggestion.

Omar: Factory farming puts toxic chemicals in our water. Chemical fertilizers and pesticides should not be used. We should keep the soil healthy by making it illegal to plant the same crops every year. Also, there are many natural pesticides in the world. We should encourage farmers to use natural pesticides. That would help solve the problem of chemical pesticides and fertilizers in our water.

Mr. Perreault: What about bacteria in our water?

Ricardo: The solution to the bacteria problem in the water is also the solution to the oxygen problem we have in the water. We should have laws that fine people and companies that don't treat waste products before they put them in the water. We should also encourage research that will find ways to clean up waste products and maybe reuse them without dumping them in the water.

Chantal: I have a suggestion for solving the problem of warmer temperatures in our waters. We can pass a law that says that water used to cool machines in plants and factories cannot be put back until it has reached a normal temperature.

Mr. Perreault: Class, you have very good ideas, and most of your solutions are things we can begin to do right away. I think you are great engineers, scientists and problem solvers. I'm proud of all of you!

Activity 2, Part 3
Answer the following questions on pollution prevention. Reread the skits on air and water pollution, if necessary.

Text 37A

1. Which fuels cause the greenhouse effect?

   (a) ____________________

   (b) ____________________

   (c) ____________________

2. What are two ways to save electricity?

   (a) ____________________

   (b) ____________________

3. Give three examples of clean energy.

   (a) ____________________

   (b) ____________________

   (c) ____________________

Text 37B

4. What are two ways to reduce acid rain?

   (a) ____________________

   (b) ____________________

5. How can oil spills be prevented?

   ____

6. What two laws are needed to reduce water pollution?

   (a) ____________________

   (b) ____________________

Activity 2, Part 4
Rewrite the underlined verbs of the following passages in the past tense.

a. The students are [1] ready to continue their discussion on pollution solutions. They want [2] to continue their discussion as soon as possible. Mr. Perreault lists [3] the causes of water pollution on the chalkboard. First he draws [4] a column and writes [5] "toxic chemicals". In that column he lists acid rain, factory waste, oil spills, chemical fertilizers and pesticides. He then draws a second, third and fourth column and writes [6] "bacteria", "oxygen" and "temperature".

1. ______________________
2. ______________________
3. ______________________
4. ______________________
5. ______________________
6. ______________________

b. Mr. Perreault: I agree [7] with you, Toni. That's a very good suggestion.

Omar: Factory farming puts [8] toxic chemicals in our water.

7. ______________________
8. ______________________

c. Chantal: I have [9] a suggestion for solving the problem of warmer temperatures in our waters. We [10] can [11] pass a law that says [12] the water that cools machines in plants and factories cannot [13] be put back until it has [14] reached a normal temperature.

Mr. Perreault: Students, you have [15] very good ideas, and most of your solutions are [16] things we can begin to do right away. I think [17] you are [18] great engineers, scientists and solution finders: I'm [19] proud of all of you!

9. ______________________
10. ______________________
11. ______________________
12. ______________________
13. ______________________
14. ______________________
15. ______________________
16. ______________________
17. ______________________
18. ______________________
19. ______________________

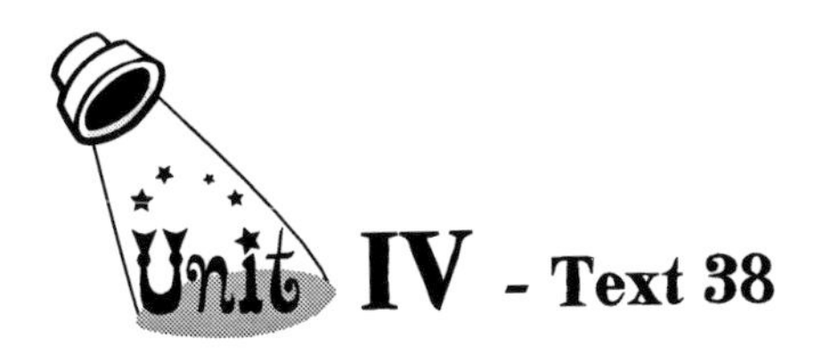

IV - Text 38

Chemical Secret
Chapter 11

Activity 1
Answer the following questions in complete sentences. Refer to Chapter 11 of the novel.

1. What do you think will happen in this chapter?

____

____

____

2. How does Mr. Wilson force John to give the "right" answers at the inquiry?

____

____

____

3. John uses science to lie about the truth. How does he do this?

____

____

____

4. At the inquiry, the lawyer shows John the newspaper article about Christine's fall into the river.

(a) Why doesn't John know about this accident until he is in the inquiry room?

____

____

____

(b) Describe John's reaction in your own words.

____

____

____

(c) Do you feel sorry for John? Why?

____

____

____

5. A rat is not a very popular animal. Why does the author compare the lawyer who saves the town from chemical waste to a rat?

____

____

____

6. What does John Duncan finally admit before he runs out of the inquiry room?

____

____

____

Activity 2, Part 1
Write an antonym for each of the following words from the letters in Activity 2, Part 2. Use a dictionary if necessary.

1. new: ____________________
2. answers: ____________________
3. upset: ____________________
4. love: ____________________
5. sick: ____________________
6. finished: ____________________
7. buying: ____________________
8. agree: ____________________
9. unessential: ____________________
10. simple: ____________________
11. cruelty: ____________________
12. strong: ____________________
13. find: ____________________
14. uncomfortable: ____________________
15. many: ____________________
16. right: ____________________
17. throw: ____________________
18. never: ____________________
19. cleaner: ____________________
20. give: ____________________

21. solution: ______________________

22. reduce: ______________________

23. night: ______________________

24. leave: ______________________

25. short: ______________________

26. wonderful: ______________________

27. remember: ______________________

28. fresh: ______________________

29. easy: ______________________

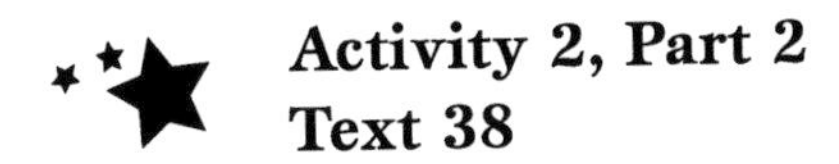

Activity 2, Part 2
Text 38

The Advice Column

"PST" is a new column in *News From the Bridges!* In this column, the Pollution Solution Team at ESDP answers questions from students about pollution and pollution solutions.

Dear PST,

I am very upset because I found out that the shampoo I use is tested on animals. I read an article about testing. I learned that 17 million rabbits, dogs, mice, guinea pigs and other animals are used in animal testing every year in North America. I love all animals, and I know animal testing means that animals suffer. Many animals go blind or get sick, and after the testing is finished, the animals are killed, but I don't know what to do. Should I stop buying shampoo?

Sincerely,
Animal Lover

Dear Animal Lover,

Many consumers get upset when they read articles or see movies about animal testing. I agree with those who say that animal testing should be used only for medical research and not for the testing of unessential products like shampoo or makeup. What can you do? It's simple. Read the labels.

There are many "cruelty-free" products you can buy. If you stop spending your money on products that are tested on animals, you send a strong message to those companies. You can also write letters to the companies to remind them that new "cruelty-free tests" can be done with computers.

Therefore, when you go shopping, read the labels and find the best "cruelty-free" shampoo for you! Tell your friends about it as well. I'm sure they will switch too.

Naturally yours,
PST

Dear PST,

One of my friends said that batteries are very bad for the environment. He said that toxic chemicals are released into our environment when batteries are made and when we throw them in the garbage. This makes me feel very uncomfortable because I use batteries in my cell phone, my Walkman, my watch and many other things! What should I do?

Worried

Dear Worried,

Your friend is right. Batteries contain one of two very toxic metals: cadmium or mercury. More than 2 billion batteries are used in North America every year. That's a lot of toxic chemicals for our environment! What can you do to help? Do not throw batteries into the garbage, because the toxic chemicals in our garbage dumps go into the ground and our water. Before you throw away your used batteries, call the public works department to find out what you can do with them. In the meantime, here are a few ideas that will help you and your friends use fewer batteries.

1. Turn things off when you are not using them.
2. Use rechargeable batteries.
3. Never use new batteries with old ones because the old ones take the power out of the new batteries.
4. Plug in portable equipment when possible.
5. Buy items or gifts that don't use batteries, like a solar calculator or a wind-up watch. This sends a message to companies that you prefer cleaner sources of energy.

Naturally yours,
PST

Dear PST,

What three words of advice do you give consumers who want to be part of the pollution solution?

Curious

Dear Curious,

My three words of advice are "reduce", "reuse" and "recycle". Remember that everything you buy was once part of the earth's natural resources.

"Reduce" means buying less and using less. How can you buy less? Buy what lasts and buy things that have as little packaging as possible. How can you use less? Think of the energy you use every time you do something! Walk, cycle, or take public transportation when possible; open windows instead of turning on the air conditioner; turn down the heat at night or when you leave the house; turn off things that use electricity when you are not using them; take short showers; wash clothes in cold water! You can find hundreds of other ways to "reduce" what you buy and how much energy you use. Remember, there are many companies today that make electrically-powered products that use less energy. You can learn more about them if you go to your library and look at consumer magazines.

"Reuse" means buying things that you can use for a long time. For example, buy a coffee cup instead of using a paper cup each time you are at the coffee shop; buy refillable containers; don't buy disposable things like paper plates, napkins and plastic knives and forks; don't throw away things that you don't want anymore. Other people can use your furniture, clothes, books, toys, dishes and many other things.

"Recycle" means three things. It means recycling things made of plastic, paper, metal and food.* Don't forget that every time you recycle, you help save natural resources. "Recycle" also means buying things that can be recycled easily without hurting the ecosystem. These things are called "biodegradable". Use soaps and shampoos that are biodegradable; buy unbleached paper; buy bottles and containers that can be recycled; recycle plastic bags and dry-cleaning bags. You can find many others ways to "recycle" what you use.

If you remember the words "reduce", "reuse" and "recycle", you will make a big difference! Good luck.

Naturally yours,
PST

*P. S.: You can recycle plants, fruit and vegetables by "composting". Ask your biology teacher about it. Maybe you can begin a composting project at home, at school, or in your neighbourhood.

Dear PST,

I want my family to become a Pollution Solution Family right away. What should I tell my parents?

Impatient

Dear Impatient,

It is wonderful that you want your family to become part of the Pollution Solution Team. You will find that it is not difficult. A family becomes a member of the Pollution Solution Team because of what it chooses and what it uses. And when you become a member of our team, you help make the air you breathe cleaner and the water you drink healthier. Here are some of the simple rules for pollution solution families.

Your family can make a difference by what it uses. You can use natural products like pure soap, vinegar and baking soda instead of household cleaners. Buy laundry detergents that do not contain phosphates. In your garden, use natural fertilizers and pesticides instead of chemical fertilizers and pesticides. Always use regular plates, forks, towels and containers instead of disposable ones. Remember that everything you put in your garbage, sink or garden will soon be in your land, air and water.

Your family can also be part of the pollution solution by eating vegetarian meals and by buying fresh fruit and vegetables from local farmers instead of produce that was transported by trucks. You can also buy in "bulk". One large bottle of orange juice creates less garbage than 12 small cans. And always buy things in reusable or recyclable containers and bottles.

Good luck, and welcome to the Pollution Solution Team!

Naturally yours,
PST

Activity 2, Part 3
Answer the following questions in complete sentences. Refer to the letters in Activity 2, Part 2.

1. Why are batteries toxic?

____

____

____

2. What are the three Rs of pollution prevention?

____

____

____

3. Why shouldn't people use paper cups or plastic utensils?

____

____

____

4. Why isn't shampoo a "cruelty-free" product?

____

____

____

Activity 2, Part 4
Journal Entry 11

Journal Entry 11

Write an advice column on pollution prevention.

1. Write the first letter as if you are a character in the novel who is asking for help.
2. Answer this letter, offering at least two possible solutions.

IV - Text 39

Chemical Secret
Chapter 12

Activity, Part 1
Answer the following questions in complete sentences. Refer to Chapter 12 of the novel.

1. In what three ways has the author prepared the reader for the ending of the novel?

____

____

____

2. What has happened to John since the inquiry?

____

____

____

3. What has happened to John's relationship with his daughter since the inquiry?

____

____

____

4. Why is it difficult for John to read the magazines he has in his apartment?

____

____

____

5. Where is John going at the end of this chapter?

____

6. Do you like or dislike the ending of this novel? Why?

____

____

____

____

____

____

7. The title of this chapter is “The Future”. What is the “future” the author is talking about in this novel?

Activity, Part 2
Journal Entry 12

Journal Entry 12

Imagine you are the author. In two or three paragraphs, write a new ending for this novel. Include some dialogue.

Achevé d'imprimer en juillet 2008
sur les presses du
Centre franco-ontarien de ressources pédagogiques